Metalwork Technology

Also by G. H. Thomas
Introduction to Metalwork, Books 1 and 2 (Macmillan)
Design Technology in Metal and Plastics

Metalwork Technology
METRIC EDITION

G. H. Thomas

Head of Faculty of Craft, Design and Technology,
Tarring High School, Worthing
Examiner in Engineering Workshop Theory and Practice
for the Associated Examining Board

John Murray 50 Albemarle Street London

ACKNOWLEDGMENTS

The author wishes to thank the headmaster of West Tarring School, Mr R. A. Williams, M.A., for his encouragement and the school secretary, Mrs P. J. Amos, for her help with the script. Some of the questions forming a section of the book are reproduced by kind permission of the Boards listed on page 236. (Imperial terms and quantities have been metricated.)

The cover photograph is reproduced by courtesy of Messrs T. S. Harrison and Sons Ltd.

© G. H. Thomas 1966, 1972
First Published 1966
Reprinted 1968, 1971
New edition (in metric units with additional material) 1972
Reprinted 1973, 1975, 1977, 1979, 1981, 1982

Printed in Hong Kong by Wing King Tong Co Ltd

0 7195 2654 X

CONTENTS

PREFACE

This book has been written to prepare pupils for the ordinary level of the General Certificate of Education in the Craft of Metalwork, Engineering Workshop Theory and Practice and the Certificate of Secondary Education. It will be found useful too for the Craft Examinations of the City and Guilds of London Institute.

Many pupils find difficulty in following complicated technical instructions. Consequently, an attempt has been made here to explain the technical processes in a manner that will be exceedingly easy to follow: by presenting them in an ordered sequence of numbered steps, and by providing very numerous line drawings to complement the brief text. An accurate, clear drawing, accompanied by a concise explanation, can often convey more than pages of print.

The section on examination questions has been arranged so that it can be used as a basis for a course in theory. The questions have been selected in such a way that they cover the courses laid down by the above examining bodies.

It is hoped that this book will provide that fresh approach to the subject that is often advocated.

PREFACE TO THE METRIC EDITION

An international conference held in Paris in 1960 finally agreed a modern, coherent form of the metric system known as Système International d'Unités (International System of Units), commonly abbreviated to SI. Practically every country in the world is changing to this international "language" of measurement, which rationalizes the main metric units of measurement and standardizes their names and symbols. In 1965 the British Government announced that SI would be adopted. . . . "sector by sector until that system can become in time the primary system of weights and measures for the country as a whole".

The British Standards Institution has already prepared and published most of the necessary metric standards, over twelve hundred of them. These standards are written around the recommendations of the International Organization for Standardization (ISO) and therefore have an international background. ISO recommendations have virtually universal acceptance and provide the basis for most national standards produced in recent years.

Many sectors of industry are already manufacturing metric articles. The target date for the substantial completion of the change is 1975 but there will be some usage of the imperial system beyond this. Consequently some imperial information (e.g. details of imperial threads, imperial micrometers, etc.) has been retained in this book.

Most GCE and CSE Boards are now setting papers with dual units or setting alternative papers in metric units. By 1975 it is expected that all examination papers will be set in metric units.

All the changes in this metric edition have been made with reference to or in conjunction with BSI, the Metrication Board and numerous Engineering Associations and Manufacturers.

1 MATERIALS

Properties of Metal

Most engineering materials are metallic: they can be classed as:

1 *Ferrous metals* which contain chiefly iron with small proportions of other metals.

2 *Non-ferrous metals* which contain little or no iron.

3 *Alloys*

Pure metals are little used in engineering: they rarely possess the required properties, and some are difficult to produce in the pure state. Hence, metals are more commonly used in the form of alloys.

Metals have many physical and chemical properties which affect their working qualities.

1 *Relative density*. This is the ratio between the weight of the metal and the weight of an equal volume of water.

2 *Colour*. Besides being a means of distinguishing metals, colour is useful in decorative work.

3 *Fusibility*. This is the property of becoming liquid when heated. Different metals have different melting points.

4 *Conductivity of heat and electricity*. Copper and silver are the best conductors of both heat and electricity.

5 *Magnetic properties*. Iron and steel are the most important magnetic metals but others are slightly magnetic, e.g. cobalt and nickel. Some irons and steels become permanently magnetized but others lose their magnetism immediately the magnetic field is removed. These latter are used for electromagnets.

6 *Elasticity*. The ability to regain shape after deformation.

7 *Hardness*. This is the resistance the metal offers to being scratched, cut or worn. There are a number of standard hardness tests (e.g. Brinell) by means of which the hardness of metals can be compared.

8 *Malleability*. The property which allows a metal to be hammered or rolled without breaking.

9 *Ductility*. The quality of being able to be drawn into fine wire. Ductility often increases with heat. It bears little relation to malleability, e.g. lead is malleable but not ductile.

10 *Toughness*. The resistance to fracture or deformation. Toughness decreases with heating.

11 *Brittleness* is the opposite of toughness. Brittle materials break easily with a sharp blow, are usually hard and are neither ductile nor malleable.

12 *Tenacity*. The measure of tenacity is tensile strength and is the property of materials to resist fracture when stretched. Tenacity is one of the most important mechanical properties of metals and is very important in all structures which have to stand up to high stress, e.g. high tensile steels.

Processes

1 *Work hardening*. Many metals become hard and lose ductility when cold worked, i.e. bent, hammered, twisted, etc. Annealing then becomes necessary before further work can continue.

2 *Forging*. The shaping of metal by hammering when red hot.

3 *Welding*. Uniting metals by hammering at white heat (forge welding) or uniting by fusion (oxy-acetylene or electric arc).

4 *Extrusion*. Forcing plastic metals through holes of the desired shape.

5 *Drawing*. Pulling ductile metals through holes in draw plates to reduce the size of those metals, e.g. wire drawing.
6 *Spinning*. Forcing fast-revolving sheet metal over metal or wood formers.
7 *Casting*. The pouring of molten metal into previously prepared sand or steel moulds.
8 *Pressing*. Stretching and shaping sheet metal by means of a press tool.
9 *Annealing*. Restoring metal to its softest state to enable further cold working to continue.
10 *Normalizing*. Relieving stresses set up by working.
11 *Hardening*. Producing maximum hardness.
12 *Tempering*. Relieving some of the brittleness after hardening.

Ferrous Metals

CAST IRON

1 Grey cast iron has most of the carbon present as graphite. It is relatively soft, tough and can readily be machined.
2 White cast iron has most of the carbon present as iron carbide, making the iron hard and brittle. It is difficult to machine.

CHILLED CASTINGS

These are used where it is necessary to have a hard, durable surface. Parts of the mould are made of iron instead of sand and the poured cast iron, coming into contact with these plates, will be cooled quickly. The chilled part of the casting will be changed into white cast iron and will be harder than the rest of the casting.

MALLEABLE CAST IRON

This is cast iron that has undergone a heat treatment to make it softer and more malleable. The castings are packed round with iron oxide, heated in a furnace and allowed to cool slowly. The carbon is removed from the surface of the casting by oxidation. The process is used for castings that have to withstand shock or, after casting, have to be further worked on.

WROUGHT IRON

Although once in general use, wrought iron has now been superseded by mild steel. It is expensive, about three times the price of mild steel, but for some purposes is superior to it.

PURE IRON

This is difficult to produce and is used nowadays only for rotor stampings and transformer cores.

STEEL

An alloy of iron and carbon, with a carbon content up to 1.5%.

Low carbon or mild steels have a carbon content varying from 0.1% to 0.3% and are used for general engineering purposes.

Black mild steel is covered with a black scale formed by oxidation during hot rolling. The edges of black mild steel strip and bar are slightly rounded.

Bright mild steel or bright drawn mild steel is obtained by cleaning black mild steel and then cold rolling it. This gives a bright clean finish and the sections are true to size to fairly close limits (0.05 mm). It is stronger but less ductile than black mild steel.

Terne plate is mild steel sheet coated with lead.

Tinplate is mild steel sheet covered with a protective coating of tin. Thicknesses range from 0.17 to 0.03 mm in steps of 0.01 mm and in steps of 0.05 mm above 0.03 mm.

Galvanized iron is mild steel sheet covered with a thin layer of zinc.

C.R.C.A. sheet is cold rolled close annealed bright mild sheet. Bright mild steel sheet is annealed out of contact with air to maintain its bright surface and at the same time leave it in a softened condition.

MEDIUM CARBON STEELS

These have a carbon content varying from 0.3% to 0.7%. As the carbon content increases so the strength and hardness increases but the steel becomes less ductile.

HIGH CARBON STEELS (cast steels or tool steels).

These have a carbon content varying from 0.7% to 1.5%. The higher the carbon content the harder but more brittle the steel. All steels in this group can be hardened and tempered.

ALLOY STEELS

These contain carbon and small quantities of other metals as well in order to produce special qualities.

Nickel increases the toughness.

Chromium imparts stainless properties, adds to the hardness and increases resistance to corrosion.

Tungsten gives the steel the ability to cut at high temperatures without softening, e.g. H.S.S.

Manganese adds strength and resistance to wear.

Molybdenum increases the hardness.

Cobalt increases the hot hardness.

Vanadium increases the hardness.

HIGH SPEED STEELS

Plain carbon steels suitably heat treated will not stand a heat of more than 300 °C before becoming soft (i.e. their temper becomes drawn). High speed steel will retain its hardness at high temperatures (600 °C) and consequently will cut at a high speed. The composition varies, but a typical composition is 0.75% carbon, 4% chromium, 1% vanadium, 18% tungsten and the rest iron.

SILVER STEEL

This is a high carbon steel (1.0% carbon) and may also contain a small proportion of chromium. It contains no silver, has a ground accurate finish and is usually sold in 330 mm lengths.

HIGH TENSILE STEELS

These usually contain nickel and chromium and combine toughness with high strength.

STAINLESS STEELS

The composition of stainless steels varies according to their purpose and method of fabrication. All contain at least 12% chromium and the carbon content is usually low, about 0.3%. They are costly and need care in handling (see "The Working of Stainless Steels" on page 232).

There are three groups of stainless steels.

1 The Martensite group contains all the cutlery type steels. The chromium content is 13% and the steels can be heat treated.

2 The Ferritic group contains 13% to 20% chromium and is low in carbon. They are moderate in ductility and are magnetic.

3 The Austenitic group are all chromium-nickel alloys. They are non-magnetic and have high ductility. Supplied mainly in sheet form and cold formed to shape.

SINTERED CARBIDE ALLOYS

E.g. tungsten carbide (an alloy of tungsten and carbon). These alloys, usually used for cutting tools, are formed by a sintering process (heating to a very high temperature) at 1500 °C. They are costly to produce, are extremely hard and cannot be ground on ordinary grinding wheels. They cut at speeds four times as fast as H.S.S. Because of their cost and extreme brittleness they are used in the form of tool tips.

HEAT TREATMENT OF STEELS

The heat treatment of carbon steels depends on the carbon content. When carbon steel is heated to its critical temperature (about 900 °C) the iron and carbon combine to form iron carbide. It is this iron carbide which causes the hardening of high carbon steels, but it can be formed only if the carbon percentage is sufficiently high. Mild steels have insufficient carbon to form iron carbide, hence cannot be hardened. Quenching (sudden cooling) the high carbon steel at this critical temperature "freezes" iron carbide in solution, leaving the steel very hard.

HARDENING H.C.S.

1 Heat to a cherry red (900 °C) and quench in brine, water, oil or blast of air.

Precautions:

1 Heat very slowly at first, then more fiercely.

2 Avoid prolonged heating and overheating. This causes enlargement of the grain structure, making it coarse and weak.

3 Quench vertically to avoid distortion.

B

TESTS FOR FERROUS METALS

TEST	CAST IRON	WROUGHT IRON	MILD STEEL	CARBON STEEL	HIGH SPEED STEEL
APPEARANCE	Grey, sandy surface showing casting line.	Red, scaly surface with rolling marks	Fine, smooth surface with a bluish sheen.	Smooth, black surface.	Smooth, fine surface.
DROP ON A STONE FLOOR	Dull, with no ring.	Dull, but a higher sound than C.I.	A medium ringing sound.	A fine, ringing sound.	Gives a sound midway between M.S. and C.S.
CUT HALF WAY THROUGH BAR AND BEND	Snaps easily.	Bends well before breaking.	Bends well before breaking.	Bends very little and snaps suddenly.	Bends little, if any, before breaking.
APPEARANCE OF FRACTURE	Large, grey crystals with the free carbon showing as dark specks.	Fibrous structure, coarse and grey.	Fine, grey crystalline structure.	Very fine crystalline structure.	Fine, grey structure.
FILE	A very hard skin with dark grey filings.	Pins badly.	Files well.	Harder to file than M.S.	Harder to file than M.S. but easier than C.S.
MACHINE IN A LATHE	Turns well after getting under the hard skin.	Turns well but with a poor finish. Swarf long and spiral.	Turns easily and well. Swarf long and spiral.	Harder to turn than M.S. with swarf that breaks up small.	Turns well with long chips.
HEAT RED AND QUENCH	No change but may crack.	No change.	No change but may harden a little according to carbon content.	Becomes very hard and brittle.	Becomes hard and brittle.

4

TEST	CAST IRON	WROUGHT IRON	MILD STEEL	CARBON STEEL	HIGH SPEED STEEL
HEAT RED AND HAMMER	Crumbles.	Works easily and well.	Works easily and well.	Works well but harder than M.S.	Difficult to work.
HEAT RED AND COOL SLOWLY	No change.	No change.	No change.	No change unless already hard.	Becomes hard and brittle.
GRIND ON A GRINDSTONE	Dull, red non-bursting sparks.	Yellow, non-bursting sparks.	Streaks of long, bright, yellow sparks, some of them bursting.	Bushy streams of bright, yellow, bursting, star-like sparks, very like "sparklers".	Red sparks that tend to cling to the wheel.

FERROUS METALS

	CAST IRON	WROUGHT IRON	MILD STEEL	HIGH CARBON STEEL
MELTING POINT IN °C	1240	2000	Varies according to composition.	Varies according to composition.
COMPOSITION	An alloy of iron and carbon with small amounts of silicon, phosphorus, sulphur, etc. Carbon content between 1·5% and 4·5%.	99% iron with slight impurities. (iron silicate)	An alloy of iron and carbon. Carbon content up to 0·35%.	An alloy of iron and carbon. Carbon content varies from 0·5% to 1·5%.
PROPERTIES	Brittle, with a hard skin. General properties will vary according to the proportions of combined and free carbon.	Malleable and ductile with a high tensile strength. Quickly recovers from overstrain.	Malleable, ductile and very uniform in texture.	Malleable and ductile but not to the same extent as mild steel. Can be hardened and tempered.

	CAST IRON	WROUGHT IRON	MILD STEEL	HIGH CARBON STEEL
TESTS	Dull note when dropped. Easily snaps. Crumbles if forged. Dull sparks off the grinder.	Dull note when dropped but higher than C.I. Bends well cold and hot. Yellow non-bursting sparks off the grinder.	Medium note when dropped. Bends well cold and hot. Long, bright, yellow sparks off grinder, some bursting.	High ringing note when dropped. Bushy, yellow, star-like sparks off the grinder.
WORKING QUALITIES	Has a hard skin but underneath the skin the metal is fairly soft. Cannot be forged but casts very well. Grey cast iron is easy to machine but white cast iron is difficult.	When heated remains in a pasty state before the melting point is reached. Hence it forges and forge welds well. Cannot be cast. Machines well but with a poor finish. Pins when being filed.	Bends well cold, particularly black mild steel. Welds and forges well. Machines well and with a good finish. Files well.	Not very easy to file, saw or machine. Forges reasonably well but not as easily as mild steel.
USES	Machine tool bases, bodies and slideways, the graphite content helping the movement of one part on another. Marking out tables and surface plates. Vice bodies, lathe face plates and chuck bodies. Cylinder blocks, piston rings.	Haulage gear, anchor chains, crane hooks, boiler plates.	General structural work. Nuts, bolts, screws, tubes, small tools (non-cutting) Vice screws and handles. Tinplate is mild steel covered with tin. Galvanized sheet is mild steel covered with zinc. Terne plate is mild steel covered with lead.	Cutting tools. Files, chisels, saws, drills, taps, dies, screwdrivers, knives, scribers, lathe tools, reamers, hammer heads, pliers, punches. Gauges, springs. Superseded by H.S.S. for machine cutters because of the temper becoming drawn with heat.

MILD STEELS, TOOL STEELS AND CAST IRON

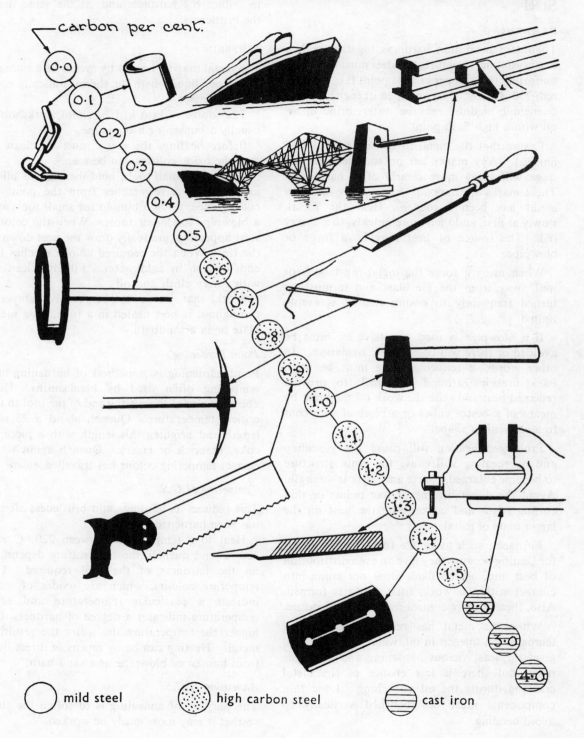

carbon per cent.

0.0
0.1
0.2
0.3
0.4
0.5
0.6
0.7
0.8
0.9
1.0
1.1
1.2
1.3
1.4
1.5
2.0
3.0
4.0

○ mild steel   ⊙ high carbon steel   ⊖ cast iron

To Harden and Temper High Carbon Steel

HARDENING

To obtain maximum hardness together with a fine crystalline structure, the steel must be heated uniformly to its upper critical point (i.e. a cherry red, 750 °C to 850 °C) and then quenched. The quenching medium may be water, brine or an oil with a high flash point.

Ensure that the metal to be hardened is well finished. Any marks left on the metal at this stage will show more clearly after hardening. These marks are impossible to remove once the metal has been hardened. Heat the metal, slowly at first, and then more quickly, to a cherry red. The source of heat may be a forge or blowpipe.

When using a forge the metal must be kept well away from the air blast and it must be turned frequently to ensure that it is evenly heated.

If a blowpipe is used, excessive air must be avoided or there will be excessive oxidation. In other words, a reducing flame must be used. Pack firebrick around the work to provide reflected heat and raise the work off the brick by means of asbestos cubes or a piece of wire bent to a convenient shape.

Prolonged heating will cause heavy scaling and overheating will cause the grain structure to become enlarged, coarse and weak in strength. Avoid the direct heating of fine points or thin cutting edges and concentrate the heat on the larger mass of metal.

Furnaces, such as muffle furnaces, are better for heating because they give an even distribution of heat and, as the flame does not come into contact with the work, little oxide is formed. Also, there is more control over the temperature.

When the metal has reached the required temperature, quench in oil, water or brine. Oil gives the least vicious hardening and brine the most, but there is less chance of the metal cracking during the oil quenching. Long thin components must be quenched vertically to avoid bending.

Hardening is followed by tempering in order to reduce the hardness and, at the same time, the brittleness.

TEMPERING

The metal may be heated by means of a bunsen, blowpipe, liquid bath or thermostatically controlled furnace.

The source of heat in the school workshop is usually a bunsen or a blowpipe.

Before heating, the metal must be clean so that the oxide colours can be seen.

To temper small tools, hold them in gas pliers and heat some few inches from the point or cutting edge, using a bunsen for small tools and a blowpipe for larger tools. When the colours start appearing, gradually draw the heat down to the tip. When the required colour reaches the end, quench in cold water. Finally, clean up with emery cloth and oil.

Work that needs to be evenly tempered throughout is best heated in a tube, on a metal plate or in a sandbath.

Point hardening

Point hardening is a method of hardening and tempering often used by blacksmiths. Heat about 50 mm of the cutting end of the tool to the critical temperature. Quench about a 25 mm length and brighten this length with a piece of coke, firebrick or emery. Quench again when correct tempering colour has travelled down.

Tempering H.C.S.

This reduces its hardness and brittleness after it has been hardened.

Heat to a temperature between 220 °C and 300 °C and quench, the temperature depending on the hardness of the tool required. The tempering colours, which are oxides of iron, indicate a particular temperature and each temperature indicates a degree of hardness, the higher the temperature the softer the resulting metal. Heating can be by means of direct heat from bunsen or blowpipe or a sand bath.

Annealing H.C.S.

The purpose of annealing is to soften the steel so that it may more easily be worked.

TEMPERING CHART

°C			
220°		Pale Straw	
230°		Medium Straw	
240°		Dark Straw	
250°		Brown	
260°		Light Purple	
270°		Dark Purple	
300°		Blue	

Heat slowly to the required temperature (bright red) and cool very slowly, e.g. under hot ashes. Slow cooling allows the iron carbide to separate out into iron and carbon.

Normalizing H.C.S.

Normalizing is a process which refines the structure of the steel and removes strains caused by cold working.

Heat to a bright cherry red and cool in air.

Case-hardening of mild steel

This is a method of forming a hard skin of H.C.S. on wrought iron or mild steel by adding carbon. Steel case-hardened has a tough core and a very hard skin that resists wear. The process is useless for any tools that have to be eventually ground.

Heat to a bright red and plunge in "Kasenit".

Reheat to a bright red. It is at this stage that the carbon gets absorbed by the steel. Quench to harden the skin.

Box-hardening

This is a form of case-hardening.

Work to be treated is packed in steel boxes together with a carbon compound and then heated to 900°C for some hours. Quenching afterwards hardens the skin.

Non-Ferrous Metals and Alloys

ANNEALING

Cold working of most metals distorts the crystalline structure rendering them hard and brittle. The metals then need softening (annealing) so that they can be further worked upon.

Copper. Heat to a dull red—overheating causes heavy black scaling—and cool slowly in air or quench in water (the effect is the same). Pickling in dilute sulphuric acid can follow to remove any oxide scale formed during heating. The pickling is a cleaning process only and has nothing to do with the actual annealing.

Brass. Heat to a dull red and cool slowly. Sudden cooling causes fracture.

Aluminium becomes annealed at 350 °C and melts at 660 °C. Soap turns black at 400 °C. To anneal aluminium, therefore, coat with soap and heat with a gas flame until the soap turns black. Cool slowly or quench.

NON-FERROUS METALS

	ALUMINIUM	COPPER	LEAD	TIN	ZINC
M.P. °C	660	1080	327	232	419
COLOUR	Bluish white.	Reddish brown or salmon pink – a colour that darkens on exposure.	A dull metallic lustre when bright but quickly deepens to a bluish grey.	Bright and silvery, with a yellowish tinge.	Bluish white.
PROPERTIES	Very light in weight malleable, soft, ductile and a good conductor of electricity.	Very malleable and ductile. Excellent conductor of heat and electricity – hence its use for soldering bits, electric wire.	Very soft and malleable. Resists corrosion very well and is not affected by water and acids. Heavy.	Soft, malleable and fairly ductile. Keeps its lustre and has a high corrosion resistance.	Has a distinct grain due to rolling. Fairly hard and brittle. At 100-150°C becomes ductile but at 200°C again becomes brittle.
WORKING QUALITIES	Being malleable and ductile can be rolled into thin foil, drawn into wire, spun into deep shapes and bent into boxes. Cannot be soldered by ordinary methods but can be welded and brazed. Polishes well. Casts well. Work hardens. In its pure form its tensile strength is too low for most engineering purposes	Can be cast, rolled, forged, spun, drawn into tubes and wire and beaten into very deep shapes. Can be joined by soft soldering, brazing and welding. Polishes well. Work hardens.	Can be worked and shaped at ordinary temperatures without work hardening. Can be joined by soft soldering and welding (called lead burning). Casts well.	Being malleable can be rolled into thin foil but is often not used today for this purpose because of its cost. For the same reason it is rarely used in its pure state. If a thin bar of tin is bent, a distinct noise, called "tin cry", can be heard, due to the deformation of the crystalline structure.	Easily bent and folded to shape. Does not work harden and is easily worked when slightly warm. Can be easily soldered but because of its low melting point extreme care is needed.

11

USES	ALUMINIUM	COPPER	LEAD	TIN	ZINC
	Kitchen and cooking utensils. Reflectors of light and heat. Electric cables. Foil (0·005mm thick). Engine parts. Aircraft parts. Tubes, tins, boxes. Aluminium alloys.	Decorative articles, boxes, bowls, wire, rivets, tubes. Electric and wireless parts. Soldering bits. Boiler Tubes. Used as the base for many alloys, eg brass and bronze.	Cable sheathing. In the form of sheeting for roofing and lining containers (mostly in the chemical industry). Battery elements. Water piping. Used as a base for many alloys.	Rarely used in its pure state except as a dip for mild steel to form tinplate and as a protective coating on copper wire. A common constituent of many alloys, eg. bronze.	Used for galvanizing (ie. as a protective coating on sheet steel). In the form of sheeting for roofing and containers. A constituent of many alloys, eg. brass.

NON-FERROUS ALLOYS

ALLOY	COMPOSITION	PROPERTIES	WORKING QUALITIES	USES
1. BRASSES ENGLISH STANDARD	Copper 66% Zinc 34%	Soft and ductile.	Works fairly well and can be submitted to limited hammering and bending when cold. Cannot be worked hot. Solders and brazes well.	Sheet, rod, wire, screws, rivets, castings.
2. MUNTZ METAL	Copper 60% Zinc 40%	Not very malleable or ductile when cold. Often called "yellow brass."	Not suitable for cold working, but works well hot.	Castings and forgings.
3. CARTRIDGE BRASS	Copper 70% Zinc 30%	Bright yellow in colour. Malleable and ductile.	Excellent for cold working, rolling and drawing.	Pressings, stampings and drawn sections.
4. GILDING METAL	Copper 80% Zinc 20%	Very malleable and ductile. Resists corrosion well. Golden colour. Takes a high polish.	Works well cold by bending, rolling, drawing. Solders and brazes well.	Architecture. Cheap jewellery. Decorative beaten work.

ALLOY	COMPOSITION	PROPERTIES	WORKING QUALITIES	USES
5. MANGANESE BRONZE	Copper 83% Zinc 12% with other metals in small amounts	Is really a brass rather than a bronze. Hard, tough with a high tensile strength. Yellow in colour but sometimes with a brown skin.	Hard and difficult to work but casts well and wears well.	Machine parts. Engine frames. Marine units, e.g. ships' propellers.
BRONZES 1. GUNMETAL	Copper 88% Tin 10% Zinc 2%	Strong, tough and resists corrosion well. Reddish yellow in colour and polishes well, but the surface quickly darkens on exposure.	Casts well and turns well.	Used chiefly in the form of castings. Steam pipe fittings, marine fittings, pump units. Gears.
2. BELL METAL	Copper 78% Tin 22%	Most sonorous of all the copper alloys.	Casts very well. Machines well.	Bell making.
3. ALUMINIUM BRONZE	Copper 89.5% Tin 0.5% Aluminium 0.5 – 10%	The addition of aluminium trebles the strength of the copper, makes it very hard, changes its colour from red to gold and enables it to resist corrosion, wear and oxidization at high temperatures.	Malleable when hot or cold. Can be rolled, drawn, spun and forged. Solders and brazes well.	Electrical and architectural work. Chemical and paper-making industries. Sewage works and underwater fittings.
4. PHOSPHOR BRONZE	Copper 89.5% Tin 10.0% Phosphorus 0.5%	Reddish yellow colour. Strong and tough with a high tensile strength. Resists corrosion well. Has a low coefficient of expansion.	Can be cast, rolled and drawn into wire. Machines well.	Mainly used for bearings. Springs.

13

ALLOY	COMPOSITION	PROPERTIES	WORKING QUALITIES	USES
ALUMINIUM ALLOYS 1. DURALUMIN	Al. 95% Copper 4% Manganese and Magnesium.	Has the approx. strength of mild steel with the weight of aluminium. Very susceptible to corrosion over a period of time. Age hardens.	Bends, folds and works well cold but quickly work hardens. Cannot be soldered by normal methods. Can be forged, stamped, spun, bent and hammered to shape.	Aircraft parts. Vehicle parts. Pulleys, con. rods, bolts, nuts, rivets, screws, etc. Components where lightness of weight and strength are important.
"WHITE METAL" BABBITS METAL	Tin 88% Antimony 8% Copper 4%	Fairly soft but harder than tin. Wears well under normal speed conditions.	Works well cold. Casts well.	Chiefly used for bearings in bronze or brass shells, eg. big end bearings.
2. PEWTER	Tin 82% Lead 18%	Soft and malleable.	Shapes and works easily. Can be cast, rolled and spun. Needs a special low melting point solder.	Used to be used for drinking utensils and kitchen ware. Decorative work.

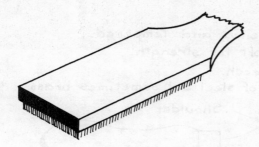

File Card

Chalking to Prevent Pinning

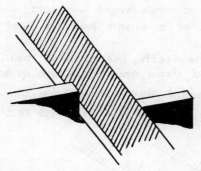

Use of Safe Edge

PINNING is the clogging of the file teeth with particles of metal causing the file to lose its cutting efficiency and badly score the work. Soft metals are more apt to pin than hard metals. The "pins" can be removed, if not too stubborn with a file card. Failing this, they will have to be pricked out with a sharp point. Chalking the surface of the file helps to prevent pinning.

CARE OF FILES
1. Work fitted loosely in the vice allows the file to chatter, thereby distorting or chipping the teeth.
2. The file teeth are brittle and easily broken so care should be taken both in their use and in their storage.
3. Never use a new file on welded joints, brazed joints, surface of a casting or a "burnt" soldering bit.
4. Use new files on brittle metals like brass and soft cast iron and when slightly worn: then use them on steels.
5. Never allow the file to slip over the work. It dulls the teeth.
6. Never use a small file when a large file will do the work better.
7. Clean the teeth as soon as they become pinned.
8. Never use a file without a handle. It is dangerous.

FILES

<u>BLADE</u>, made of high carbon steel hardened and tempered.
<u>TANG</u>, made of high carbon steel, left soft for strength.
<u>HANDLE</u>, made of wood, usually ash or beech.
<u>FERRULE</u>, to prevent handle splitting, made of steel but sometimes brass.

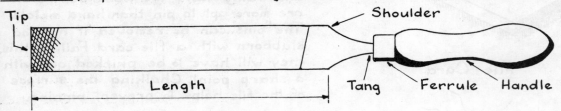

Tip   Shoulder   Length   Tang   Ferrule   Handle

<u>CUT</u> means the particular way in which the teeth are cut, single cut, double cut or rasp cut.
  SINGLE CUT FILES are used for cutting hard metals. They have an unbroken series of cuts, parallel with each other but running at an angle to the length of the file.
  DOUBLE CUT FILES are used for general purposes. They have two series of cuts running across each other, one series being finer than the other. One cut runs at an angle of 45° to the length of the file, the other at 70°.
  RASP CUT FILES are used for relatively coarse work on soft materials. Each tooth is cut separately by means of a single pointed tool or punch.
<u>GRADE</u> indicates the degree of coarseness of the teeth, the grades being rough, bastard, second cut, smooth and dead smooth. Each grade of cut has teeth of different pitch in different sizes. A 100mm smooth file has 60 teeth in 25mm, a 300mm smooth file has 40 teeth in 25mm.

FILE TEETH - ENLARGED
The file grooves, being cut at an angle to the length of the file, provide side rake on the teeth.

<u>CROSSFILING</u> is used for general work, roughing down, squaring etc.
1. Hold the work in the vice firmly and as low as possible.
2. Arrange the work so that it can, if possible, be filed horizontally.
3. Ensure that the grip on the file, as well as the body position, is correct. The arm, as far as the elbow, should be in a straight line, horizontal and level with the top of the work. The joint of the right wrist must be held firm.
4. Use slow full length file strokes with pressure on the forward stroke and relieving the pressure on the back stroke.

SECTION	SHAPE and SIZE	DETAILS and USES
Flat	100 mm to 450 mm	Parallel for two thirds of its length, tapering in width and slightly in its thickness. Faces are double cut and edges single cut. A general purpose file.
Hand	100 mm to 450 mm	Parallel in width and tapering slightly in thickness. Faces are double cut or single cut. One edge is single cut, the other uncut and called a safe edge. A general purpose file useful when filing up to a shoulder.
Warding	100 mm to 200 mm	Very similar to the flat file in shape but thinner and parallel in thickness. Not made in large sizes. Used for narrow slotting, grooving and apertures too narrow for a hand file.
Square	100 mm to 400 mm	Tapers for one third of its length. Double cut on all faces. Used for slotting, grooving and finishing square edges.
3-square Triangular	100 mm to 400 mm	Tapers in length, with angles of 60°. Double cut on all faces. Used for filing awkward corners and angles less than 90°.
Round	100 mm to 400 mm	Tapers in length. Usually double cut, the teeth being formed by straight chisel cuts intersecting one another. Used for filing concave curves, easing out holes, etc. Small sizes are often called rat-tails.

SECTION	SHAPE and SIZE	DETAILS and USES
Half-round	100mm to 450mm	Tapers towards the tip. The curved face is not semi-circular but a segment of a circle. Used for general purposes and for concave curves.
Knife	100mm to 300mm	Wedge-shaped in section with the tang offset. Used for filing awkward shapes, sharp corners and angles that are less than 60°.
Pillar	150mm to 300mm	Similar in shape to the hand-file but narrower. Useful for work where a handfile is too wide.
Mill	150mm to 350mm	Similar to the hand file. The edges may be square, rounded or one rounded and one square. Used for saw sharpening.
Rasps	Various shapes and lengths.	The teeth are punch cut and not chisel cut so that single teeth are thrown up. Used for soft materials, eg. wood, leather.

CHISELS

CHISELS are usually made of octagonal high carbon steel, hardened and tempered to a degree of hardness (varying from brown to purple) depending on the size of the chisel and the metal to be cut.
The head is left soft, otherwise it would crack under the impact of the hammer.
Alloy steels are better for chisels than H.C.S. but they are more expensive and more difficult to recondition if the temper becomes drawn.

NAME and SHAPE	DETAILS	USES
Flat Chisel	Size is specified by the width of the cutting edge (varying from 5 to 25mm) and the length in proportion. The point angle varies according to the material being cut – 65° for tool steel. 50° for mild steel. 30° for aluminium. The cutting edge may be straight or slightly curved according to the work. The head is chamfered to slow down the burring caused by hammering.	chisel held at oblique angle Cutting off in the vice work from each end Chipping a surface Cutting sheet on cutting block

NAME and SHAPE	DETAILS	USES
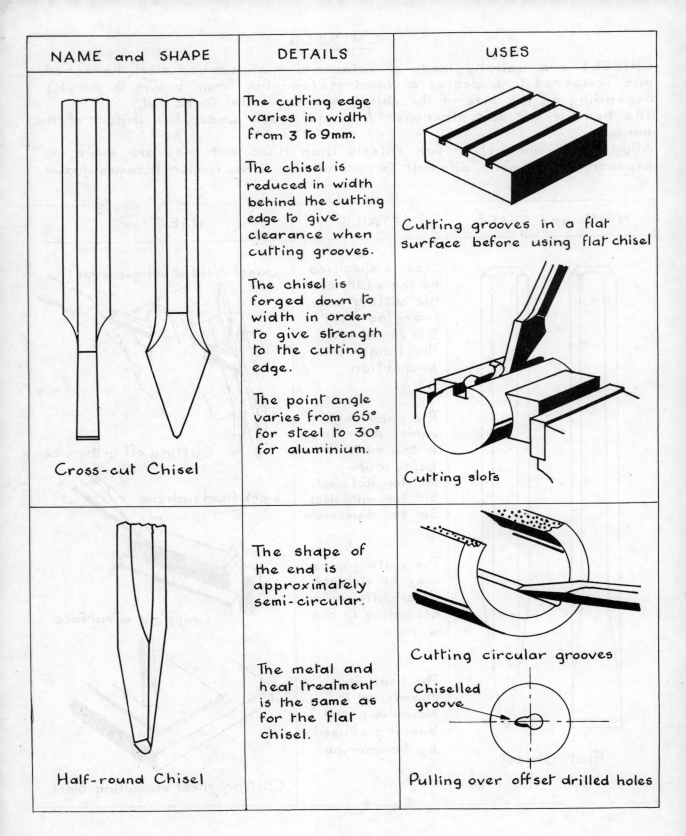 Cross-cut Chisel	The cutting edge varies in width from 3 to 9mm. The chisel is reduced in width behind the cutting edge to give clearance when cutting grooves. The chisel is forged down to width in order to give strength to the cutting edge. The point angle varies from 65° for steel to 30° for aluminium.	Cutting grooves in a flat surface before using flat chisel Cutting slots
Half-round Chisel	The shape of the end is approximately semi-circular. The metal and heat treatment is the same as for the flat chisel.	Cutting circular grooves Chiselled groove Pulling over offset drilled holes

NAME and SHAPE	DETAILS	USES
Diamond-point Chisel	The end is forged down to a four-sided taper. The extreme end is then ground at an angle, making it diamond-shaped. Metal and heat treatment the same as for the flat chisel.	Cleaning out corners Pulling over off-drilled centres

PUNCHES

NAME	DETAILS	USES
1 2 Centrepunches	**Material.** 1. Round H.C.S. knurled for grip or 2. Octagonal H.C.S. **Heat Treatment.** Hardened and tempered to a brown or brownish purple. Only the cutting edge is heat treated the head being left soft to withstand the impact of the hammer. The punches vary in diameter from 5 mm for light work to 20 mm for heavy work. The point angle is 90°. Type 1 has a round head and shank. Type 2 has a round shank but a square head to prevent rolling off the bench.	Used to position a drill for drilling 1. The punch mark must be large enough to take the chisel edge of the drill. right wrong 2. The punch mark must be accurate in position. If not it must be pulled over by hammering whilst the punch is tilted at the desired angle. Final positioning is made with the punch vertical. 1 2 3. A light punch mark is made first and then it is deepened only after its position has been checked.

NAME	DETAILS	USES
Dot Punch	Made of H.C.S. and heat-treated the same as the centre-punch. The same general shape as the centre-punch but finer and usually with a ground point angle of 60°.	Used to more clearly define lines that have to be filed down to.
Pin Punches Tapered, Parallel	The same material and heat treatment as the centrepunch. Tapered punches vary in size from 3 mm dia. at the end of the taper to 6 mm dia. Parallel punches vary in dia. from 1·5 mm dia. to 8 mm dia.	Used for extracting cotter pins, rivets, etc.
Bell Punch	Plain or spring-loaded types are marketed. The punch is made of H.C.S. hardened and tempered to a brown, the head being left soft. The body is made of M.S. usually knurled for grip. The dia. of bar to be centred is limited by the size of the bell of the punch.	Used for finding and punching the centre of the end of round stock. It is often used before centre drilling when the bar cannot be conveniently gripped in the lathe.

TOOL	DETAILS and USES

HAMMERS

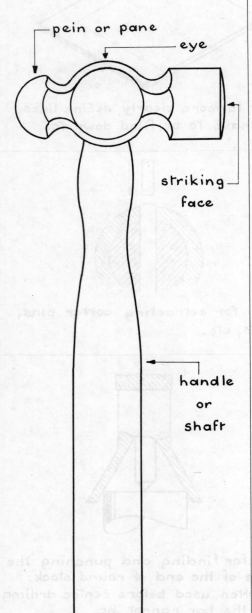

pein or pane

eye

striking
face

handle
or
shaft

HEAD - made of high carbon steel with approximately 0·6% carbon.

FACE and **PEIN** - tempered to a straw.

EYE - left soft for increased strength. The eye is thin-walled and weak and if left hard would fracture under the continued shock of impact.

Hammers are specified by weight, from 0·1 to 1·35 kg For general benchwork a head of about 0·4 kg is used.

SHAFT or **HANDLE** - made of ash or hickory, straight-grained and free of knots. It is fitted to the head by means of a metal or wooden wedge. Head and shaft should be square to each other when fitted.

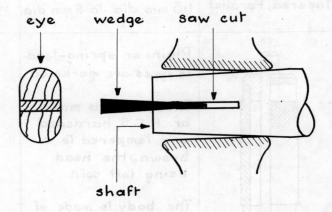

eye   wedge   saw cut

shaft

The eye is tapered in its length and when the wedge is driven home the head becomes a firm fixture on the shaft.

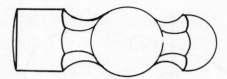

BALL PEIN

General purpose hammer. Ball pein used for riveting.

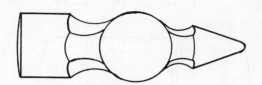

CROSS PEIN

Has the pein at right angles to the shaft. Used for drawing down and riveting in awkward places.

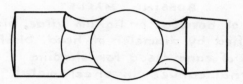

STRAIGHT PEIN

Has the pein in line with the shaft. Used for riveting in awkward places and for awkward bending of sheet.

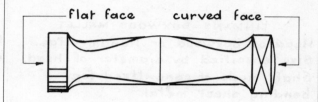

flat face   curved face

PLANISHING HAMMER

Often with one face flat and the other convex. Faces polished and free of defects. Used for finishing beaten work.

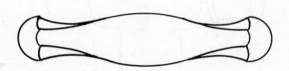

BLOCKING HAMMER

The end faces are well radiused and polished. Used for the shaping of sheet metal.

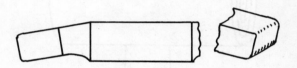

COLLET and RAISING HAMMERS

Of varying shape and size. Faces well finished. Used for raising and stretching sheet metal.

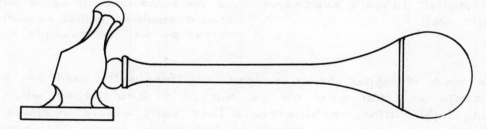

REPOUSSÉ HAMMER

Handle made of lancewood. Used with repoussé punches for shaping sheet metal.

MALLETS and SOFT HAMMERS

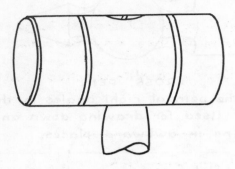

TINMAN'S BOXWOOD MALLET

Head of boxwood or lignum vitae.
Size specified by diameter of head.
Shaft made of cane. Used for
bending sheet·metal.

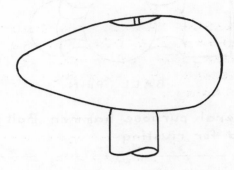

BOSSING MALLET

Head of boxwood or lignum vitae. Size
specified by diameter of head. Shaft
made of cane. Used for shaping
internal curves in sheet metal.

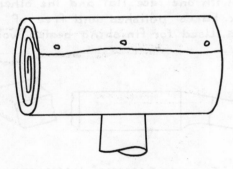

RAWHIDE MALLET

The head is of rawhide, rolled tightly
and pinned. Size specified by dia.
of head. Gives a softer blow than a
boxwood mallet. Is more expensive
but wears well.

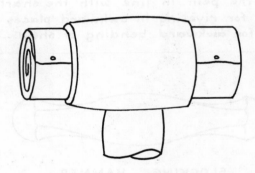

RAWHIDE HAMMER

The head consists of a tubular
casting with a roll of rawhide a
push fit in each end. The rawhide can
be renewed when it wears out. Heavier
than a rawhide mallet. Available with
copper as well as rawhide inserts.

Hammers made of copper, brass or lead are frequently used for blows
on any component that must not be marked or bruised, eg. when
assembling tight-fitting machine parts. They vary widely in shape and
size but all must have some provision for firmly fixing the head to
the shaft.

HACKSAWS

HACKSAW FRAMES are made non-adjustable or adjustable for length to enable them to take blades of different lengths. They may be made of rectangular section steel or tube.
HANDLES may be of the pistol grip type or straight-handled like a file handle.

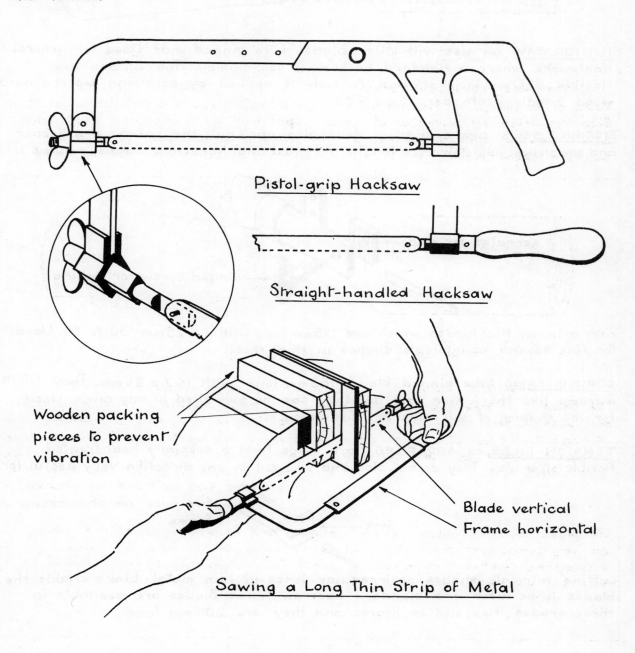

Pistol-grip Hacksaw

Straight-handled Hacksaw

Wooden packing pieces to prevent vibration

Blade vertical
Frame horizontal

Sawing a Long Thin Strip of Metal

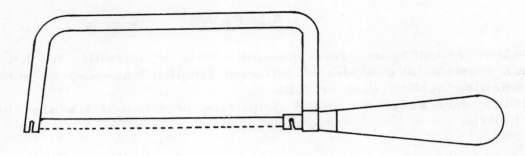

JUNIOR SAW for use with 150mm blades with pinned ends. Used for general light work where a standard hacksaw is too clumsy. The blades are flexible, 150mm in length and tension is applied by screwing up the hard-wood handle. Teeth per 25mm - 32.

PIERCING SAWS are similar in general shape but the frames are deeper and sometimes adjustable for length. Serrated and hardened clamps ensure a

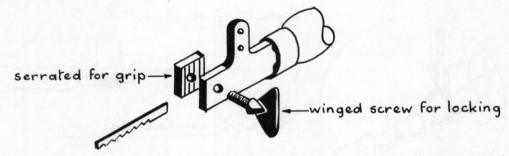

serrated for grip →

→ winged screw for locking

firm grip on the blades, which are 125mm long with t.p.25mm 32 to 80. Used for fine sawing of intricate shapes in thin sheet.

COPING SAWS take pinned blades 165mm long, with 14 t.p.25mm. They fit in a frame like the junior saw but they can be swivelled at any angle. Used for the shaping of soft materials like wood.

TENSION FILES, eg. "ABRAFILES", are made from a specially heat treated flexible steel wire. They do not clog and will cut in any direction. Very useful for

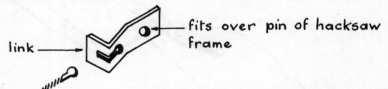

→ fits over pin of hacksaw frame

link →

cutting intricate shapes or irregular holes in thin metal. Links enable the blades to be used in a standard hacksaw frame. Blades are available in three grades, fine, medium, coarse and they are 200 mm long.

HACKSAW BLADES

The **LENGTH** of a blade is measured from the centre points of the fixing holes. Blades for hand use are 250 or 300mm long and 13mm wide. Blades for power use are 300 to 750 mm long and from 25 to 63mm wide.

The **SET** of a blade enables the blade to make a cut wider than the thickness

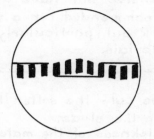
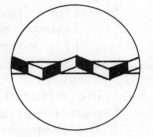
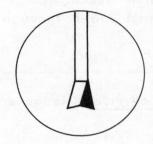

Fine Blade	Coarse Blade	End View

of the blade and prevents it from jamming in the cut. Fine blades have the teeth set in groups each side but coarse blades have alternate teeth set to left and right with sometimes every third tooth left straight to clear the cut of chippings.

HAND BLADES

TYPE	* T.P. 25mm	USES
Flexible. Made of low tungsten steel with only the teeth hardened.	18 to 32	Recommended for the less skilled user. Teeth chip off when misused but the blade rarely breaks.
All hard. Made of low tungsten steel, hardened and tempered right through.	18 to 32	More rigid and remain sharp longer than flexible blades but they are very brittle. Useful for accurate sawing by skilled workers.
High Speed Steel. Hard right through.	18 to 32	Hard and remain sharp over a long period but relatively brittle and expensive. They can cut faster because the temper does not get drawn. Most useful for cutting hard materials like annealed H.C.S.

* ISO Proposal 1970. Size of teeth specified by 1. Teeth per 25mm
or 2. Pitch in mm.

MACHINE BLADES

TYPE	T.P.25mm	USES
All hard. Low tungsten steel hardened and tempered right through.	10 to 24	Their relative cheapness is an advantage but they cannot be run at so fast a speed nor will they last as long as H.S.S. blades.
High Speed Steel. Hardened right through.	4 to 24	They are expensive but have a long life. Recommended for a wide range of work but particularly for hard materials.

CHOICE OF PITCH is governed by
1. The material to be cut — the softer the metal, the coarser the blade.
2. The shape and thickness of the material to be cut. At least three teeth must be in contact with the material at a given time. Therefore fine blades must be used for tubing and thin metals.

DIAMETER	HARD METALS	SOFT METALS
Up to 3mm	32	32
3-6mm	32	24
6-12mm	24	18
12-25mm	18	14

PRECAUTIONS IN THE USE OF A HAND HACKSAW

1. Choose a blade of the right type.
2. Choose a blade of the right length with the right number of t.p.25mm for the material to be cut.
3. Fit the blade in the frame with the teeth pointing away from the handle.
4. Correctly tension the blade. Take up the slack on the wing nut and then apply three full turns.
5. Ensure that the work is secured rigidly.
6. If the work is irregular in shape, arrange it in the vice so that sawing does not start across a corner.
7. Arrange the work in the vice so that the sawing, if possible, is vertical.

8. Use long steady strokes, releasing the pressure on the back stroke.
   50 strokes a minute is recommended when using low tungsten blades.
   60 strokes a minute is recommended when using high speed steel blades.

WRONG		RIGHT
Pitch too fine — the teeth will clog.	Soft Material	Correct pitch giving ample chip clearance.
Pitch too coarse - insufficient number of teeth in contact.	Hard Material	Correct pitch giving sufficient teeth in contact.
Pitch too coarse - insufficient no. of teeth in contact.	Thin Tube	Correct pitch giving plenty of teeth in contact.
Pitch too coarse - the teeth straddling the material.	Thin Section	Correct pitch - three consecutive teeth in contact.

FAULT	CAUSE
Blade breakage	Stroke out of line, excessive tensioning, insufficient tensioning, sawing against a sharp corner, material insecurely fixed, blade jamming in cut.
Excessive tooth wear	L.T.S. blade instead of H.S.S. blade, wrong tooth size, blade fixed wrong way round in frame, hard spot in material, insufficient or excessive pressure, excessive speed.
Tooth breakage	Wrong tooth size, sawing against a corner, material insecurely fixed.
Crooked cutting	Insufficient tensioning, hard spot in the material, excessive pressure, material insecurely fixed.

SCRAPERS

SCRAPERS are used to make a surface more accurate than is possible by filing. Only a very small amount of metal is removed and it is useless to scrape a surface before it has been worked as accurately as possible by other methods. They are made of H.C.S. hardened and tempered to a straw. Worn files can be made into very good scrapers.

NAME and SHAPE	DETAILS	USES
Handle removed Flat Scraper	The handle is usually similar to a file handle but is sometimes of metal, round and knurled. The blade is made of H.C.S. hardened and tempered to a straw. The end may be forged out as shown or left parallel. The cutting edge may be left straight but is more often curved to prevent the corners digging in. 1 Oilstone 2 Sharpening	To make a surface accurately flat. Procedure. 1. Clean the work and surface plate. 2. Apply a <u>thin</u> layer of prussian blue (mechanic's blue) to the plate. 3. Place the work on the plate and move it to and fro once or twice. 4. High spots will show blue. These are removed by scraping. 5. Repeat until as much of the surface as possible is covered with blue.

NAME and SHAPE	DETAILS	USES
Half-round Scraper	Material and heat treatment the same as for the flat scraper. The blade is curved and tapered in its length. The upper face is convex and the under face is slightly concave. It is sharpened on the convex face, deburring the concave face, if necessary with a curved oilstone slip.	Pressure with left hand Circular motion with right hand **Scraping a Bearing** 1. Clean journal and bearing. 2. Smear a thin film of blue on the journal. 3. Lower into bearing and revolve. 4. High spots will show blue. Scrape these high spots. 5. Lower again, repeat if necessary. 6. Repeat with top half of the bearing in position.
Triangular Scraper	Material and heat treatment the same as for the flat scraper.	Not used as much as the flat or half-round scrapers but is very useful for working in awkward corners where the use of the other scrapers is impossible.

THE CHOICE OF TOOL and method of using it for marking out and measuring will be governed by the accuracy required. If a dimension on a drawing is given as a fraction without any qualification, e.g. quality of fit, then it may be assumed that the marking out need not be made with a precision instrument.

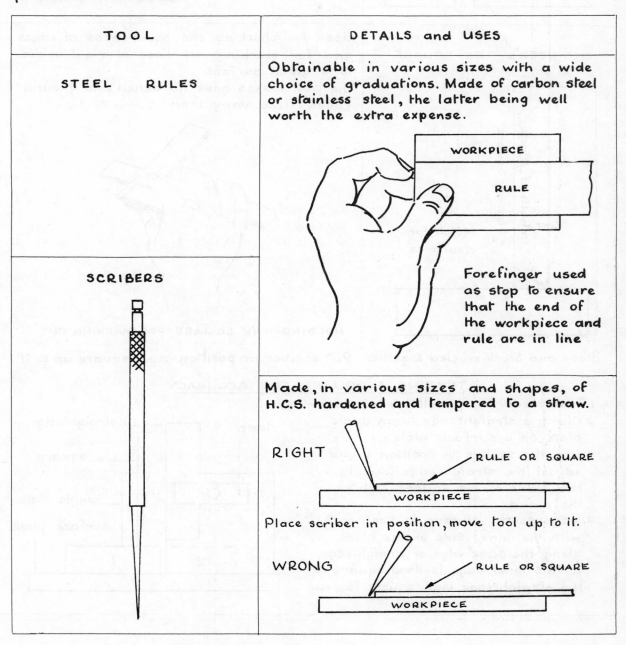

TOOL	DETAILS and USES
STEEL RULES	Obtainable in various sizes with a wide choice of graduations. Made of carbon steel or stainless steel, the latter being well worth the extra expense.
	WORKPIECE / RULE / Forefinger used as stop to ensure that the end of the workpiece and rule are in line
SCRIBERS	Made, in various sizes and shapes, of H.C.S. hardened and tempered to a straw.
	RIGHT — RULE OR SQUARE / WORKPIECE / Place scriber in position, move tool up to it.
	WRONG — RULE OR SQUARE / WORKPIECE

TOOL	DETAILS and USES
STRAIGHTEDGE bevelled 	Used for the accurate checking of surfaces for straightness. Two patterns are listed, one of hardened steel with a bevelled edge and the other of ribbed cast iron. Made in sizes from 50mm to 2·5m long and with an accuracy up to 0·002mm.
ENGINEER'S TRY-SQUARE 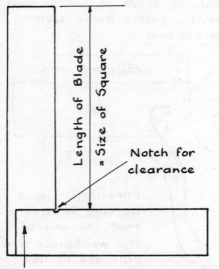 Length of Blade = Size of Square Notch for clearance Blade and Stock riveted together	Used for checking the squareness of edges and for marking out lines at right angles to a given surface. The best makes have hardened and ground faces. Sizes vary from 50mm to 1m.  **HOLDING THE SQUARE FOR MARKING OUT** Put scriber in position - move square up to it

TESTING A SQUARE FOR ACCURACY

1. Test blade for parallel with micrometer.
2. Clamp a straightedge to an angle plate on a surface plate.
3. Lay the square in position 1 and adjust the straightedge true to the blade of the square. Tighten the clamp.
4. Reverse the square to position 2, with the inner side of the blade along the same edge of straightedge. If this inner edge is dead square to the straightedge then square is true.

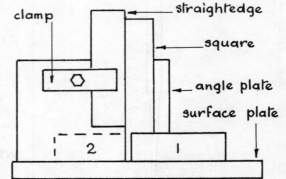

clamp — straightedge — square — angle plate — surface plate

TOOL	DETAILS and USES

COMBINATION SET

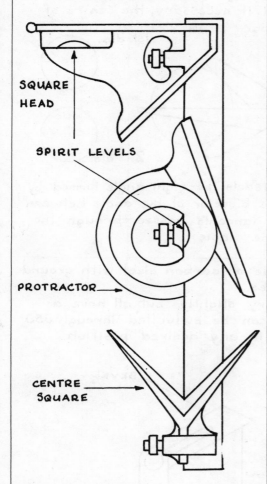

SQUARE HEAD

SPIRIT LEVELS

PROTRACTOR

CENTRE SQUARE

A set of four instruments in one —

1. A steel rule grooved at the back along which the other three instruments, known as heads, can slide.
2. The main head has one edge at 90° and the other at 45° to the rule. It is fitted with a spirit level. Used as a square, mitre square, depth gauge, etc.
3. A protractor enables the rule to be set at any desired angle.
4. A centre square is used to find the centres of circular bars.

All the heads can be locked at any desired position on the rule by knurled nuts.

Use of head as depth gauge

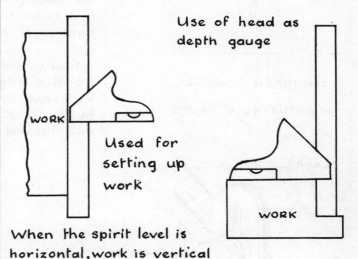

WORK

Used for setting up work

WORK

When the spirit level is horizontal, work is vertical

BOX SQUARE

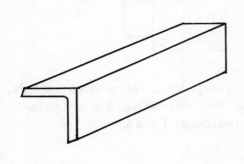

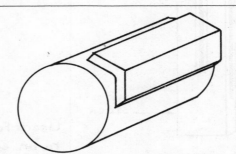

Similar to angle iron in shape. Used for scribing lines along the length of a bar

TOOL	DETAILS and USES
CENTRE SQUARE 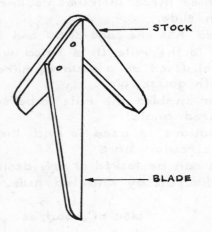	Made in various shapes. Used for marking lines diametrically across the end of a bar, and so to find, if necessary, the centre of the end of a bar. 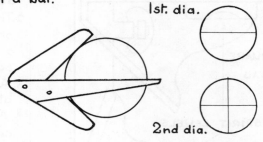 The blade bisects the right angle formed by the stock. (The bisector of the angle between two common tangents passes through the centre of the circle.)
ENGINEER'S BEVEL **or ADJUSTABLE BEVEL** 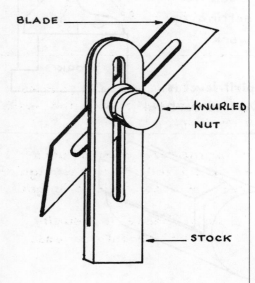	Usually made of carbon steel with ground parallel edges. Patterns vary slightly but all have a blade that can be swivelled through 360° and locked in any desired position. 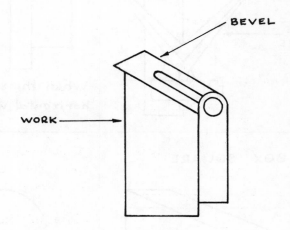 Used for marking lines at a given angle to an edge or for checking the angular accuracy of inclined faces.

TOOL	DETAILS and USES
DIVIDERS 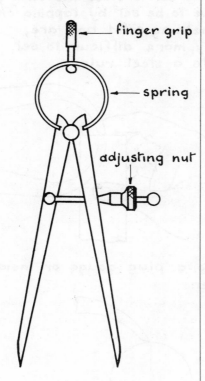 finger grip — spring — adjusting nut	Used for 1. scribing circles and curves 2. stepping off distances. 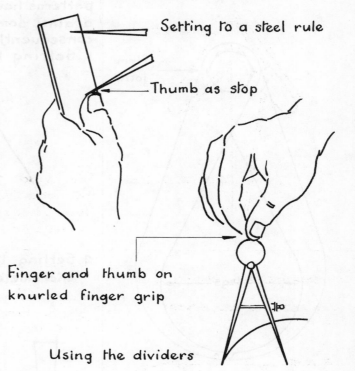 Setting to a steel rule — Thumb as stop — Finger and thumb on knurled finger grip — Using the dividers
TRAMMEL POINTS 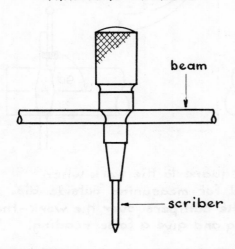 beam — scriber	Used for drawing large diameter circles or stepping off distances beyond the limits of a pair of dividers. The heads or points are always used in pairs and are fixed to a rectangular or round beam of a convenient length. One of the pair of heads is usually fitted with a fine adjustment for ease of setting.

TOOL	DETAILS and USES

OUTSIDE CALLIPERS

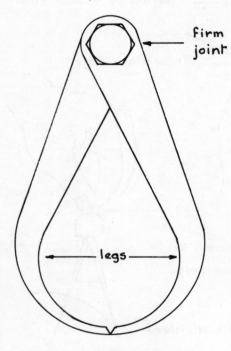

Firm joint pattern

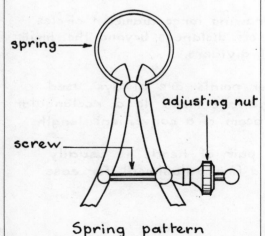

Spring pattern

Spring callipers with screw and adjusting nut are easy to set to size. The firm joint patterns have to be set by tapping one leg against something solid and are, consequently, more difficult to set.

1. Setting to a steel rule.

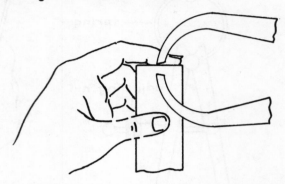

2. Setting to a plug gauge or inside micrometer.

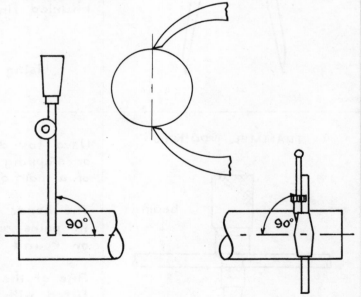

Must be held square to the work when checking. Used for measuring outside dia. Never force the callipers over the work — the legs will spring and give a false reading.

TOOL	DETAILS and USES

TOOL

INSIDE CALLIPERS

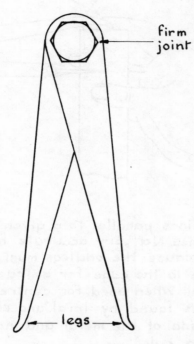

firm joint

Firm joint pattern

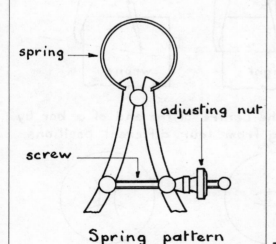

spring

screw

adjusting nut

Spring pattern

DETAILS and USES

Constructional details are the same as the outside callipers.
Used for checking inside diameters. One leg is held in contact with the bore while the other is rotated through an arc to get the correct "feel". No force should be used to do the measuring.

Methods of Setting

A flat face to act as a stop

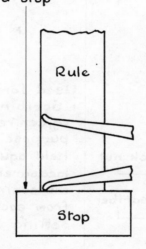

Rule

Stop

1. To a steel rule

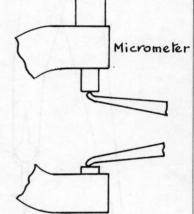

Micrometer

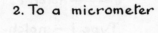

2. To a micrometer

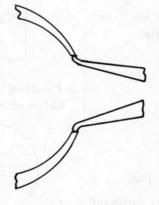

3. To outside callipers

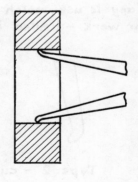

4. To a ring gauge

43

TOOL	DETAILS and USES

TOOL

ODD LEG CALLIPERS
(JENNY OR HERMAPHRODITE CAL'S)

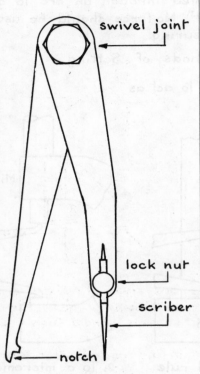

swivel joint

lock nut

scriber

notch

Type 1 - notched leg.

Easy to use, notch hooks on rule or work — limited in scope.

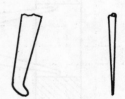

Type 2 - curved leg.

Curved leg needs finger support for setting - less limited in scope.

DETAILS and USES

Body made of steel with a scriber of H.C.S. hardened and tempered to a straw. The size is set by a steel rule using the fingers to support the leg

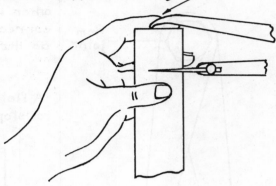

Used for

1. Scribing lines parallel to a given edge, eg, centre lines. Not very accurate for this purpose because the oddlegs must be held square to the edge for a true measurement. When used for centre lines the centre is found by trial and error from each side of the metal and not by setting to a rule.

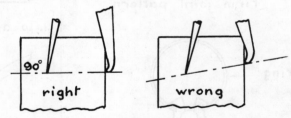

90°

right   wrong

2. Finding the centre of the end of a bar by estimating from four different positions.

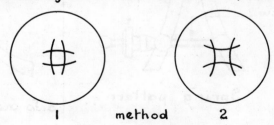

1   method   2

TOOL	DETAILS and USES

VEE BLOCKS

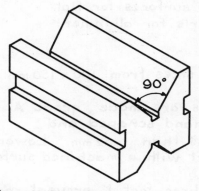

Small Vee Block

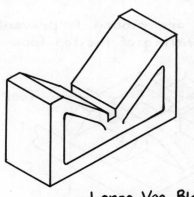

Large Vee Block

Made in pairs exactly alike in shape and size, and often with two vees, one larger than the other. The sloping faces are at 90° with a groove at the base of the vee for clearance.

Small sizes are made of H.C.S. hardened and ground and provided with a clamp for holding the work.

clamp

work

vee block

Larger sizes are made of C.I. and are not provided with a clamp because the weight of the work is enough to hold it in position.

Used for supporting round stock for marking out or for drilling.

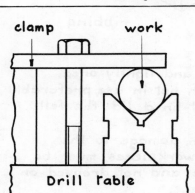

clamp   work

Holding work for drilling

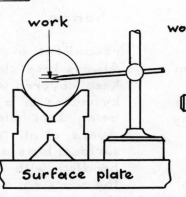

work

Surface plate

Marking centre lines

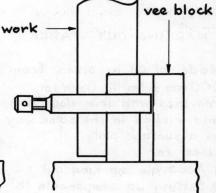

work   vee block

Holding round stock vertically

TOOL	DETAILS and USES

SURFACE PLATE

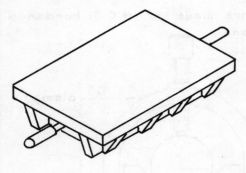

Surface plates are used for:
1. Accurate marking out.
2. Checking of surfaces for flat.
3. Checking parts for alignment height, etc.

Made of C.I. in sizes from 100 x 150 mm to 1m square.
Various grades are made, grade A plates being hand scraped and accurate to less than 0.02mm. Lower grades are left with a machined surface.

Provided with three feet to prevent rock and give stability, and with two handles for carrying.
The undersides are ribbed to prevent warping and twisting of the top face

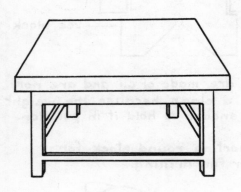

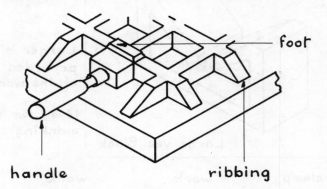

foot

handle   ribbing

MARKING-OUT TABLE

Made of C.I. in sizes from 300mm x 1m to 6m x 1m.
Provided with four stout legs and ribbed in the same way as a surface plate.
Used for
1. Accurate marking out.
2. Setting up components to be checked for accuracy, parallelism, alignment etc.

Precautions in use.
1. Always keep clean and lightly oiled.
2. Keep covered when not in use, preferably by means of a felt-lined lid, the felt being kept oiled.
3. Avoid, at all times, damage to the surface. Tools and workpieces must be handled with care and not dropped on the working surface.
4. Never use it for work for which it is not intended.

TOOL	DETAILS and USES
ANGLE PLATE 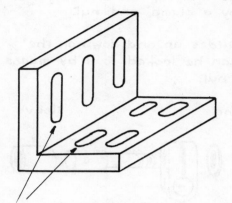 Slots for bolting down	Made of cast iron and machined accurately on the outer faces and the edges. They range in size from 75mm to 300mm long. Used for supporting work for marking out and machining. 1. Supporting the work and rule for marking out. 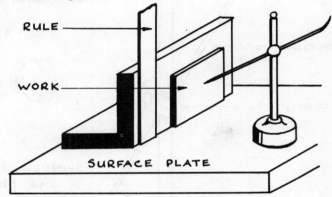 RULE WORK SURFACE PLATE
ENGINEER'S PROTRACTOR 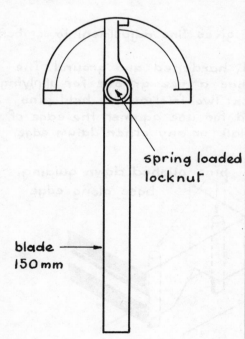 spring loaded locknut blade 150mm	2. Supporting work for turning. 3. Supporting work for drilling. 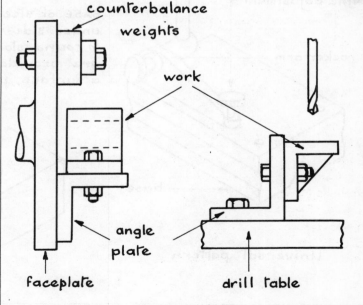 counterbalance weights work angle plate faceplate drill table

TOOL	DETAILS and USES

SURFACE GAUGE OR SCRIBING BLOCK

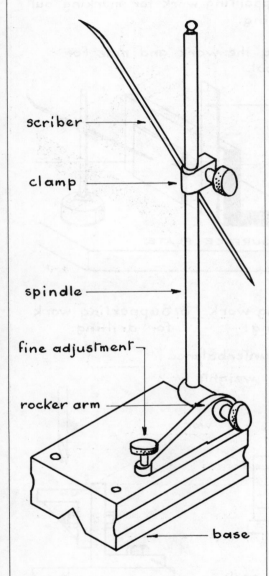

scriber

clamp

spindle

fine adjustment

rocker arm

base

Universal pattern

SCRIBER made of H.C.S. hardened and tempered to a straw. One end is straight and the other curved. Fully adjustable on the spindle and capable of being locked in position by a clamp and nut.

CLAMP. This slides up and down on the spindle and can be locked to it by means of a knurled nut.

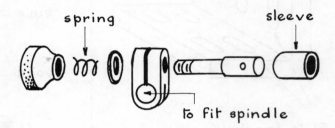

spring

sleeve

to fit spindle

SPINDLE fixed to base and able to swivel in one plane. It is locked to the rocker arm by means of a collar and knurled nut.

ROCKER ARM gives fine adjustment to scriber.

BASE of steel, hardened and ground. The under side has a vee groove for applying to round stock. Two frictionally held pins are provided for use against the edge of a surface plate or any other datum edge.

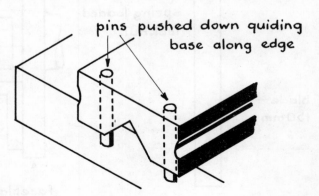

pins pushed down guiding base along edge

TOOL	DETAILS and USES

TOOL

SURFACE GAUGE
plain type

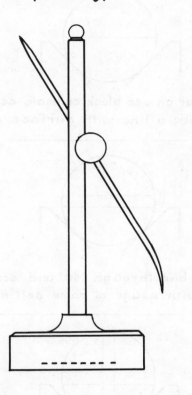

DETAILS and USES

USES
1. Marking out on a surface plate or marking-off table.

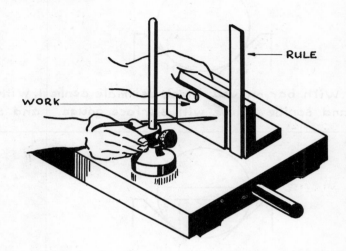

RULE

WORK

2. Testing for parallelism or alignment.

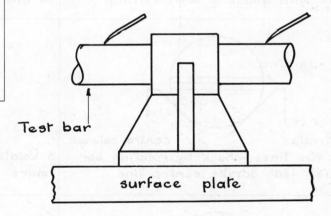

Test bar

surface plate

Testing the bore of a casting for parallel with the base.

3. Trueing work in the lathe.

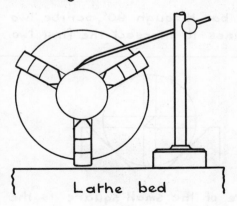

Lathe bed

4. Finding the centre of the end of a bar - see next page.

FINDING THE CENTRE OF THE END OF A BAR WITH A SURFACE GAUGE

METHOD 1	METHOD 2
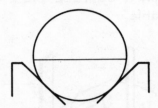	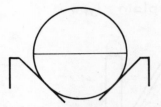
1. With bar on vee block estimate centre and scribe a line with surface gauge.	1. With bar on vee block estimate centre and scribe a line with surface gauge.
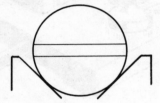	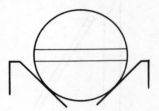
2. Rotate bar through 180° and scribe a line with gauge at same setting.	2. Rotate bar through 180° and scribe a line with gauge at same setting.
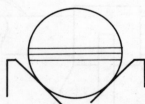	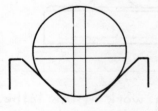
3. Estimate centre between these two lines, check by rotating bar through 180°. Scribe centre line.	3. Rotate bar through 90°, scribe two more lines to intersect the first two.
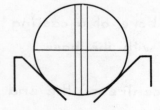	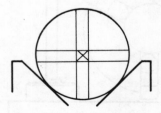
4. Rotate bar through 90° and scribe a second centre line to intersect the first.	4. Centre of the small square is the bar centre.

TOOL	DETAILS and USES
PARALLEL STRIPS 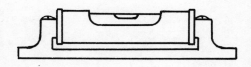	Used for supporting work horizontally on the marking-off table. Made of either C.I. machined and scraped or H.C.S. hardened and ground. 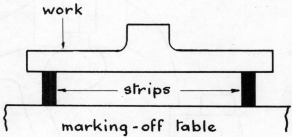 The length of the strips is unimportant but each pair must be exactly the same in width with all faces square and parallel.
SPIRIT LEVEL	When the bubble is central the level is horizontal. Useful for levelling machine beds and tables. Provided a drill table is horizontal, then the spirit level becomes useful for setting surfaces parallel to it, thus ensuring drilling square to a surface.

FITTER'S VICE

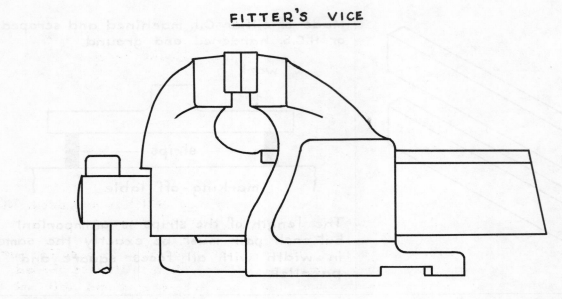

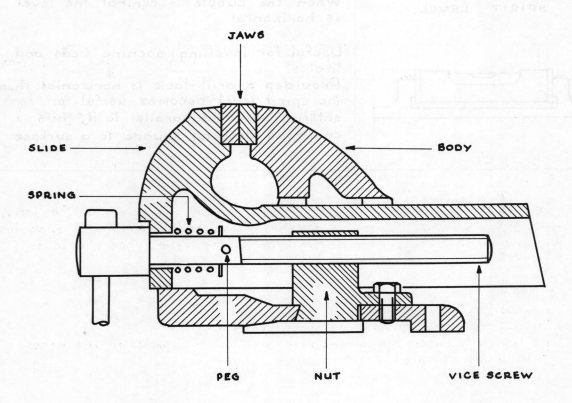

JAWS

SLIDE

BODY

SPRING

PEG

NUT

VICE SCREW

<u>BODY</u> - of cast iron or steel, the latter being more expensive but stronger.

<u>JAWS</u> - of hardened steel, serrated on the inside to help the grip and capable of being renewed when worn. To avoid damage to finished

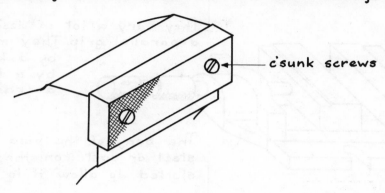

c'sunk screws

work by the jaws, clamps of steel, copper, lead or fibre are used. The jaws give a parallel grip throughout their full movement.

<u>SCREW</u> - machined with a square thread which engages with a solid nut in the vice body. Some vices are fitted with a buttress thread and quick release mechanism. These are time-saving but will not stand up to heavy work. In use a lever pulls a half nut away from the screw, thus disengaging it.

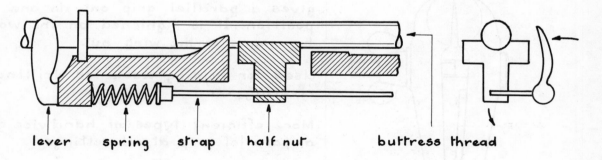

lever   spring   strap   half nut   buttress thread

Vices are made in various sizes and specified by the width of the jaws, a common size being 100mm. The height of the bench should be such that the worker's elbow is level with the top of the vice when he is in position for filing.

ALWAYS 1. Keep the vice clean.
2. Oil the screw regularly.
NEVER 1. Use the vice as an anvil for hammering on.
2 Use a hammer or wrench to tighten the jaws or the screw will be strained.

TOOL	DETAILS and USES
MACHINE VICE 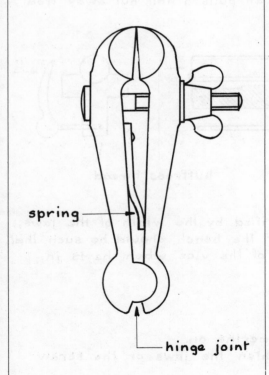	Machine vices are used to hold work for drilling, shaping, etc. They vary a lot in design but all give a parallel grip. They may be tightened by a knurled handle, by a tommy bar or by a cranked handle. The body of the vice may be made of steel or cast iron, the base being slotted to allow it to be bolted down. For light drilling the vice can be held by hand.
HAND VICE 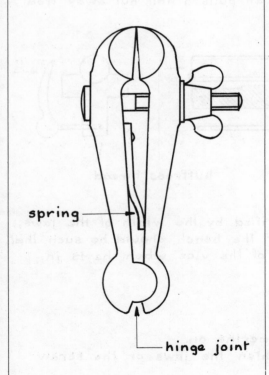 spring hinge joint	The most common pattern is the Lancashire hand vice as shown, but it is relatively inefficient because it works on the same principle as the leg vice and gives a parallel grip only in one position. It is tightened on the work by means of the wing nut. Used for holding work for drilling, riveting, etc. More efficient types of hand vice give a parallel grip at all settings. 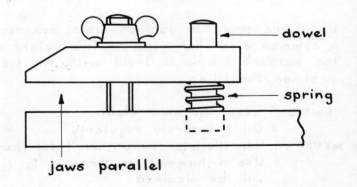 dowel spring jaws parallel

TOOL	DETAILS and USES
TOOLMAKER'S CLAMP 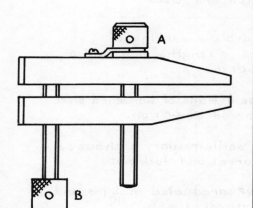	Made of case-hardened mild steel. A clip screwed to the top jaw prevents the jaws falling together when being adjusted. Gives a parallel grip in all positions. The jaws are adjusted to approx. the correct position and final tightening done by first tightening screw A and then screw B. Various sizes are made with jaws from 50 to 150 mm long. Used for holding small pieces together for assembling, riveting or screwing.
PLIERS 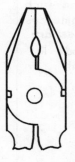  Combination Flat Nose 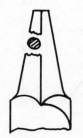  Round Nose End Cutters	Pliers are useful general purpose holding tools. They are made in many shapes and sizes. The size is denoted by the overall length, a common size is 125 or 150 mm. Combination pliers are provided with cutting edges and they will hold round and flat material. Flat nose pliers are used for flat material. Round nose pliers are used for round material. End cutters are used for cutting wire, etc. **NEVER USE PLIERS FOR WORK FOR WHICH THEY ARE NOT INTENDED.**

5   GAUGES

TOOL	DETAILS and USES
EXTERNAL MICROMETER	Used for the accurate measuring of external diameters or lengths to a limit of 0·001 in. or 0·0001 in. SPINDLE and SCREW made of hardened steel with a ground thread of 40 t.p.i. FRAME - roughly semicircular in shape, holding anvil, barrel and lock nut. BARREL or SLEEVE graduated in $\frac{1}{10}$ ths. and $\frac{1}{40}$ ths. for a length of 1 inch. THIMBLE rotates around the barrel and is divided on its circumference into 25 divs. RATCHET. This provides the correct feel. Measurement is over a distance of one inch on the smaller micrometers but micrometers are made to read up to 24 in. These are usually provided with extension rods to increase the range of measurement.

ratcher, thimble, locking ring, barrel, spindle, anvil, frame, spindle lock

Alternative spindle lock

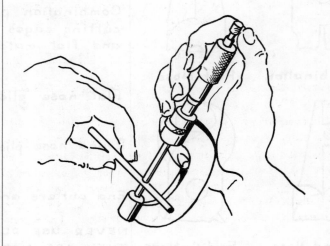

The micrometer in use

PRINCIPLE OF THE IMPERIAL MICROMETER

<u>The screw</u> is threaded 40 t.p.i. Therefore with one complete revolution of the thimble, the spindle moves $\frac{1}{40}$th. or 0·025 in.

<u>The thimble</u> is divided on its circumference into 25 parts. If the thimble is turned along one of these divisions the spindle will move $\frac{1}{25}$th. of $\frac{1}{40}$th.= 0·001." Therefore each division on the thimble represents 0·001 in.

<u>The barrel</u> carries a datum line with each tenth divided into four parts, ie. $\frac{1}{40}$ths or 0·025 in. When the micrometer is closed the "0" on the thimble coincides with the "0" line on the barrel.

READING THE MICROMETER

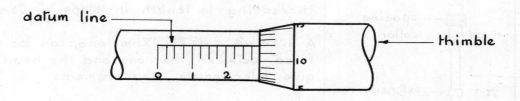

1. Read the largest whole number visible on the barrel - 2   = 0·200
2. Read the complete subdivisions after the 2 on the barrel - 3 = 0·075
3. Read the figure on the thimble before the datum line - 10   = 0·010
4. Read the extra divisions before the datum line - 2   = 0·002
                                                             0·287

Some micrometers read to 0·0001 in. They are similar to the 0·001 in. micrometer but they have a vernier attachment on the barrel, ten graduations on the vernier being equal to nine divisions on the thimble.

PRECAUTIONS IN THE USE OF THE MICROMETER

1. The micrometer is a precision instrument. Treat it with care at all times.
2. It must not be allowed to come into contact with harmful materials, eg. filings.
3. Do not allow tools to come in contact with it on workbench or machine.
4. Spindle, anvil and work must be wiped clean before using.
5. It must be held square to the work when measuring.
6. Do not use force when obtaining the correct "feel."
7. Store away safely in a container immediately after use.
8. Do not set the micrometer to a size and try to push it over the work.
9. A periodic check on its accuracy is needed.

TOOL	DETAILS and USES
INTERNAL MICROMETER 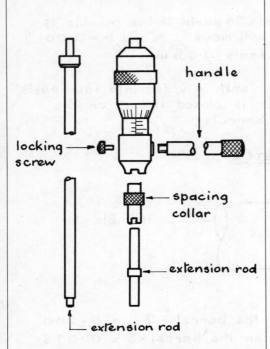	The INTERNAL MICROMETER is used for the accurate measuring of internal diameters. The HEAD is similar to the barrel and thimble of the external micrometer but its range of adjustment is only 13mm. The length is usually 25mm which means that that is the smallest bore it will enter. EXTENSION RODS are bars of different lengths that can be fixed and locked in position to increase its range. Each head is usually accompanied by a set of rods increasing in length in steps of 25mm. A SPACING COLLAR, 12mm long, can be fixed between the rods and the head to give intermediate measurements. A HANDLE can be screwed into the head for reaching into deep holes.

Labels on diagram: handle, locking screw, spacing collar, extension rod, extension rod

METRIC MICROMETER

Metric micrometers are similar in construction to the imperial micrometer. They have threads of metric pitch and read in millimetres. The range of measurement is over 25 mm, eg. 0 to 25mm, 25 to 50 mm etc.

The screw has a pitch of $\frac{1}{2}$ mm and therefore the spindle moves 0.5 mm for each turn of the thimble.

The barrel is graduated in millimetres and half millimetres.

The thimble is divided into 50 parts, therefore a movement of one division on the thimble moves the spindle $\frac{1}{50}$ th of $\frac{1}{2}$ mm = $\frac{1}{100}$ mm = 0.01mm.

The readings are taken in the same order as the imperial micrometer.

METRIC MICROMETER

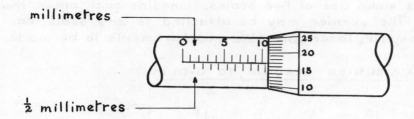

1. Highest whole number visible on the barrel - 10 = 10·00 mm
2. Additional subdivisions visible on the barrel - 1 = 0·50 mm
3. Figure visible on thimble before datum line - 15 = 0·15 mm
4. Any additional divisions on thimble before datum - 2 = 0·02 mm

                                                         10·67 mm

MICROMETER DEPTH GAUGE

Range usually 0 to 25mm
with extension rods to
increase the range.

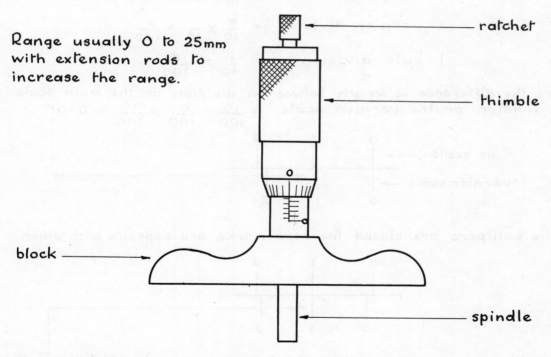

A standard depth gauge with a micrometer attachment to give
readings to 0·01 mm.
Used for the accurate testing of depths of holes, shoulders, recesses, etc.

VERNIER SCALES

VERNIER SCALES always make use of two scales, alongside each other, that are slightly different. The vernier may be attached to any scale, eg. protractor, rule, micrometer, to enable fine measurements to be made.

A VERNIER READING TO 0·01 in.

FIXED SCALE or RULE SCALE marked in inches and $\frac{1}{10}$th. in.
VERNIER SCALE. A length of $\frac{9}{10}$ths is divided into 10 parts.

$$10 \text{ vernier divisions} = \frac{9}{10} \text{ ths.}$$

$$1 \text{ vernier division} = \frac{9}{10} \times \frac{1}{10} = \frac{9}{100}$$

$$1 \text{ rule division} = \frac{1}{10} = \frac{10}{100}$$

Therefore the difference in length between a division on the main scale and a division on the vernier scale $= \frac{10}{100} - \frac{9}{100} = \frac{1}{100} = 0·01$

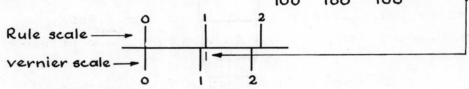

When the callipers are closed the zero marks are opposite each other.

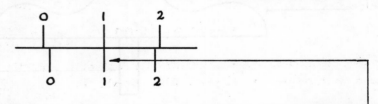

When the callipers are opened 0·01 the 1st. line on each scale will be opposite. When the callipers are opened 0·02 the 2nd line on each scale will be opposite until the zero mark on the vernier is opposite the first $\frac{1}{10}$ division on the main scale when the callipers will be set to $\frac{1}{10}$th.

TO TAKE A READING

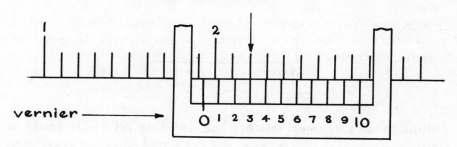

1. Read the biggest whole number on main scale before "O" on vernier: 1. = 1·0
2. Read the number of tenths before the "O" on vernier: 9, = 0·9
3. Read on the vernier scale the number alongside the line
   that coincides with any line on the main scale: 3.   = 0·03

                                              Total reading = 1·93

A VERNIER READING TO 0·001 in.

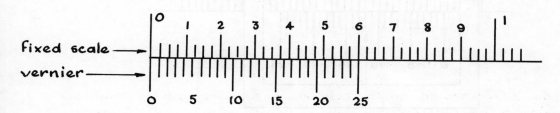

FIXED SCALE graduated in inches, $\frac{1}{10}$ ths. and $\frac{1}{40}$ ths.

VERNIER SCALE. A length of 24 divisions on the main scale is divided into 25 parts.

$$25 \text{ vernier divisions} = \frac{6}{10} = \frac{24}{40} \text{ in.}$$

$$1 \text{ vernier division} = \frac{24}{40} \times \frac{1}{25} = \frac{24}{1000} \text{ in.}$$

$$1 \text{ rule division} = \frac{1}{40} = \frac{25}{1000} \text{ in.}$$

Therefore the difference in length between a division on the main scale and a division on the vernier scale is $\frac{25}{1000} - \frac{24}{1000} = \frac{1}{1000} = 0·001$ in.

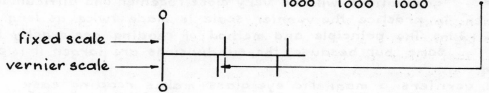

When the callipers are closed the zero marks are opposite each other.

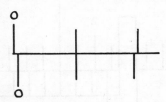

When the callipers are opened 0.001, the 1st. line on each scale will be opposite.
When the callipers are opened 0.002, the 2nd. line on each scale will be opposite.
When the zero mark on the vernier is opposite the 1st. $\frac{1}{40}$ th. division on the main scale, then the callipers will be set at $\frac{1}{40}$ th or 0.025 in.

TO TAKE A READING

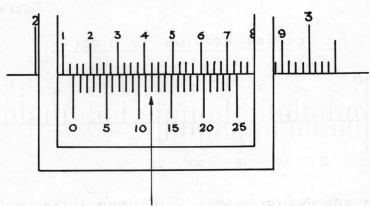

1. Read the biggest whole number on main scale before "0" on vernier: 2 = 2.0
2. Read the number of $\frac{1}{10}$ ths. on the main scale before "0" on vernier: 1 = 0.1
3. Read the number of $\frac{1}{40}$ ths. on the main scale before "0" on vernier: 1 = 0.025
4. Look for the line on the vernier scale that coincides with any

line on the main scale. The number at this line is $\frac{1}{1000}$ ths.   12 = 0.012
                                                        Complete reading = 2.137

With this type of vernier the scale will be relatively short in length
$\frac{24}{40} = \frac{6}{10}$ ths., which means that when subdivided into 25 parts the
                graduations will be very close together and difficult to read.
Very often, in practice the vernier scale is made twice as long.
ie. $\frac{48}{40} = 1\frac{2}{10}$ ths. The principle and method of reading are exactly the
                same but because the subdivisions are larger it is easier
to read.
For all verniers a magnetic eye glass makes reading easy.

METRIC VERNIER

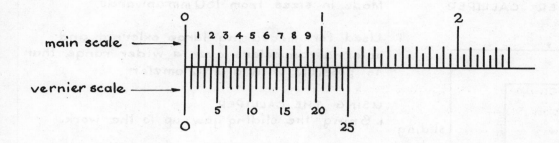

main scale

vernier scale

The MAIN SCALE is graduated in millimetres and half millimetres.
The VERNIER SCALE. A length of 12mm on the main scale is divided
into 25 parts

$$25 \text{ vernier divisions} = 12 \text{ mm}$$

$$1 \text{ vernier division} = \frac{12}{25} = 0.48 \text{ mm}$$

$$1 \text{ rule division} = 0.5 \text{ mm}$$

Therefore the difference in length between a division on the main
scale and one on the vernier scale = 0.5 - 0.48 = 0.02 mm

TO TAKE A READING

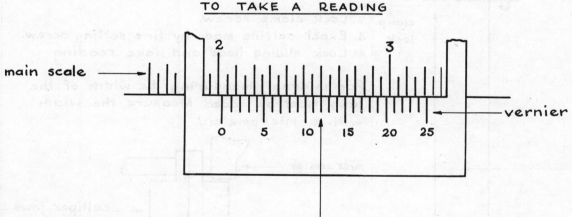

main scale

vernier

1. On the main scale read the complete number of mm and ½ mm
   before the zero on the vernier   = 20.0

2. Read the mark on the vernier scale that coincides with
   a mark on the main scale. This will be the number of 0.02mm
   so that the number will have to be doubled, i.e. 12 × 0.02 = <u>0.24</u>

                                          Total reading = 20.24mm

TOOL	DETAILS and USES

VERNIER CALLIPER

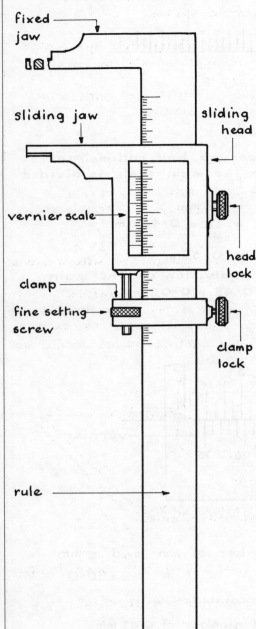

fixed jaw

sliding jaw

sliding head

vernier scale

head lock

clamp

fine setting screw

clamp lock

rule

Made in sizes from 150 mm upwards.

Used for measuring large external and internal diameters over a wider range than is possible with a micrometer.

USING THE CALLIPER
1. Bring the sliding jaw up to the work.

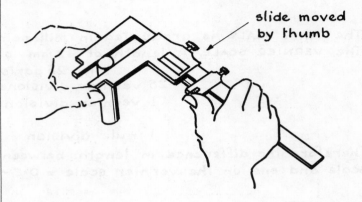

slide moved by thumb

2. Lock clamp screw.
3. Exact setting made by fine setting screw.
4. Lock sliding head and take reading.

For internal measuring the width of the jaws must be added. Measure the width with a micrometer.

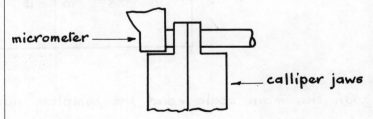

micrometer

calliper jaws

USE GREAT CARE WHEN SETTING THE CALLIPERS. Make use of the fine adjustment and never use force. The jaws can be easily strained and the callipers ruined.

TOOL	DETAILS and USES

VERNIER HEIGHT GAUGE

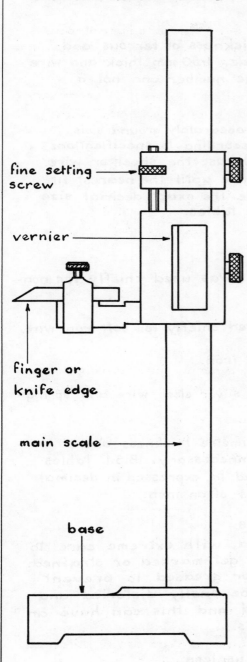

fine setting screw

vernier

finger or knife edge

main scale

base

BASE, heavy, hardened steel with a ground finish on the underside and recessed to reduce the bearing surface.

MAIN SCALE, a heavy gauge rule graduated like a vernier calliper in millimetres.

VERNIER, reading to 0·02 mm with a lock and fine adjustment screws.

FINGER or knife edge made of steel hardened and ground.

Made in a range of sizes but those commonly in use measure to 300-450 mm.

USES - basically the same range of work as the surface gauge but where more accuracy is needed.
N. B. A height gauge is an expensive precision instrument. It must be treated with great care and must never be used for work where a surface gauge would be sufficiently accurate.

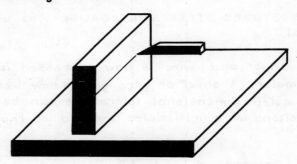

1. Accurate marking out to close limits ie. 0·02 mm.
2. Testing components for parallel.
3. Testing components for height, alignment, etc.

GAUGES

<u>WORKSHOP GAUGES</u> are used for testing components for size. They are usually a fixed size and non-adjustable.

<u>WIRE GAUGES</u> were used to determine the thickness of ferrous and non-ferrous sheet and wire. All sheet metal under 1·50 mm thick and wire under 1·50 mm dia. was specified by a gauge number and not a fractional thickness.

The gauges were hardened flat steel plates with accurately ground slots around their edges, each slot being numbered according to specifications laid down by B.S.I. (British Standard Institute) In use the sheet or wire was tried in the various slots of the gauge plate until the nearest fit was obtained and the number read off alongside. The exact decimal size of the slots could be obtained from reference tables.

The most common wire gauges used were:

THE IMPERIAL STANDARD WIRE GAUGE, I.S.W.G., was used chiefly for non-ferrous metals.

THE BIRMINGHAM WIRE GAUGE, B.W.G., was used chiefly for soft iron wire.

THE BIRMINGHAM GAUGE was used for sheet iron.

THE STUBBS STEEL WIRE GAUGE was used for silver steel wire and spring steel.

All sheet and wire is now expressed as a millimetre thickness and diameter. A sheet or wire gauge now becomes unnecessary. B.S.I. tables of metric dimensional tolerances can be referred to, expressed in decimal fractions of a millimetre instead of thousandths of an inch.

CARE OF GAUGES

All gauges should be used and treated with extreme care to ensure that the working surfaces do not get marked or strained. When not in use they should be oiled or greased to prevent corrosion. Thin gauges particularly can be easily distorted and even expanded with the heat of the hand and this can have an adverse effect when checking to fine limits.

<u>An inaccurate gauge is useless</u>

TOOL	DETAILS and USES
RING GAUGE 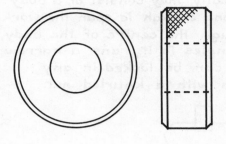	Used, in conjunction with a male plug gauge of the same nominal size, for testing external diameters. Limited in use because 1. It does not provide any limits. 2. It has to be tried over the end of a shaft and this is often inconvenient, eg. when working on centres. 3. It needs to be worked along the whole length of a shaft in order to test whether it is parallel.
SLIP GAUGES 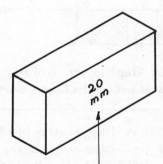 All faces parallel 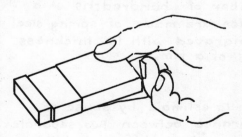 Slip gauges "wrung" together to form a block	Slip gauges or block gauges are rectangular pieces of hardened steel with very accurate parallel faces. They were invented by the Swedish engineer Johannson in 1903 and are often called Johannson blocks. They are very expensive and are sold in sets, eg. from 25·00 mm to 25·20 mm in steps of 0·02 mm making 11 slips in all. Metallic faces, when made very accurately flat, can be "wrung" together by carefully cleaning them, pressing them together and slightly twisting them. The two faces will adhere together and considerable force is necessary to separate them. In this way it is possible to "wring" a group of slip gauges together and handle them as one gauge block, the overall accuracy being to within 0·0002 mm. Used to verify dimensions or, combined in a frame, as accurate calliper gauges.

TOOL	DETAILS and USES

DEPTH GAUGE

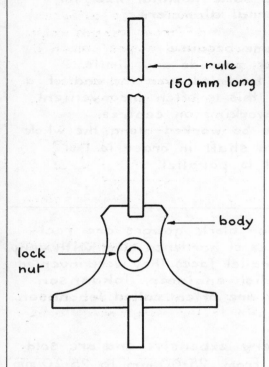

- rule 150 mm long
- body
- lock nut

DEPTH GAUGES vary in general form, some being very simple in design and others being elaborate with micrometer or vernier adjustments. Basically, they consist of a body which must be long enough to span the work concerned. Through the centre of the body, and at right angles to it, runs a narrow steel rule that can be locked in any desired position with a knurled nut.

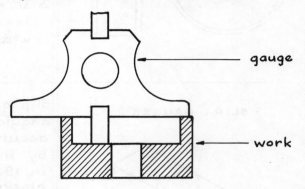

- gauge
- work

Used to measure the depths of holes, recesses and the distances between surfaces.

FEELER GAUGES

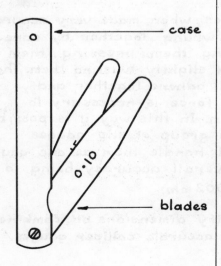

- case
- 0
- 0·10
- blades

Sets of feeler gauges look like multi-bladed penknives. A case is provided with a set of leaves or blades of different thicknesses, the thickness of each blade being equal to a certain number of hundredths of a mm. The blades are made of spring steel and each is engraved with its thickness in hundredths of a mm.

They are used to estimate, by sense of touch, the clearance between two separate components by inserting different blades or combination of blades until the thickness is found that will just go between the two surfaces.

TOOL	DETAILS and USES
SCREWCUTTING GAUGE or thread gauge 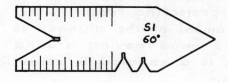 **Type 1** 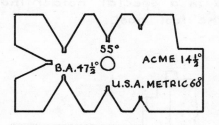 **Type 2**	Hardened steel plate with thread angles cut in the profile. Type 1. All angles the same, so a different gauge is needed for different thread angles. Type 2. All common thread angles cut on the same gauge. Used for 1. Testing the correct included angle of a lathe screwcutting tool. 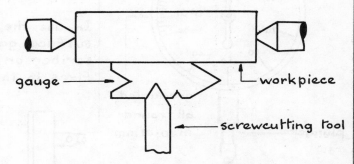 2. Setting the screwcutting tool at right angles to the component to be threaded.
SCREW-PITCH GAUGE 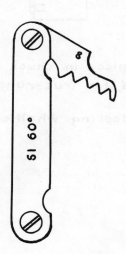	These resemble feeler gauges in general appearance, but the blades, of hardened steel, instead of being of varying thicknesses, have their edges cut with teeth corresponding in size and shape to different screw threads. Each blade of the set can be swivelled out of the holder and is marked with its t.p. 25mm or pitch. 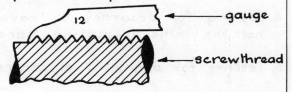 Used for determining the pitch of a thread by selecting a blade which fits.

TOOL	DETAILS and USES

DIAL INDICATOR
or clock gauge

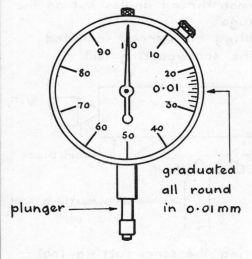

plunger →

graduated
all round
in 0·01 mm

The dial indicator is a sensitive instrument for comparing or testing the accuracy of surfaces. It gives no direct reading of size. The main dial is like a clock face and has a plunger projecting from it. The amount of movement of the plunger is registered by a hand moving around the dial which is graduated to read to 0·01 or 0·002 mm.

In use the indicator is clamped to the surface gauge spindle in place of the scriber or used in a special holder that fixes in the lathe tool post.

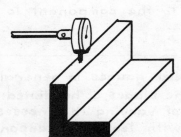

1. Testing for parallel.

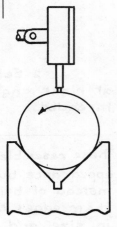

2. Testing for roundness.

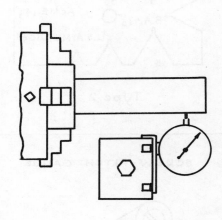

3. Workpiece in chuck being tested for true-running.

4. Testing for accuracy of traverse on a lathe, ie. testing whether or not the lathe is cutting parallel.

5. Testing for alignment of centres.

6. Testing tailstock set-over when taper turning.

7. Testing alignment of stroke, etc., on a shaper.

TOOL	DETAILS and USES

LIMIT GAUGES

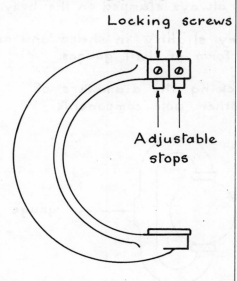

Locking screws

Adjustable stops

Adjustable Limit Calliper or Gap Gauge

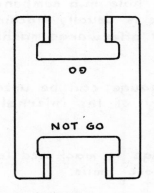

GO

NOT GO

Limit Plate Gauge

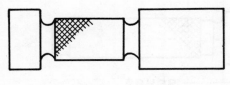

Limit Plug Gauge

LIMIT SYSTEMS

When a component has to be made to a particular size the problem arises as to the degree of accuracy that is needed on that particular component. The less accurately a component has to be made, the cheaper it will be, because many methods will be available to make it and less skill will be needed.

A limiting degree of accuracy will also make possible the interchangeability of parts.

For these reasons a working drawing should always state the permissible allowance - up and down - on the nominal size. This is called tolerance.

Tolerance is always stated as a number of hundredths of a mm above or below a nominal diameter.

eg. 1. $20.00 \begin{array}{c} +0.02 \\ -0.02 \end{array}$ means that the top limiting size is 20.02 mm and the bottom limiting size is 19.98 mm.

eg. 2. $20.00 \begin{array}{c} +0.02 \\ -0.00 \end{array}$ means that the tolerance is 0.02 mm above the nominal diameter with no allowance below that diameter.

LIMIT GAUGES are used where tolerances are given because the measuring of the work can be done more quickly and definitely.

They are usually double-ended, one end being machined to the lower limit (GO) and the other to the upper limit (NOT GO) Often the "GO" end is made longer than the "NOT GO" end because it would wear rapidly if short and would also tend to wedge in the hole. The "NOT GO" should never enter the hole so need only be long enough to carry its size.

TOOL	DETAILS and USES

CALLIPER GAUGE
or snap gauge

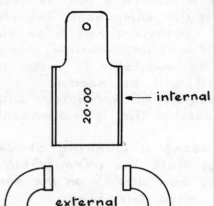

Often called snap gauges in the smaller sizes. Size is always stamped on the body.

They can vary slightly in shape and are often in the form of limit gauges.

Used for checking the diameters of shafts and other male components.

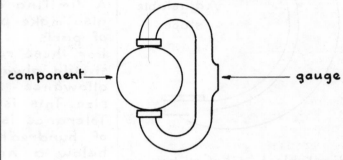

PLUG GAUGE

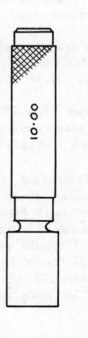

When machining a hole in a component to fit a shaft, the hole is usually machined first and the shaft afterwards machined to a fit.

A standard plug gauge can be used to check the accuracy of the internal machining.

The end of the gauge is machined to a standard size to close limits.

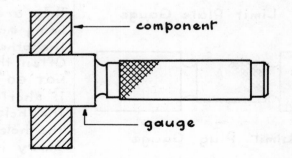

CARE OF GAUGES

1. Treat with extreme care to ensure that the working surfaces do not get marked.
2. When not in use oil them and store away carefully.
3. Thin gauges need particular care because they can expand and distort slightly with the heat of the hand.
4. Never use a gauge for work for which it is not intended.

MATERIAL FOR GAUGES

1. OIL-HARDENING STEEL. Less distortion occurs during hardening than when using a water-hardening steel.

2. CARBON STEEL, hardened and tempered or left "dead" hard. Warping often occurs during quenching and allowance for this has to be made so that the gauge can be ground after heat treatment.

3. MILD STEEL, case hardened. Useful for small temporary gauges. There is a risk of some distortion during heat treatment and no subsequent grinding is possible.

FITS

The system of fits and limits has been developed to ensure:
1. Interchangeability of parts.
2 The desired degree of fit on mating parts.

NOMINAL SIZE is the size by which a part is normally specified.

LIMITS are the two extreme sizes for that dimension, the high limit being the largest permissible size and the low limit the smallest.

TOLERANCE is the difference between the high and low limits.

FIT between two mating parts is the relationship between those two parts, allowing either clearance or interference.

THE NEWALL SYSTEM of limits is the one most widely used in this country. Tolerances are given under four headings and these vary for different diameters. The four headings are - running fits, push fits, force fits, driving fits. Tables can be referred to under these headings to obtain the correct tolerance for any given diameter.

6 SOLDERING AND BRAZING

SOLDERING is the process of joining metals together by means of heat and a suitable alloy.

SOFT SOLDERING is a low temperature form of soldering.

HARD SOLDERING, which includes brazing and silver soldering, is a high temperature form of soldering.

FLUXES are necessary for the following reasons:
1. They keep the metal clean during heating.
2 They break down the surface tension of the solder enabling it to flow.
3. Some fluxes, acid fluxes, clean the metal to a limited extent.
Paste fluxes, ie. non-corrosive fluxes, usually have a resin base.
Acid fluxes must not be used for electrical joints because they set up corrosion.
All fluxes should be thoroughly washed off after soldering.
Hard soldering fluxes, borax type, are removed by applying salt while the metal is hot or by immersion in an acid bath.
Aluminium is very difficult to solder as no effective flux so far has been discovered that is capable of preventing the formation of oxides and at the same time breaking down the surface tension.

SOFT SOLDERING makes use of soft solder which is an alloy of tin and lead with sometimes the addition of antimony and bismuth.
USES - for joints on light articles that will not have to withstand much heat and where great strength is not needed.
FLUXES - various, according to metal being soldered. See chart.
HEAT - low temperature, varying with composition of solder, supplied by soldering bit, bunsen or blowpipe.

METAL	FLUX
Brass	Zinc chloride or ammonium chloride
Copper	" " " "
Gunmetal	" " " "
Steel	" " " "
Britannia Metal	Tallow or olive oil
Pewter	" "
Lead	Tallow or resin
Tinplate	Zinc chloride
Galvanised Iron	Dilute hydrochloric acid
Zinc	" " "
Electrical Joints	Resin or "Fluxite"

SOLDERING BITS

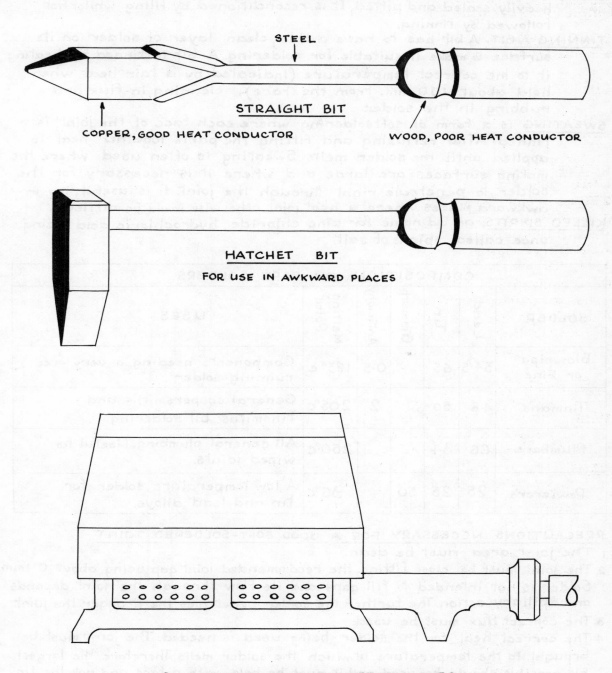

STEEL

STRAIGHT BIT

COPPER, GOOD HEAT CONDUCTOR

WOOD, POOR HEAT CONDUCTOR

HATCHET BIT

FOR USE IN AWKWARD PLACES

GAS HEATER FOR SOLDERING BITS

A "BURNT" IRON is a soldering bit that has been overheated and become heavily scaled and pitted. It is reconditioned by filing whilst hot followed by tinning.

TINNING A BIT. A bit has to have a thin, clean layer of solder on its surface to make it suitable for soldering. A bit is tinned by heating it to the correct temperature (indicated by a fair heat when held about 100 mm from the face), cleaning in flux and rubbing in the solder.

SWEATING is a form of softsoldering where each face of the joint is tinned. After refluxing and fitting the parts together heat is applied until the solder melts. Sweating is often used where the mating surfaces are large and where it is necessary for the solder to penetrate right through the joint. It is useful, too, in awkward places where a neat joint otherwise would be difficult.

KILLED SPIRITS, an old name for zinc chloride, hydrochloric acid being once called spirits of salt.

COMPOSITION OF SOFT SOLDERS						
SOLDER	Lead	Tin	Bismuth	Antimony	Melting Point	USES
Blowpipe or Fine	34·5	65		0·5	183°c	Components needing a very free running solder.
Tinman's	48	50		2	205°c	General coppersmith's and tinsmith's bit soldering.
Plumber's	66	34			250°c	All general plumbing. Useful for wiped joints.
Pewterer's	25	25	50		96°c	A low temperature solder for tin and lead alloys.

PRECAUTIONS NECESSARY FOR A GOOD SOFT-SOLDERED JOINT

1. The joint area must be clean.
2. The joint must be close fitting, the recommended joint gap being about 0·1mm. Solder is not intended to fill gaps and its flow through the joint depends on capillary action. The further the solder penetrates the stronger the joint.
3. The correct flux must be used.
4. The correct heat for the solder being used is needed. The joint must be brought to the temperature at which the solder melts. Therefore the largest bit possible should be used and it must be held with a face and not the tip in contact long enough for heat to flow by conduction. Insufficient heat is a common failing.
5. The bit must be in good condition, not "burnt", and properly tinned.
6. The joint must be washed after soldering.

HARD SOLDERING - Brazing and Silver Soldering.

BRAZING makes use of a solder, often called spelter, which is an alloy of copper and zinc in strip, wire or granulated form.

USES - joints that are relatively strong and (or) have to withstand a reasonable heat.

FLUX - borax.

HEAT - bright red (900°c approx.) supplied by a blowpipe.

PRECAUTIONS NECESSARY FOR A GOOD BRAZED JOINT

1. The joint must be clean.
2. The joint must be reasonably tight. The gap necessary will vary according to the particular joint, averaging 0.10mm.
3. The right flux must be used.
4. The work should be packed round with firebrick to conserve heat.
5. The correct heat for the solder being used must be obtained. Remember that the joint must be heated to the temperature at which the solder melts.
6. Avoid prolonged heating. This causes scale to work into the joint.
7. Concentrate the heat on the larger mass of metal so that both parts of the joint are brought to the correct heat together.
8. Dip the solder into flux before applying.
9. Allow the strip solder to become heated by conduction from the hot metal and not by means of direct heat from the flame.
10. Use the minimum amount of solder.

COMPOSITION OF HARD SOLDERS							
SOLDER	Silver	Copper	Zinc	Cadmium	Melting Point	FLUX	USES
B.S. GRADE A	61	29	10	-	735°c	"Tenacity"	Has a high conductivity, therefore used for electrical joints.
B.S. GRADE B	43	37	20	-	780°c	"Tenacity"	General purposes and where the high M.P. is no disadvantage.
B.S. GRADE C (Easyflo)	50	15	16	19	630°c	"Easyflo"	For jointing dissimilar metals. Fluidity and low M.P. makes it easy to use.
SOFT SPELTER B.S. GRADE B	-	50	50	-	880°c	Borax	For medium strength joints.
MEDIUM SPELTER B.S. GRADE A	-	54	46	-	885°c	Borax	For strong joints.
HARD SPELTER B.S. GRADE AA	-	60	40	-	890°c	Borax	For very strong joints.

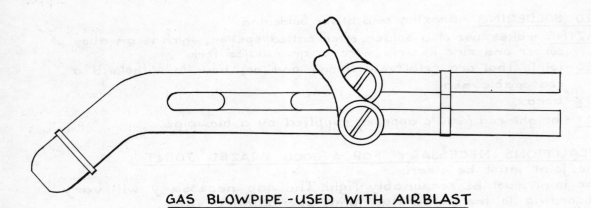

GAS BLOWPIPE - USED WITH AIRBLAST

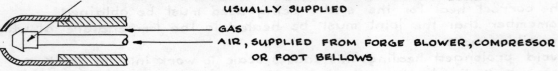

A SET OF INTERCHANGEABLE NOZZLES OF DIFFERENT BORE
USUALLY SUPPLIED

← GAS
← AIR, SUPPLIED FROM FORGE BLOWER, COMPRESSOR
    OR FOOT BELLOWS

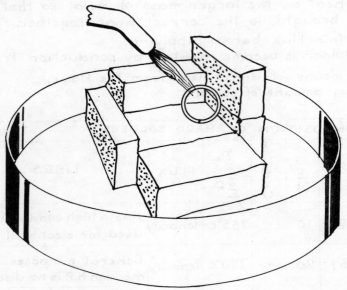

BLOWPIPE IN USE ON A BRAZING HEARTH. A BRAZED JOINT IN A RING IS
BEING MADE. NOTE THAT FIREBRICKS ARE WELL PACKED ROUND TO GIVE
REFLECTED HEAT AND THAT HEAT IS FIRST BEING APPLIED AT A POINT
FURTHEST FROM THE JOINT CAUSING THE METAL TO EXPAND, BRINGING THE
JOINT CLOSE TOGETHER.

SILVER SOLDERING makes use of a solder which is an alloy of copper zinc and silver.

<u>USES</u> - The solder melts at a low temperature and is therefore useful for brass. A range of solders is available that melt at different temperatures and by using them work can be built up in parts using the higher melting point solders first.

<u>FLUX</u> - For solders that melt below 750°C use "Easyflo" flux. For solders that melt above 750°C use "Tenacity". This flux is also particularly useful for large assemblies in steel and for stainless steel. Both fluxes are removed by light wire brushing after soaking in hot water.

<u>HEAT</u> - varying between 610°C and 830°C according to the composition of the solder.

<u>PRECAUTIONS NECESSARY FOR A GOOD JOINT</u> - as for brazing

METHODS OF HOLDING WORK TOGETHER FOR SOLDERING.
1. Gas pliers.
2. Joints, eg. dovetail.
3. Rivets.
4. Screws.
5. Binding wire.
6. Split pins.
7. Cramps. Various cramps can be designed and made for holding particularly awkward soldering jobs.

SCREW THREAD TERMS

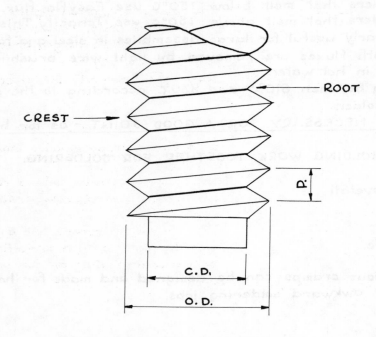

P. = PITCH

C.D. = CORE DIA.   OR ROOT DIA.

O.D. = OUTSIDE DIA.   OR NOMINAL DIA.

The MAJOR DIAMETER or NOMINAL DIAMETER is the outside diameter across the crests.

The MINOR DIAMETER or CORE DIAMETER is the inside diameter from root to root.

The CREST is the tip of the thread.

The ROOT is the base of the thread.

PITCH is the distance from a point on one thread to a similar point on the next.

LEAD is the distance a nut will travel in one revolution along a bolt. On single start threads the pitch is equal to the lead but they become different on multiple start threads.

MULTIPLE START THREADS are threads with more than one start. A double start thread has two threads of the same size running round the bolt together but starting from opposite sides of the bolt. With such a thread the lead becomes twice the pitch. Multiple threads increase the movement of the nut without changing the pitch of the thread.

SCREWS

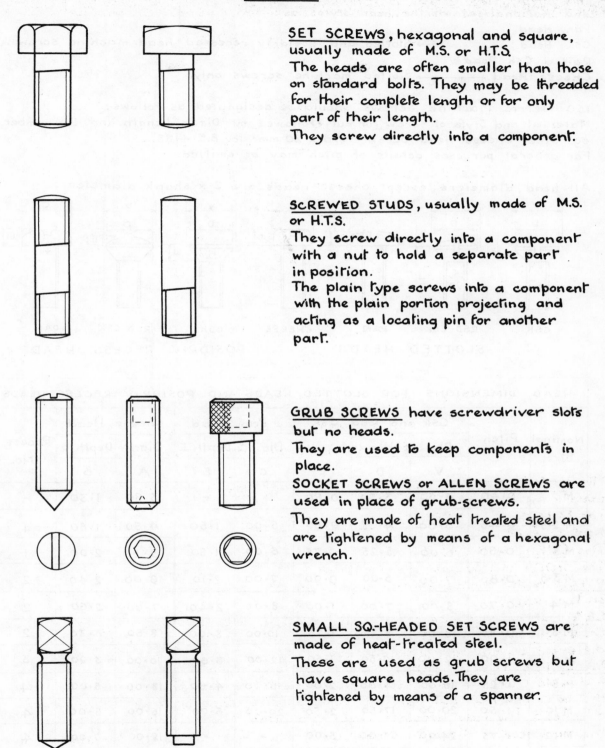

SET SCREWS, hexagonal and square, usually made of M.S. or H.T.S.
The heads are often smaller than those on standard bolts. They may be threaded for their complete length or for only part of their length.
They screw directly into a component.

SCREWED STUDS, usually made of M.S. or H.T.S.
They screw directly into a component with a nut to hold a separate part in position.
The plain type screws into a component with the plain portion projecting and acting as a locating pin for another part.

GRUB SCREWS have screwdriver slots but no heads.
They are used to keep components in place.
SOCKET SCREWS or **ALLEN SCREWS** are used in place of grub-screws.
They are made of heat treated steel and are tightened by means of a hexagonal wrench.

SMALL SQ.-HEADED SET SCREWS are made of heat-treated steel.
These are used as grub screws but have square heads. They are tightened by means of a spanner.

This standard is based on the proposals of the 150 Technical Committee TC2 and rationalises all the head styles as :

Pan Head
Csk Head
Raised Csk Head   → Slotted and posidriv recessed head machine screws.
Cheese Head   → Slotted machine screws only.

150 Metric Machine Screws should be designated as follows :
Material and Style of screw (or nut) Followed by Dia. x Length and B.S. number, eg. Steel Cheese Head Screw - M6 x 20 mm to B.S. 4183.
For general purposes details of pitch may be omitted.

All head diameters, except cheese heads are 2 x shank diameter.

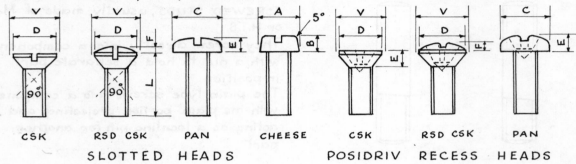

SLOTTED HEADS   POSIDRIV RECESS HEADS

Nominal Size	Pitch	Csk and Rsd Csk.			Pan Head		Cheese Head		Recess No.
		Dia. of Head			Dia. C	Depth E	Dia. A	Depth B	
		V.	D	F	c	E	A	B	
M 2	0.40	4.00	3.50	0.50	-	-	3.80	1.30	-
M 2.5	0.45	5.00	4.38	0.60	5.00	1.50	4.50	1.60	1
M 3	0.50	6.00	5.25	0.75	6.00	1.80	5.50	2.00	1
M 3.5	0.60	7.00	6.00	0.90	7.00	2.10	6.00	2.40	2
M 4	0.70	8.00	7.00	1.00	8.00	2.40	7.00	2.60	2
M 5	0.80	10.00	8.75	1.25	10.00	3.00	8.50	3.30	2
M 6	1.00	12.00	10.50	1.50	12.00	3.60	10.00	3.90	3
M 8	1.25	16.00	14.00	2.00	16.00	4.80	13.00	5.00	4
M 10	1.50	20.00	17.50	2.50	20.00	6.00	16.00	6.00	4
M 12	1.75	24.00	21.00	3.00	-	-	18.00	7.00	4

HEAD DIMENSIONS FOR SLOTTED HEADS AND POSIDRIV RECESS HEADS

THREAD FORM	NAME	SIZES	USES
	1. B.S.W. British Standard Whitworth	$\frac{1}{8}''$ to 3"	Has a relatively coarse pitch and is used for general machine construction where quick and easy assembly of parts is needed and for threads in soft materials.
	2. B.S.F. British Standard Fine	$\frac{3}{16}''$ to 2"	Fine pitch. Used for lock nuts, adjusting nuts and parts that have to withstand vibration.
	3. B.S.P. British Standard Pipe	$\frac{1}{8}''$ to 3"	Fine pitch. Used for gas, water and steam pipes where screwed pieces of large outside diameter and fine pitch are needed.
	4. B.S.G. (B.) British Standard Gas (or Brass)	$\frac{1}{8}''$ to 2"	Once the standard thread for gas piping, and, later electrical fittings but now falling out of use.
	B. A. British Association	Nos. 0-10 0.236 to 0.066. Full sets range down to No. 30.	A metric thread with pitch and diameter sizes in mm. Used generally for small instrument work but is also replacing B.S.W. in the smaller diameters. The even sizes, Nos. 2, 4, 6 etc., are commonly used.

THREAD FORM	NAME	SIZES	USES
	B.S.C. British Standard Cycle (previous C.E.I.)	$\frac{1}{4}"$ to 2"	Confined to screwed units for use on cycles and motor cycles.
	A.N.F. A.N.C. American National Fine and Coarse (formerly Sellers)	$\frac{1}{16}"$ to 2"	American standard threads. Equivalent to the B.S.F. and B.S.W. threads.
	U.N.F. U.N.C. Unified National Fine and Coarse	$\frac{1}{4}"$ to 2"	Crest may be rounded or flat. These are the standard threads agreed upon between Britain, U.S.A. and Canada. Intended to replace existing thread systems in these countries and aid interchangeability.
	ISO (International Standards Organization) Metric BS. 3643	1mm to 100mm	The ISO Metric thread replaces the B.A., B.S.W. and B.S.F. thread forms. The thread is in a coarse and fine series. The coarse series approximates to B.S.F. and is the one for general use. The fine series is for components needing very fine threads.

THREAD FORM	NAME	SIZES	USES
	Square	No limit in size	No accepted standard relationship between diameter and pitch. Steadily being replaced by the acme thread. Creates no bursting stresses as do vee-shaped threads and little friction, therefore used for machines and power transmission.
	Acme	No limit in size	More easily cut than the square thread. It also works more easily with split nuts, eg. lathe lead screws, than the square thread which it has replaced for many purposes. Used for the transmission of power and motion. The flank of the thread slopes at 14·5°.
	Buttress	No limit in size	Used for quick release mechanisms, eg. vices.

SCREW CUTTING BY HAND METHODS

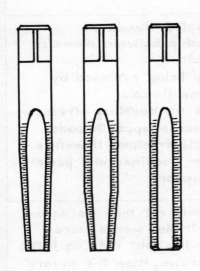

INTERNAL THREADS are cut by means of TAPS. Taps are made of H.S.S. or H.C.S. hardened and tempered. Both types are very brittle and need care in use. They are made in sets of three.

TAPER TAPS taper for two thirds of their length and are used first, to start the cutting of the thread. No other tap is necessary for tapping thin plate because the taper tap will cut a full thread at the top end.

SECOND TAPS or INTERMEDIATE TAPS taper for one third of their length and follow the taper taps in use. Some sets have these taps omitted.

BOTTOMING TAPS or PLUG TAPS are parallel for their complete length except for a chamfer lead. They are used last of the set and are always necessary when a blind hole has to be tapped.

| Taper Tap | Second Tap | Bottoming Tap |

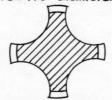

Cutting Edge

Flute

Land

No land drag. Strong. Efficient. Regrinding reduces effective diameter.

Increased land drag causes scoring of the thread surface.

Maximum cutting efficiency. Minimum of land drag.

TAPPING SIZE or TAPPING DRILL is the size of hole drilled before tapping any given thread. Its size will vary with different types of thread and with different screw diameters. Theoretically, the tapping size should be equal to the core diameter but in practice it is found that the taps, besides cutting freely, also exert a "squeezing" action on the metal, forcing it towards the crest of the thread. If the tapping hole were not slightly larger than the core diameter the squeezing action would cause the tap to bind and possibly break in the hole. For general work it has been found that there is little loss of strength when only 85% of a thread is formed, ie. a hole drilled too large for a full thread to be formed. This makes for easier tapping and consequently less breakages.

The tapping size can be obtained by
1. Referring to tables.
2. Subtracting twice the depth of thread from the outside diameter and adding a little for clearance.
3. Measuring the core diameter from a taper tap of the right size and adding a little for clearance.

CLEARANCE SIZE is the size of hole drilled that will clear the outside diameter of a screw. The amount of clearance will vary according to the class of work, e.g. washers have large clearances while holes to clear locating dowels have fine clearances.

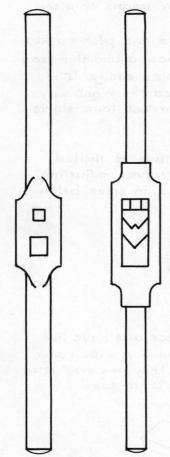

**Solid
Tap Wrench**

**Adjustable
Tap Wrench**

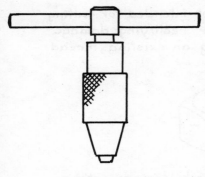

**Chuck Pattern
Tap Wrench**

TAP WRENCHES are used to hold the taps for cutting. Many types are made including plain (non-adjustable) and adjustable. Both these grip the square shank of the tap. The chuck pattern is only suitable for the smaller sizes of tap and they grip, by means of three jaws, on the round shank of the tap.

TAP BREAKAGES
REASONS FOR BREAKAGE –see under precautions.
EXTRACTION OF BROKEN TAPS
1. If sufficient of the tap is projecting and not too long a length embedded in the hole, it is sometimes possible to unscrew it with a pair of pliers.
2. Large taps can often be unscrewed or broken into pieces with an old punch or chisel.
3. Most often annealing of both tap and work is necessary. Then the tap can be drilled out and the hole retapped. Annealing of the tap is impossible if the tap is broken in a metal that has a melting point below the annealing temperature, eg. brass.
4. Two patterns of tap extractor are made, one of which requires the annealing and drilling of the tap first. This type has a tapered left hand thread which, with anticlockwise turns, has the effect of unscrewing the tap. The second type, only usable on large taps, has a set of prongs that fit inside the flutes. No annealing and drilling is necessary.

TAP SHARPENING
A dull tap will give a poor finish and possibly bind in the hole and break. Small taps can be reground on the chamfer but larger taps must be sharpened by grinding in the flutes. For this a tool and cutter grinder is needed.

LUBRICATION
The use of a lubricant is important. It disperses the heat, assists in the disposal of the chips and helps to give a better finish.

Steel, copper, bronze – oil or soluble oil.
Aluminium – paraffin or soluble oil.
Brass, cast iron – dry.

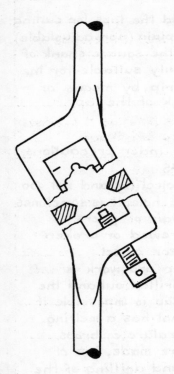

EXTERNAL THREADS are cut by means of dies which fit into die stocks.

Dies have the size, kind of thread and pitch marked on the leading face. This face has a chamfer lead to enable the cutting to start more easily. It is important that the die be placed the right way round in the stock so that the correct face starts the cutting.

CIRCULAR DIES or split dies have a limited adjustment for size provided by three adjusting screws. They are most often used in sizes below 12 mm.

Centre screw expands die

Side screws lock die

Rectangular Die Stock
(one half-die removed)

RECTANGULAR DIES or two-piece dies have two parts to each size, numbered 1 and 2. A wide range of adjustment for size is possible. They are most often used for cutting fairly large diameter threads.

DIE NUTS or solid dies are not intended for cutting threads from the solid but for rectifying damage to existing threads or running an existing thread down to size.

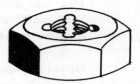

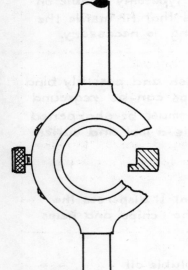

Circular Die Stock

For screwing B.S.P. threads a stock is made with a guide bush which enables the die to cut squarely. They are superior to the standard type of stock particularly for cutting large diameter fine threads.

PRECAUTIONS IN THREADING

PRECAUTION	RESULT IF NOT OBSERVED
1. Use the tap before the die because the taps are non-adjustable for size, the dies are.	Badly fitting nut.
2. Use the taps in correct order, taper tap first.	Difficulty in starting the thread. Possible tap breakage.
3. Ensure that the tap is entered squarely in the tap wrench.	Drunken thread.
4. Ensure that the die sits squarely in the stock with no chips underneath.	Drunken thread.
5. Ensure that the die is the right way round in the stock.	Difficulty in starting the thread. Inefficient cutting.
6. Chamfer the rod end before starting the die.	Difficulty in starting.
7. Use the correct size tapping drill.	Oversize holes result in partial threads, undersize holes result in breakage of taps.
8. Ensure that a blind hole is drilled deeper than the depth of thread required to allow clearance for chippings.	Thread too shallow in depth. Possible tap breakage.
9. Check for square once cutting has started.	Drunken thread.
10. Ensure that there is no vertical leverage of the wrench or stock.	Drunken thread.
11. Use a cutting solution where necessary.	Overheating, consequent blunting. Seizure, consequent breakage. Ragged or stripped thread.
12. Give backward turns to break off the chippings.	Ragged or stripped thread.
13. Take care when bottoming in a blind hole.	Tap breakage.
14. When tapping deep blind holes withdraw the tap occasionally to clear the hole of chippings.	Thread too shallow in depth. Tap breakage.
15. Take a roughing cut with the die first and then follow with a finishing cut.	Poorly finished thread. Thread undersize.

MAKING USE OF B.A. and B.S.F. THREADS

It is suggested that B.S.W. threads be dispensed with as soon as possible but the B.A. and B.S.F. series approximate to the ISO metric threads as regards diameter and pitch, but they are not interchangeable because the thread angles are different.

The chart shows how B.A. and B.S.F. threads can be used in place of metric threads so that imperial screwing tools can be made use of.

ISO Metric	Imperial Equivalent	Metric		Imperial	
		Tapping Size	Clearance Size	Tapping Size	Clearance Size
2	8 B.A.	1·7	2·2	51	43
2·5	6 "	2·2	2·8	44	34
3	4 "	2·8	3·6	34	27
4	0 "	3·7	4·8	26	12
5	0 "	4·8	6·0	12	B
6	1/4" B.S.F.	5·4	6·5	3	F
8	5/16" "	6·8	8·2	H	P
10	3/8" "	8·4	9·8	21/64"	W
11	7/16" "	9·5	11·3	3/8"	11·3mm
12	1/2" "	11·2	13·0	7/16"	13·0mm

TAPPING and CLEARANCE SIZES ISO METRIC

Diameter	Pitch	Tapping Drill	Clearance Drill
2	0·4	1·6	2·1
2·5	0·45	2·05	2·6
3	0·5	2·5	3·1
4	0·7	3·3	4·1
5	0·8	4·2	5·1
6	1·0	5·0	6·1
8	1·25	6·8	8·2
10	1·5	8·5	10·2
11	1·5	9·5	11·2
12	1·75	10·2	12·2

See Reference Data for full chart of ISO Metric Threads.

The tapping sizes given are for 75% depth of thread.

For threads 3 mm to 12 mm dia. clearance = nominal dia.+ 0·1mm.
For threads above 12 mm dia. clearance = nominal dia.+ 0·4 or 0·5mm.

The tapping size can be found by subtracting the pitch from the nominal dia.

RIVETS FOR GENERAL ENGINEERING PURPOSES, B.S. 4620: 1970

DEFINITIONS

1. NOMINAL DIAMETER – The diameter of the shank.
2. NOMINAL LENGTH, other than countersunk and raised countersunk – The length from the underside of the head to the end of the shank.
3. NOMINAL LENGTH, of countersunk and raised countersunk – The distance from the periphery (boundary line) of the head to the end of the rivet measured parallel to the axis of the rivet.
4. MANUFACTURED HEAD – The head on the rivet as received from the manufacturer.

Rivets may be made by hot or cold forging methods. Hot forging is used to shape rivets in the larger sizes, above 14 mm diameter.
The radius under the head of the rivet must run smoothly into the face of the head and shank.

COLD FORGED SNAP HEAD RIVET

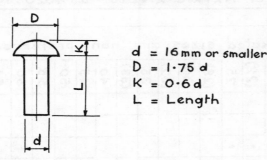

d = 16 mm or smaller
D = 1·75 d
K = 0·6 d
L = Length

Used for general plate work where strength is needed and for work where countersinking would weaken the parts.

COLD FORGED UNIVERSAL HEAD RIVET

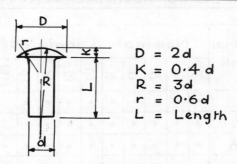

D = 2d
K = 0·4 d
R = 3d
r = 0·6 d
L = Length

The head has a large spread and little projection, therefore used for fairly soft plate or where a large projection of head is a disadvantage.

COLD FORGED FLAT HEAD RIVETS

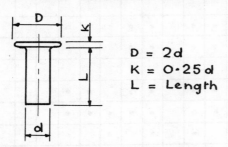

D = 2d
K = 0·25 d
L = Length

Used chiefly for tinsmithing or other thin plate work. Often galvanised.

90° COUNTERSUNK HEAD RIVETS

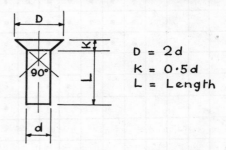

D = 2d
K = 0·5 d
L = Length

The most common form of countersunk rivet. Used where a flush surface is needed.

NOMINAL SHANK DIAMETERS FOR METRIC RIVETS – B.S. 4620:1970

Rivet Shape	Shank Diameter in millimetres															
	1	1·2	1·6	2	2·5	3	3·5	4	5	6	7	8	10	12	14	16
Snap	•	•	•	•	•	•	+	•	•	•	+	•	•	•	+	•
Universal	•	•	•	•	•	•	+	•	•	•	+	•	•	•	+	•
Flat	•	•	•	•	•	•	+	•	•	•	+	•	•			
Countersunk	•	•	•	•	•	•	+	•	•	•	+	•	•	•		

+ = Non-preferred sizes. (i.e. not first choice)

PREFERRED NOMINAL LENGTHS OF METRIC RIVETS – B.S. 4620:1970

Nominal Shank Dia.	Nominal Length (Bracketed sizes are non-preferred)																									
	3	4	5	6	8	10	12	14	16	(18)	20	(22)	25	(28)	30	(32)	35	(38)	40	45	50	55	60	65	70	75
1	•	•	•	•	•	•	•	•	•		•															
1·2	•	•	•	•	•	•	•	•			•															
1·6	•	•	•	•	•	•	•	•	•	•		•	•													
2	•	•	•	•	•	•	•	•			•	•	•													
2·5	•	•	•	•	•	•	•	•	•			•	•													
3		•	•	•	•	•	•	•	•			•	•													
(3·5)																										
4				•	•	•	•	•	•			•	•													
5			•	•	•	•	•	•	•	•	•	•	•	•	•		•	•								
6				•	•	•	•	•	•	•	•	•	•	•	•		•	•		•						
(7)																										
8					•	•	•	•	•	•	•	•	•	•	•		•	•		•	•		•	•		
10						•	•	•	•	•	•	•	•		•		•		•	•	•	•				
12												•	•		•		•		•		•	•				•
(14)																										
16																			•	•	•	•	•	•		•

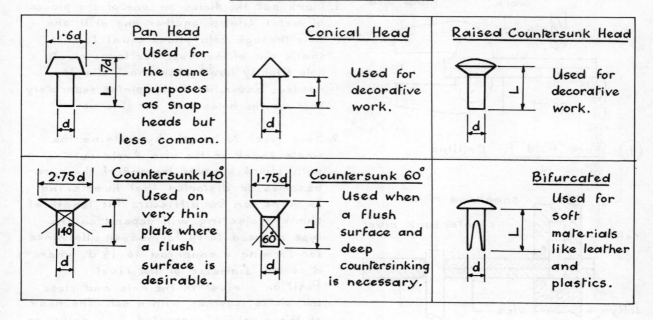

Pan Head	Conical Head	Raised Countersunk Head
1·6d, **·7d**, d — Used for the same purposes as snap heads but less common.	d — Used for decorative work.	d — Used for decorative work.
Countersunk 140° — 2·75d, 140° — Used on very thin plate where a flush surface is desirable.	**Countersunk 60°** — 1·75d, 60° — Used when a flush surface and deep countersinking is necessary.	**Bifurcated** — Used for soft materials like leather and plastics.

RIVETING

RIVETING is a method of joining metals together that is used when the parts have to remain assembled.

RIVETS are made of metals that are malleable — steel, copper, brass, aluminium and aluminium alloys.

RIVET SIZES AND ALLOWANCES

1. The rivet diameter should not exceed three times the thickness of the plates and should not be less than the thickness of the plates.
2. The shank projection for forming a round head is $1\frac{1}{2}D$ where D is the diameter of the rivet.
3. The allowance for filling a countersinking is $\frac{3}{4}D$.

RULES FOR RIVETING

1. Mark the position of the holes on one piece of metal and centrepunch.
2. Clamp the pieces together.
3. Using a drill equal to the shank diameter drill <u>one</u> hole through the pieces. When using large diameter rivets a drill slightly larger than the shank diameter is used.
4. Countersink this one hole if necessary.
5. Close the plates together with a rivet set, having first positioned the rivet.
6. Hammer in the first rivet forming a round head with a rivet snap or filling the countersinking as is necessary.
7. Drill all remaining holes and rivet.

STEPS IN RIVETING

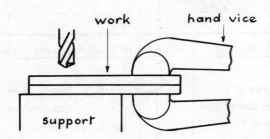

work   hand vice

support

① Work Held for Drilling

1. Mark out the holes on one of the pieces of metal. Clamp together and drill one hole through both plates equal to the shank dia. of the rivet. For large rivets a hole slightly larger than shank dia. is needed. Never drill the plates separately because the holes will not line up.

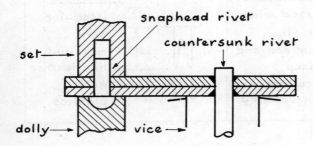

snaphead rivet

countersunk rivet

set →

dolly →   vice →

② Closing the Plates Together

2. Saw rivet to length by holding the waste shank in the vice. Avoid cutting with pliers because the end of the rivet becomes so distorted that hammering to shape can be difficult. The length of shank projecting will depend on the type of head to be formed, eg. allowance for forming a snaphead is $1\frac{1}{2}$ d, where d is the diameter of the rivet. Position a rivet in the hole and close the plates together with a set. The head of the rivet is supported in a dolly, on a block of metal or gripped in the vice depending on the type of rivet that is being used.

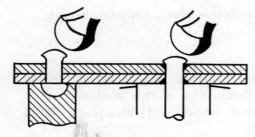

③ Hammering the Heads to Shape

3. Hammer with the flat face of the hammer enough to swell the shank of the rivet and make it a tight fit in the hole. With the ball pein of the hammer, shape the head.

4. Use a rivet snap to finish forming the head of a snaphead rivet. Rivet the second end of the countersunk rivet with the work resting on a block or on the face of an anvil.

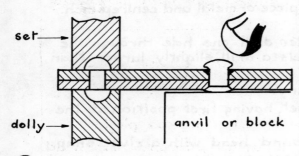

set →

dolly →   anvil or block

④ Finishing the Shape

To Remove Unwanted Rivets

1. Snapheads. File or chisel off the head and punch out with a pin punch.

2. Countersunk Heads. Centrepunch and drill out shank dia. or drill out the head only and then punch out.

FAULTS IN RIVETING

CAUSE	RESULT
1. Hole too large for shank of rivet.	Rivet bends
2. Too much of rivet shank projecting.	1. Rivet bends. 2. C'sinking partially filled. 3. Head mis-shapen.
3. Too little of rivet shank projecting.	1. C'sinking partially filled. 2. Round head partially filled.
4. Rivet head badly positioned in dolly.	Mis-shapen head (jockey cap).
5. Inefficient hammer blows.	1. Badly marked plates. 2. Partially formed roundhead or countersunk head.

CAUSE	RESULT
6. Drilling burrs not removed.	Gap left between plates
7. Neglecting to use rivet set.	Rivet forced between gap
8. Rivets not spaced correctly.	Plates split

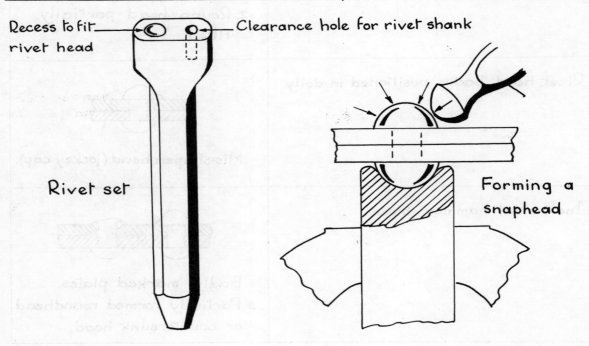

Recess to fit rivet head   Clearance hole for rivet shank

Rivet set

Forming a snaphead

FORMS OF RIVETED JOINTS

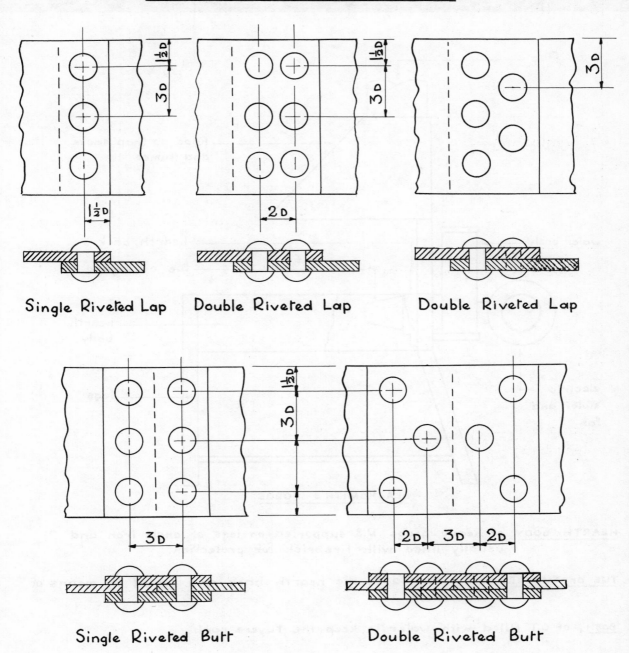

Single Riveted Lap   Double Riveted Lap   Double Riveted Lap

Single Riveted Butt   Double Riveted Butt

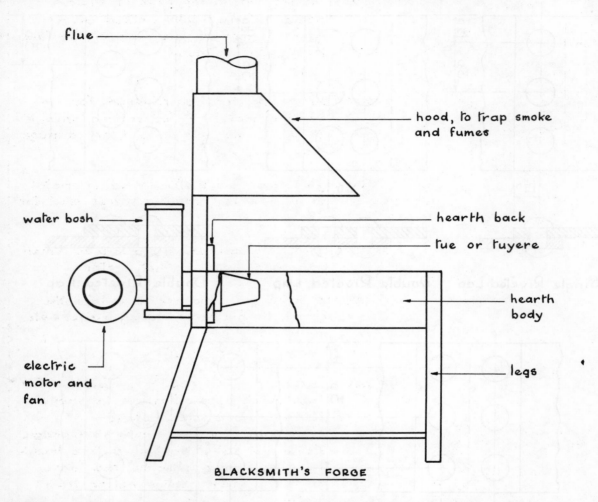

flue

hood, to trap smoke and fumes

water bosh

hearth back

tue or tuyere

hearth body

electric motor and fan

legs

BLACKSMITH'S FORGE

<u>HEARTH BODY</u>, of heavy gauge M.S. supported on legs of angle iron and usually lined with firebrick for protection.

<u>TUE or TUYERE</u>, of C.I. bolted to the hearth back and cooled by means of a water bosh.

<u>BOSH</u>, of C.I. filled with water to keep the tuyere cool.

<u>HEARTH BACK</u>, of C.I. detachable, to protect the M.S. back.

<u>ELECTRIC MOTOR</u>, of variable speed to control the blast and fitted with fan.

<u>FUEL</u>, coke "breeze," a crushed gas coke or soft coal free of sulphur.

TOOL	DETAILS and USES

TOOL

ANVIL

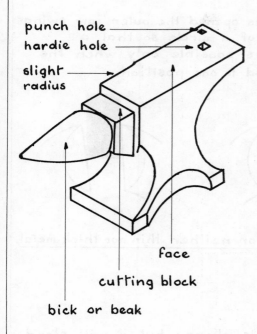

punch hole
hardie hole
slight radius
face
cutting block
bick or beak

SWAGE BLOCK

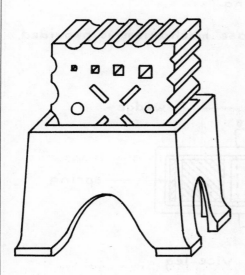

DETAILS and USES

BODY, of M.S. with a top face of H.C.S. approx 20mm thick, welded on. A short length of one edge of the face is slightly rounded.

CUTTING BLOCK, left soft. Used for resting metal on for cutting with a chisel. Being soft it will not damage the chisel.

BEAK, left soft. Used for bending metal to a radius, forming rings and for drawing down.

PUNCH HOLE. Used as a clearance when punching holes in hot metal.

HARDIE HOLE, a square hole to take the shank of bottom tools, eg. fullers etc.

WEIGHT, up to 150 kg.

ANVIL STAND, of C.I., with a seating for the anvil base. Similar in shape to the swage block stand.
Many blacksmiths prefer a wooden stand, usually part of a tree trunk because wood absorbs the force of the hammer blows better than metal.

SWAGE BLOCK, of C.I., with a series of holes of various sizes and shapes. Used for forming hot metal usually with the help of top tools.

SWAGE BLOCK STAND, of C.I., which will hold the swage block in a flat position or on its end.

TOOL	DETAILS and USES

LEG VICE

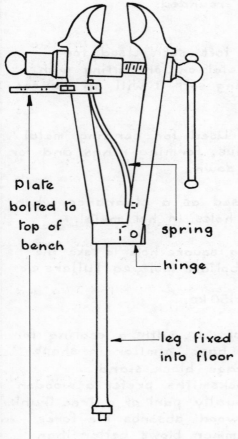

Plate bolted to top of bench

spring

hinge

leg fixed into floor

Made of wrought iron with steel-faced jaws.

When the vice is opened the outer jaw swings along the arc of a circle so that a parallel grip is possible only when the jaws are opened to one position.

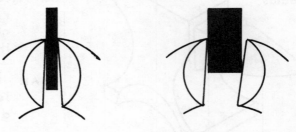

Parallel grip for neither thin nor thick metal.

The leg vice is clumsy but it will stand up to rough usage. It is suitable for holding cold or hot metal for working such as bending.

No quick release mechanism is provided.

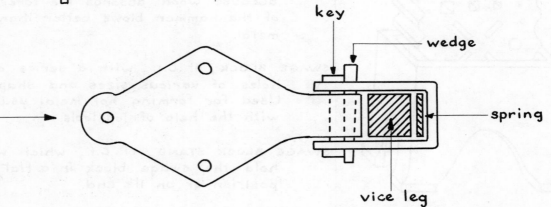

key

wedge

spring

vice leg

TOOL	DETAILS and USES

FORGING HAMMERS

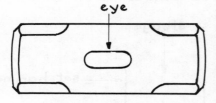

Double-Face Sledge

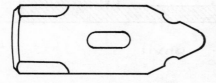

Straight Pein Sledge

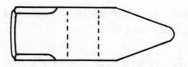

Smith's Hammer

Hammer heads are made of H.C.S. with the ends hardened and tempered and the eyes left soft for strength. The striking faces are slightly convex to prevent the corners digging in to the metal.

SLEDGE HAMMERS. In addition to the two shown, there is a cross pein sledge which has the pein at right angles to the shaft.
Weights vary from 0.9 to 6.5 kg. The handles or shafts are made of hickory or ash.
Sledge hammers are usually used by a striker working in conjunction with a smith.

SMITH'S HAMMER. The head has the face slightly convex and the other end has a cross pein which is used for drawing down, etc.
Weights vary from 0.9 to 1.3 kg and the shafts are made of knot-free hickory or ash.

HOT and COLD SETS

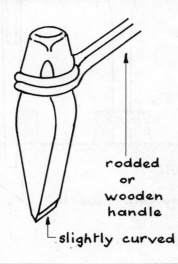

rodded or wooden handle

slightly curved

HOT SET, of H.C.S., left soft. Cutting angle 30°. Used for cutting hot metal.

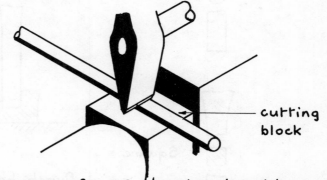

cutting block

COLD SET, of H.C.S., hardened and tempered. Cutting angle 60°. Used for cutting cold metal.

TOOL	DETAILS and USES
SET HAMMER —sledge 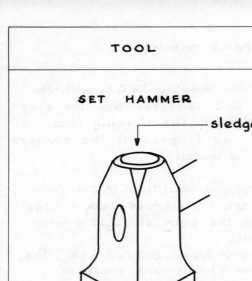	Similar to the flatter but smaller in size. Used in confined places or on small surfaces. 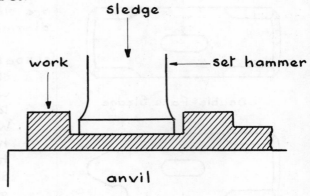 sledge work — set hammer anvil
PUNCHES and DRIFTS 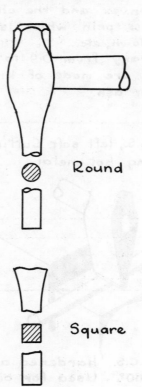 Round Square	Available with rodded or wooden handles. **PUNCHES** are used for making round or square holes in hot metal. **DRIFTS** are used to open up holes to size that have been previously punched. 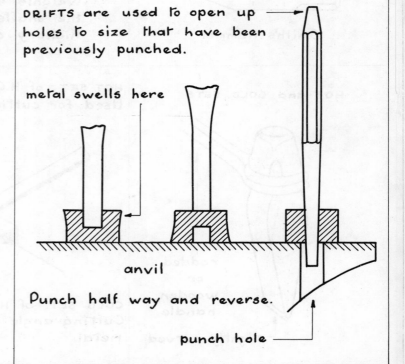 metal swells here anvil Punch half way and reverse. punch hole

TOOL	DETAILS and USES
HARDIE 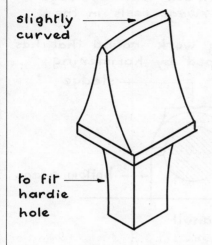 slightly curved → to fit hardie hole →	The HARDIE fits in the hardie hole of the 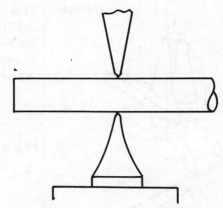 anvil. Used as a bottom chisel with a set chisel for cutting hot metal.
TOP and BOTTOM FULLERS 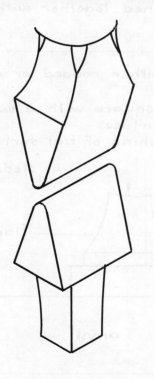	Made in pairs, the bottom tool fitting in the hardie hole and upper tool handled and held by the smith while it is struck by the striker. Specified according to the dia. of the end. 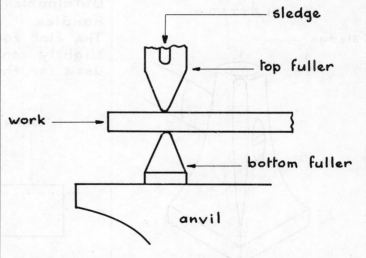 sledge top fuller work → bottom fuller anvil Used for necking, often before drawing down, or for drawing down itself.

TOOL	DETAILS and USES
TOP and BOTTOM SWAGES 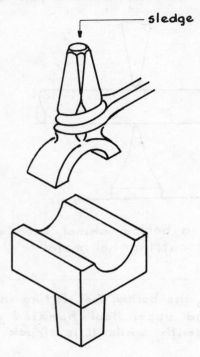	Supplied as a pair with a curvature of definite radius. The top swage is struck with a sledge whilst the bottom swage rests in the hardie hole. Used for finishing work round that has been roughly shaped by hammering. 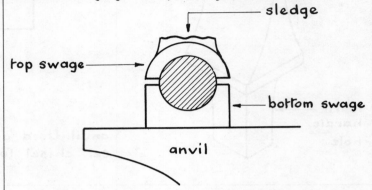 Single-handed swages have the top and bottom halves joined together with a flat spring.
FLATTER 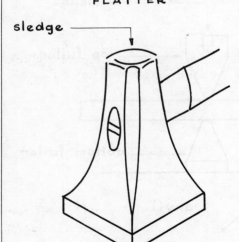	Obtainable with either rodded or wooden handles. The flat face is square with a very slightly convex surface. Used for the finishing of flat surfaces. 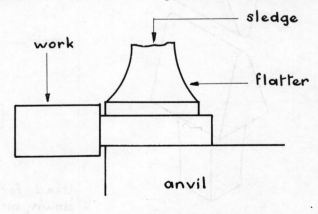

TOOLS	DETAILS and USES
TONGS	The smith needs a range of tongs of various shapes to hold the metal securely.
 Open mouth	Flat tongs - open mouth - are used for gripping flat stock that is relatively thick. They should grip along the whole length of the jaws.
 Close mouth	Flat tongs - close mouth - are used for holding flat stock that is relatively thin. They should grip along the whole length of the jaws.
 Hollow bit	Hollow bits are used for holding round stock. Size is specified by diameter.
 Vee-bit	Vee-bits are used for holding square stock. Size is specified by the size of the square.
 Pick-ups	Pick-ups are not used for holding metal for working but for picking up awkward shapes.

TOOL	DETAILS and USES
TONGS 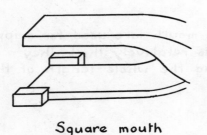 Square mouth	Used for rectangular, square and irregular stock.
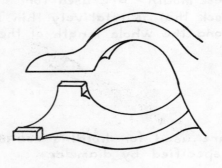 Round mouth	Used for round stock and work of irregular shape. A circular clamping ring can be pushed over the handles to hold the tongs tightly to the work and so relieve the smith of much of the grip that is necessary.

FORGING PROCESSES

DRAWING DOWN A SQUARE TAPER.

1. On the face of the anvil, hammer a short two-sided taper down to the required thickness at the end.

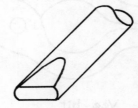

2. Rotate the metal through 90° and hammer two more short tapers, making four sides in all.

3. Whilst rotating the metal, make the taper the required length.

FORGING PROCESSES

DRAWING DOWN A ROUND TAPER

1. Follow stages 1 to 3 for a square taper, then hammer octagonal and finally round.

   Always draw square first or "piping" will result. ⟶

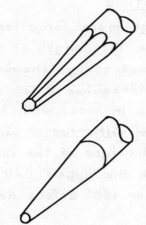

DRAWING DOWN PARALLEL

1. Draw down either
   a. single-handed, using straight pene hammer.

   or b. single-handed, using beak of anvil and flat face of hammer.

   or c. double-handed, using top and bottom fullers.

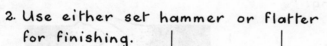

str. pene hammer

1a

Round edge of edge

hammer

1b

beak

2. Use either set hammer or flatter for finishing.

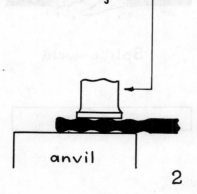

anvil

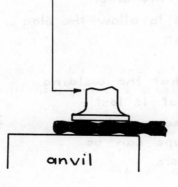

anvil

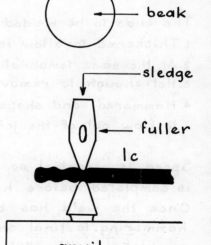

sledge

fuller

1c

anvil

2

TWISTING

1. Heat metal for a length a little more than the length of twist. An even heat is necessary. Uneven heating causes an irregular twist.
2. Grip in vice with lower limit of twist level with top of vice and hold with the under-face of the tongs (or wrench) level with the upper limit of twist. Pull through 90° or 180° before heat is lost.

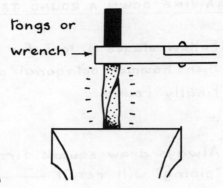

tongs or wrench →

FORGE WELDING

Hand welding is the joining of metal by hammering whilst the metal is very hot.

HEAT - Wrought iron - white heat - 1350°C
        Mild steel - yellow-white heat - 1250°C

Scarf weld

FLUX - W.I. - sand. M.S. - calcined borax.
        Flux is used to dissolve oxide scale and prevent further oxidation.

The ends to be welded must be -
1. Thickened to allow for hammering.
2. At the same temperature.
3. Hot enough to remove the slag.
4. Hammered and shaped to allow the slag to flow out of the joint.

Splice weld

Speed is essential so that the welding is completed before heat is lost.
Once the weld has been made the hammering to final shape can be completed without haste.

FORMING ANGULAR BENDS

1. Narrow stock can be bent at the end of the vice or on the top of the vice.

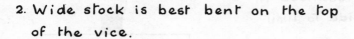

2. Wide stock is best bent on the top of the vice.

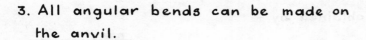

3. All angular bends can be made on the anvil.

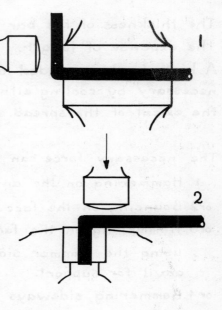

When metal is bent, the inside of the metal becomes compressed and the outside stretched. This leads to distortion. If a truly square bend is needed the metal must be upset first. See next page.

FORMING RADIUSED BENDS

1. Using beak of anvil. Hammer blow must be made in front of point of contact.

2. Using a former in the vice.

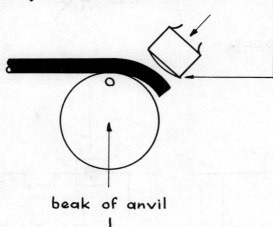

beak of anvil

1

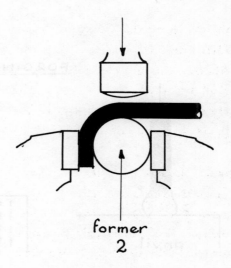

former

2

FORGING PROCESSES

UPSETTING or JUMPING-UP

1. The thickness of the bar is increased at the expense of length.

A high heat is needed and localised if necessary by cooling either side to limit the extent of the spread.

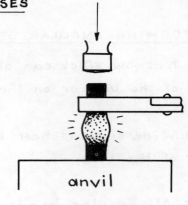

anvil

The necessary force can be obtained by –

  1. Hammering on the anvil.

or 2. Bouncing on the face of the anvil.

or 3. Hammering on the face of the anvil, using the hammer sideways and the anvil for support.

or 4. Hammering sideways with the metal supported in the vice.

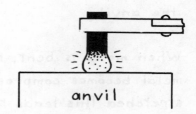

anvil

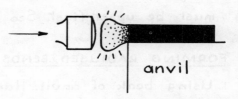

anvil

The extent of the heating and the type of blow will depend on the nature of the work. Heavy blows are usually necessary.

vice

FORGING A BOLT

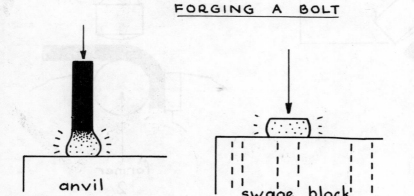

anvil

swage block

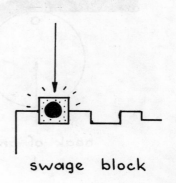

swage block

110

FORMING A CLOSED RING

1. Use a former of the desired shape and size.

2. Use the metal in a length, gripping former upright and metal horizontally in the vice.

3. Bend by hand pressure until just more than one complete ring is formed.

4. Saw through the double thickness of metal.

5. Close joint and hammer out the twist.

FORMING AN EYE

1. From mean dia. calculate circumference.
2. At this distance from the end of the bar make a rt. angled bend on the anvil.
3. With the internal angle facing upright start hammering over the beak.
4. Reverse the metal and start closing the eye.

N.B. HAMMERING MUST TAKE PLACE JUST IN FRONT OF THE POINT OF CONTACT OF METAL AND ANVIL.

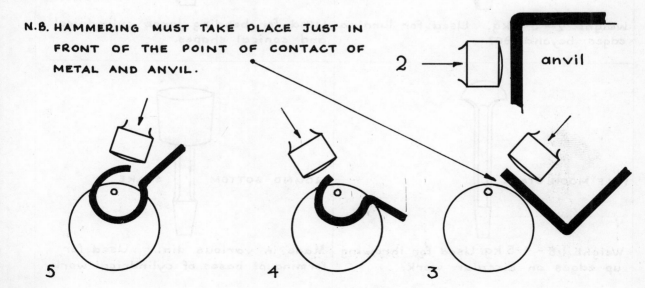

SHEETMETAL STAKES

Made of W.I. faced with steel and used for the shaping of sheet metal.

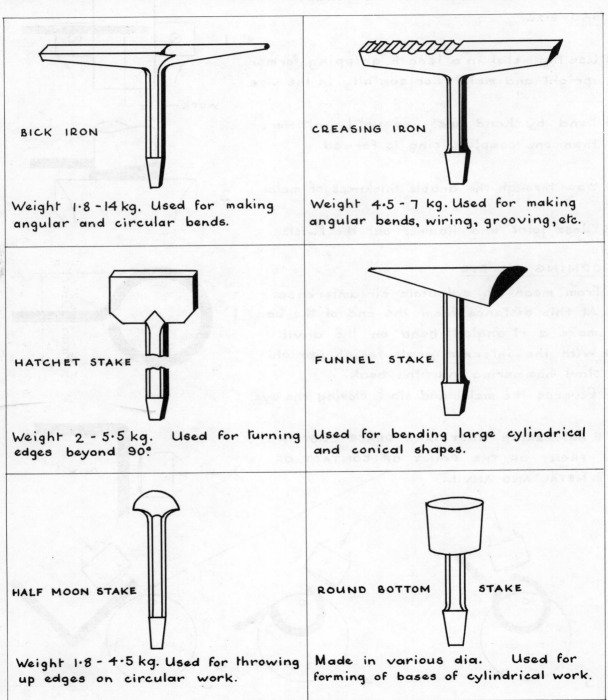

BICK IRON

Weight 1·8 – 14 kg. Used for making angular and circular bends.

CREASING IRON

Weight 4·5 – 7 kg. Used for making angular bends, wiring, grooving, etc.

HATCHET STAKE

Weight 2 – 5·5 kg. Used for turning edges beyond 90°.

FUNNEL STAKE

Used for bending large cylindrical and conical shapes.

HALF MOON STAKE

Weight 1·8 – 4·5 kg. Used for throwing up edges on circular work.

ROUND BOTTOM STAKE

Made in various dia. Used for forming of bases of cylindrical work.

TOOL	DETAILS and USES

FOLDING BARS

Used for making right-angled bends in sheet metal.

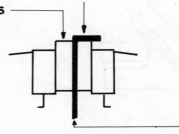

folding bars

work

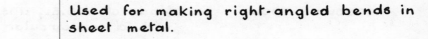

Length 250-300mm. They must be flush-fitting throughout their length.

SNIPS

Straight

Curved

Universal Pattern

These are strong, need infrequent sharpening and will cut most shapes.

Snips are used for cutting sheet metal. They must never be used for cutting wire. They are specified by their overall length, 200mm being a common size.

Straight snips are used for straight edges and external curves.
Curved snips are used for internal curves only.

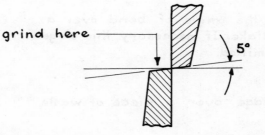

grind here

5°

Sharpen on the edges of the blades only at an angle of 5°.

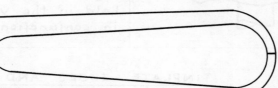
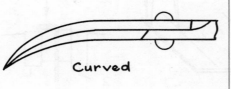
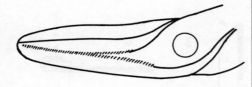

TOOL	DETAILS and USES
GROOVING TOOL 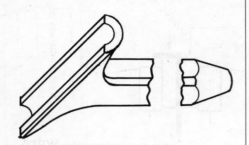	Made of H.C.S., upset at one end, cut with a semicircular groove and hardened and tempered. Sizes, specified by the diameter of the curve, are from 3mm upwards. They are used for the final forming of grooved seams and wire edges.
TUCKING HAMMER 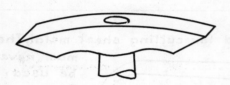	Tucking hammers have straight peins with fairly sharp corners. They are used for finishing off wired edges either by direct hammering or held in the vice and used as a stake in conjunction with a hide mallet.

TINPLATE EDGES AND JOINTS

SAFE EDGE

1. Mark out using oddlegs or dividers.

2. Bend over at right angles using folding bars and mallet.

3. Increase the angle of bend over a hatchet stake. If necessary this stage may be omitted.

4. Mallet edge over a piece of waste tinplate.

5. Mallet edge down on a stake.

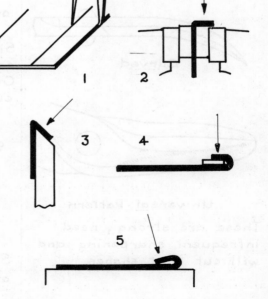

WIRED EDGE

Allowance for wiring is 2½ x dia. of wire, this allowance being added to the given height or other dimension.

1. Mark out this allowance using dividers or oddlegs.

2. Bend over at right angles in the folding bars using a mallet.

3. Mallet down the allowance over a piece of scrap metal approx. equal in thickness to the diameter of the wire.

4. Place wire in position and trap with mallet blows.

5. Bring to final shape on a flat stake, creasing iron or with a tucking hammer or grooving tool.

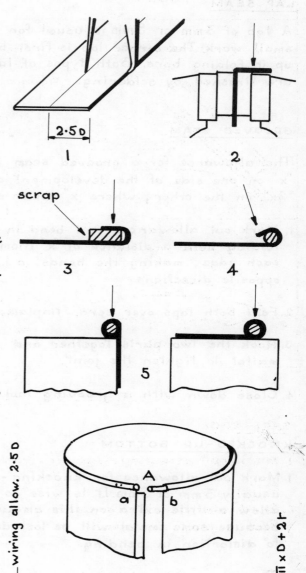

Where possible it is best to do wiring in the flat before any bending to shape. The joint of the wiring is so arranged that it is hidden when the shape is finally formed, as at "A". Difficulty may be experienced in preventing the collapse of the open part of the joint "a". This may be overcome by filling the gap with a waste piece of wire during the shaping or filing half way through the wire at "a", at a convenient spot and breaking off the wire after bending.

Circular work involving a grooved seam and wired edge gives difficulty when bringing the joint together at "A". Avoid this by cutting out an extra allowance for clearance equalling $\pi \times D + 2t$, where t = thickness of tinplate.

115

LAP SEAM

A lap of 3mm or 5mm is usual for small work. The corner lap is first bent up in folding bars. Both types of lap are finished by soldering.

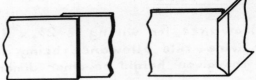

GROOVED SEAM

The allowance for a grooved seam is "x" on one side of the development and "2x" on the other, where "x" = seam size.

1. Mark out allowances and bend in folding bars a distance of "x" from each edge, making the bends in opposite directions.

2. Fold both laps over scrap tinplate.

3. Hook the two parts together and mallet to tighten the joint.

4. Close down with a grooving tool.

KNOCKED-UP BOTTOM

1. Mark out allowance for knocking-up, usually 3mm or 5mm. It is wise to allow a little extra on this amount because some metal will be lost due to distortion in bending.

2. Throw up this edge gradually on the half-moon stake. Gradual coaxing of the metal is needed to avoid too much distortion. If any ripples appear they must be malleted out before they develop too far. Rotate the edge of the metal whilst malleting.

3. Finish shape on a round-bottomed stake.

4. Set down square on a flat-faced stake.

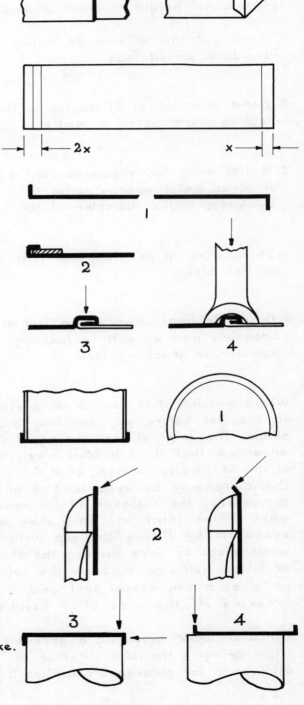

116

Hammered metalwork is that branch of the craft that is concerned with the beating to shape and the jointing together of sheet metals. The initial stages of the work follow a set procedure.

1. ESTIMATING THE SIZE OF BLANK

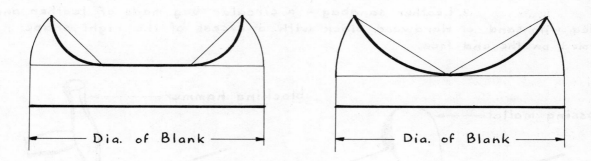

The size of blank necessary to form the desired shape must be estimated by one of the methods shown above.

2. PREPARING THE METAL

The metal is cut to shape and any irregularities removed by filing. Care must be taken to avoid scratching the surface of the metal. A pencil may be used for the marking out and if the metal has to be gripped in the vice it must be protected by using either soft metal or fibre vice clamps or by using a few layers of paper around it.

All scratches must be removed. Deep scratches are removed by bending the metal so that each scratch is accessible with a fine file. These file marks and any other fine scratches are eased out with Water of Ayr stone. This is dipped in water and rubbed over each individual scratch.

3. ANNEALING

The metal must be in a soft condition so that it can be easily shaped. It has, therefore, to be annealed. For details of the annealing of metals see under "Heat Treatment."

4. CLEANING

Before the metal can be beaten to shape it must be clean and oxides formed during the heating must be removed by dipping the work in an acid bath. This pickle, for copper, brass and gilding metal, is dilute sulphuric acid in the proportion of 1 : 8. When mixing, the acid must be added to the water and it should be kept in an earthenware trough covered when not in use. Dipping is best done when the metal is warm, not hot or it might spit and cause a serious injury. Brass tongs are used for removing the metal from the acid. Steel and iron cause discoloration of the acid pickle and copper will become deposited on any brass that is subsequently dipped. After pickling the metal is thoroughly washed and, if necessary, scrubbed with pumice powder and then dried.

117

Annealing, pickling, scrubbing and drying must be repeated during the process of shaping as soon as the metal becomes work hardened.

The metal may be shaped by hollowing, sinking, raising, expanding or contracting.

1. <u>HOLLOWING</u> is used for shallow shapes only, because the metal is stretched during the shaping and if deep hollowing is attempted the work will become too thin and weak.

<u>Tools needed</u> are 1. Boxwood bossing mallet (see under "Mallets".)
or Blocking hammer, a long headed hammer with two ball faces usually of different sizes and sometimes called a hollowing hammer.
2. Leather sandbag - a circular bag made of leather and filled with sand or Hardwood block with a recess of the right shape formed on the end face.

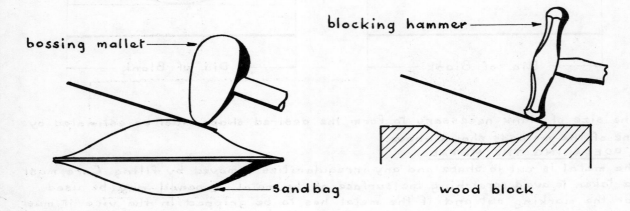

<u>Hollowing with a Mallet on a Sandbag</u>

<u>Hollowing with a Hammer on a Wooden Block</u>

The metal is held on either a sandbag or a wooden block and the blows positioned a short distance in from the edge of the metal with a mallet or hammer. The blows are continued around the circumference, the metal being rotated slowly during the process so that the mallet or hammer blows are positioned in the same place on the bag or block.

<u>Stages in Hollowing</u>

A second course of blows is made just inside the first. Shaping is continued by working in concentric circles until the required shape is obtained. Circular pencil lines, about 12mm apart, may be marked on the blank as an aid to even shaping.

The work will probably have to be annealed, pickled, washed and dried during the shaping, ie. as soon as the metal becomes work-hardened. The frequency of the annealing will depend on the metal being worked and the depth of the hollowing.

2 <u>SINKING</u> or dishing involves shaping only part of the blank, leaving a flat rim, like a plate. A bossing mallet or blocking hammer may be used in conjunction with a wooden former block.

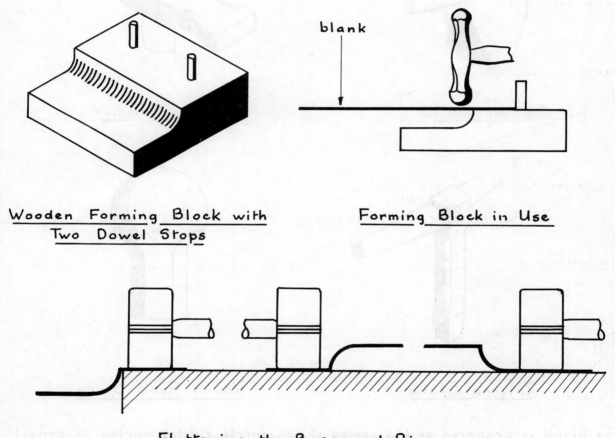

blank

Wooden Forming Block with
Two Dowel Stops

Forming Block in Use

Flattening the Base and Rim

Considerable distortion of the shape will occur during shaping and the base and rim will need flattening with a mallet on a flat plate such as a levelling plate. Frequent annealing and cleaning again is necessary.

Care will be needed to ensure that the rim and base are flat. Tight spots have to be detected and stretched with a mallet or a hammer.

3. RAISING

Deep shapes cannot be formed by hollowing and have to be raised. Whereas hollowing stretches the metal, raising contracts and thickens it.
A wedge-shaped mallet or a raising hammer is used in conjunction with a round head stake or a raising stake.

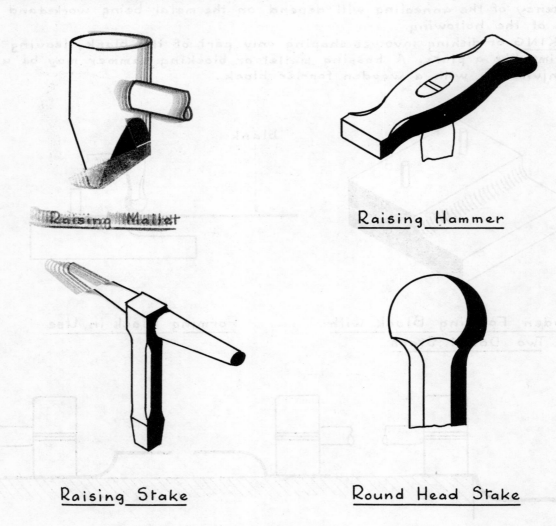

Raising Mallet

Raising Hammer

Raising Stake

Round Head Stake

The blank is prepared and a series of concentric circles marked in pencil about 12mm apart to help in positioning the stages of shaping. The blank is laid on the stake at an angle of about 30° to the horizontal and the shaping is started from the centre, working along the line of the circles until the outer edge is reached. The blows must be directed just ahead of the point of contact between stake and blank. After each completed course the metal should be annealed. Sometimes it is easier to work with the blank reversed, particularly when the shaping approaches the rim. The angle at which the hammer meets the work and the position of the point of contact of the hammer are both important. If the metal is trapped between the hammer and the stake it will become stretched and thin and little shaping will occur.

Stages in Raising

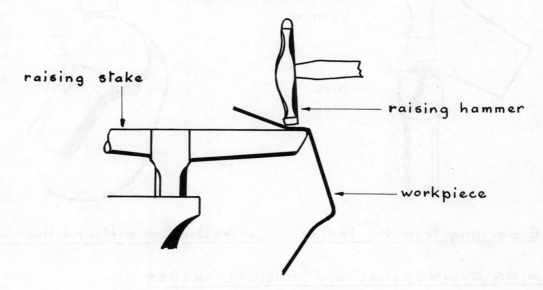

raising stake

raising hammer

workpiece

Use of Raising Stake and Raising Hammer

After raising the work will need to be planished. Planishing always stretches the metal, so it is usual to raise a shape slightly more than required so as to allow for the subsequent stretching that will take place when planishing.

4. EXPANDING and CONTRACTING

After hollowing or raising the shape may be modified by expanding (opening out the shape) or contracting (closing in the shape).

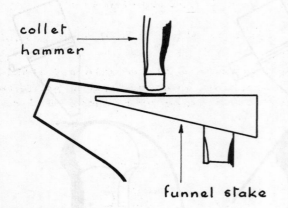

collet hammer

funnel stake

In each instance, the profile of the stake used should be as near the required finished shape as is possible.

The shape of the hammer, too, will depend on the finished shape that is required. Often a collet hammer is used, ie. a hammer with a slightly curved face and well rounded corners.

Sometimes it is possible to gain the required expansion by increased planishing over the area to be stretched.

Expanding from the Outside

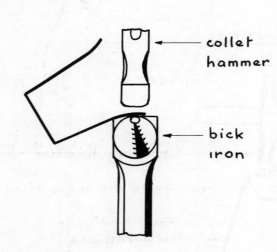

collet hammer

bick iron

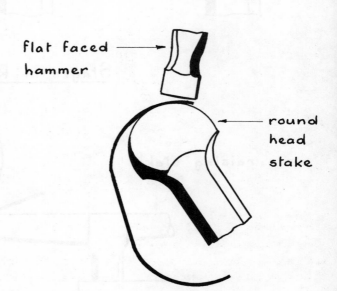

flat faced hammer

round head stake

Expanding from the Inside

Contracting on a Round Head Stake

FORMING CYLINDRICAL and CONICAL SHAPES

Cylindrical and conical shapes are developed in the normal way and, after the surfaces of the metal have been prepared, are bent up around formers of suitable section. Bick iron, funnel stake or a length of rod may be used as a former.

After bending to shape the joint is silver soldered, the grade of solder being dependent on the number of soldered joints that are needed to complete the construction.

PLANISHING

When the shaping operation has been completed, the work needs to be planished in order to 1. Even up the shape and abolish irregularities.
2. Harden the metal.
3. Close the grain of the metal so that it will take a high polish.

First, the work is annealed and then hammered on a stake with a suitably shaped hammer. Hammers and stakes for planishing must be highly polished and free of defects. Any flaw on the surface of stake or hammer will be transferred many times to the face of the work.

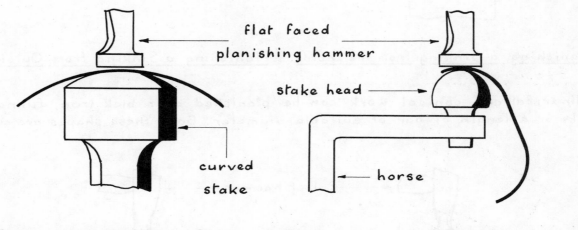

Planishing a Shallow Bowl   Planishing using a Stake and Horse

The shape of the hammer and stake will vary according to the shape of the work. General rules are —
1. Flat faced hammers are used for planishing curved surfaces.
2. Convex faced hammers are used for planishing flat surfaces.
3. The stake used should have a curvature slightly sharper than that of the work.

Concentric pencil lines marked on the work sometimes help to make sure that the whole surface is covered.

Hammering is started from the centre of the work, with relatively light blows, working in concentric circles towards the outer edge. The metal must be trapped between the stake and the hammer, ie. the hammer blow must fall where the work makes contact with the stake. If it does not, the work will be hammered out of shape. During hammering, the work is rotated while the hammer is brought down in the same position on the stake. The facets formed by the hammer should overlap slightly to make sure that no part of the surface is missed. Any parts not hammered will remain dull and rough.

No attempt should be made to exaggerate the facets. Keep them inconspicuous.

123

Curved work may be planished from the inside or outside depending on which is the easier.

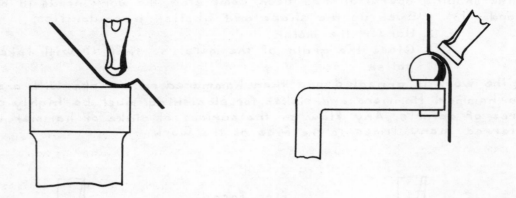

Planishing a Sinking from the Inside   Planishing a Sinking from Outside

Cylindrical and conical work can be planished on a bick iron, funnel stake or a length of bar of suitable diameter. Both these shapes are curved

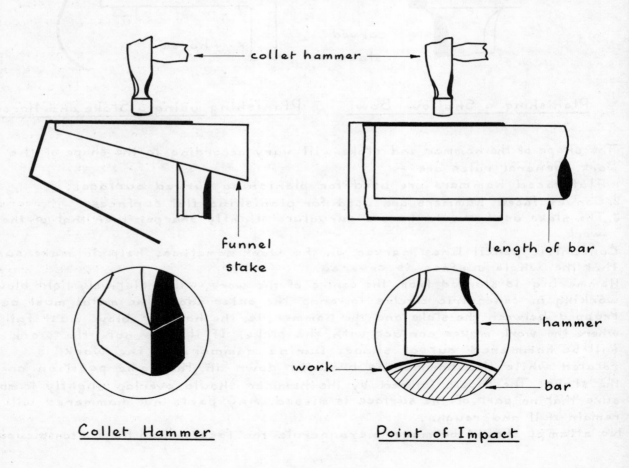

collet hammer

funnel stake

length of bar

hammer

work

bar

Collet Hammer   Point of Impact

in one direction and straight in the other. Consequently, a planishing hammer with a face of special shape is needed, a collet hammer. This hammer has a rectangular face very slightly curved in one direction and heavily curved in the other.

TRUEING AN EDGE

When the work has been planished, the foot is soldered on. At this stage, the top edge will be irregular and needs to be made true.

The work is placed on a surface plate and a line scribed round near the top edge with a surface gauge.

The waste is trimmed off with a pair of curved snips, any irregularities being removed with a fine file. For final finishing the work is up-ended and rubbed on a sheet of emery cloth resting on a flat surface, or, better still, glued on a flat board.

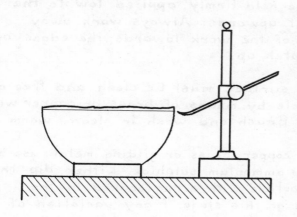

POLISHING

During the construction, the surface of the workpiece should have been carefully preserved. Any marks or scratches that have been accidentally made will need careful removal with Water-of-Ayr stone. Any excess solder may be removed by scraping.

Final polishing may be by hand or, more usual, by means of a polishing machine. The machine is, basically, an electric motor, to the shaft of which are fitted two extension spindles, machined with a tapered screw thread, a left hand thread on the left spindle and a right hand thread on the right spindle. This is necessary to prevent loosening of the mops during rotation. The mops or brushes are screwed onto these threads. The most common mops and brushes are —

a. Solid felt mop - stiff, hard and usually used for the initial dressing of castings or work that needs a lot of finishing.

b. Calico mop - formed of circular pieces of calico held together by means of a pair of central fibre washers. Some calico mops have the sections stitched together to stiffen them.

c. Swans down mop - a very soft, fine mop, used for high-class finishing.

d. Brushes - made of bristle, brass or steel wire. Used for special work.

Of this range, the calico mops are the most useful for general work.

The polish is usually bedded in a wax and supplied in the form of a bar. The type of polish used depends on —

a. The kind of metal to be polished.

b. Its surface condition.

c. Quality of finish desired.

The range of polishes available is wide but those most commonly used are rotten stone, rouge, crocus and tripoli.

Remember that polishing is a finishing process for hammered metalwork. It will not dispose of flaws but will exaggerate them.

Hints for Polishing.
1. Do not over-polish. The crispness of the planishing will be lost.
2. A piece well made will need little polishing.
3. The higher the polish, the more the flaws will show.
4. The work must be held firmly, applied low to the mop and brought upwards. Always work away from the centre of the work towards the edges or the work will catch up.

COLOURING

Before any work can be coloured, its surface must be clean and free of grease. To degrease, suspend the article by means of brass or copper wire in a hot solution of potash or soda. Brush and wash in clean, warm water and dry.

To obtain various shades of brown on copper, brass or gilding metal use a weak solution of potassium sulphide or ammonium sulphide. Either dip the article in the solution or wipe over the article with a rag soaked in the solution. A scratch brush may be used at this stage if any variation of tone is desired. Wash and dry.

PROTECTING FINISHED SURFACES

1. **Wax.** A beeswax polish applied to the surface gives limited protection. No preliminary degreasing is necessary.
2. **Lacquer,** applied by means of a brush or spray. Clean the work very thoroughly, either by boiling in soda water or by wiping over with methylated spirits. A good quality brush should be used, eg. camel hair, and it should be well-charged with lacquer. Float the lacquer on, taking care to avoid runs.

PIERCED WORK

Thin metals may be cut with a piercing saw to form a decorative pattern. The piercing saw has an adjustable frame, similar in shape to a fretsaw and used in the same way, ie. on a vee-board held in the vice. The blades are very fine and are available in 10 sizes from 0000 to 6, a gauge being chosen for the thickness of metal to be cut. The blades cut on the downward stroke.

The pattern is set out and 1·5 mm holes drilled at any convenient position for inserting the saw blade. The saw should be kept vertical and downward strokes made without too much pressure. A little candle grease applied to the blade helps to give smoother cutting. On no account force the blade.

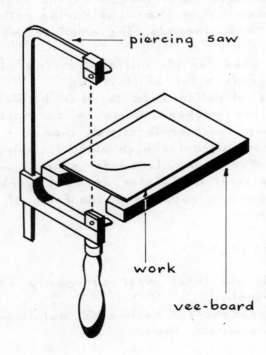

piercing saw

work

vee-board

APPLIED WIRES

Although the primary purpose of wires is to strengthen the work, they do, at the same time, add to the decorative effect. Half round wires are those most often used but a combination of wires can be used, too, by twisting them together and leaving them "in the round" or by flattening them with a planishing hammer. For twisting, the ends are held in the vice, and soldered together first if it is found difficult to hold them, while the other ends are held in a hand drill.

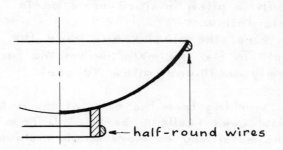

Wires Applied to a Bowl

half-round wires

The wires can be held in position for soldering to the work by means of split pins (See under "Solder Joints".). With twisted wires, in particular, the minimum of solder must be applied. Any excess is difficult, or impossible, to remove once it has run over the twists.

CHASING and PUNCHING

Chasing is a form of decoration in which grooves are made in the metal with a chasing tool and repoussé hammer. Chasing tools may be bought or made to any desired shape from 6 mm sq. H.C.S. and hardened and tempered. The tools are like chisels but the edges, instead of being sharp, are slightly rounded and highly finished. Various widths of tool are used to produce lines of different thicknesses. Punch decoration must be restrained to

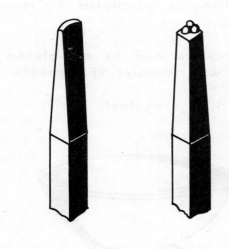

Chasing Tool   Punch

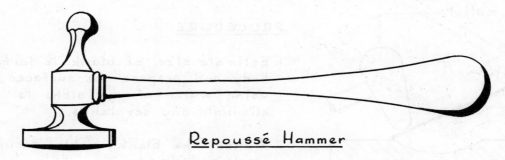

Repoussé Hammer

be effective. In use the punch is hammered into the face of the metal. An impression is formed the same shape as the head of the punch. The pattern is mapped out first in pencil.

For punching and chasing the metal may be held on a suitable stake or on a pitch block. The pitch block is a box about 25mm deep inside and of a size to take the work. It is filled with a pitch mixture of 2 parts pitch, 1 part plaster of paris and a little tallow.

To mix, heat the pitch slowly and mix in first the plaster and then the tallow. Pour in the box and allow to cool. To fix the metal, warm the face of the pitch slightly, press the metal firmly on it and allow to cool.

REPOUSSÉ WORK

This consists of beating up a pattern, working from the back of the metal while it is held on a pitch block. The metal used needs to be thin, 0.7mm or less. It is fixed to the pitch as above. The metal may be more easily removed if its under surface is coated with tallow before fixing to the pitch. The design is drawn on the metal and a chasing tool used to incise the outline. The metal is peeled off and the work reversed on the block. The design now will show itself in relief. The parts to be modelled are beaten into the pitch using round-nosed punches. The modelling is completed by reversing the metal and working from the front face.

BUILT-UP WORK

It is rarely that a piece of hammered metalwork can be completed from one piece of metal. More often work will consist of separate units soldered together.

EXAMPLE OF BUILT-UP WORK - A bowl with a ring foot.

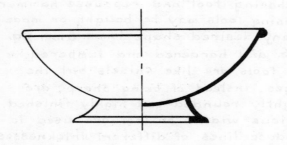

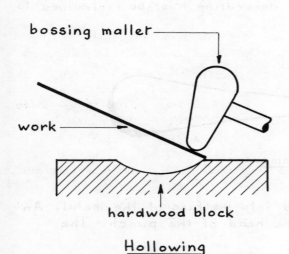

bossing mallet

work

hardwood block

Hollowing

PROCEDURE

1. Estimate size of blank to form the body and prepare the surfaces, using water-of-ayr stone to eliminate any scratches.

2. Anneal the blank, pickle, scour, wash and dry.

3. Beat out the shape with a bossing mallet or blocking hammer on a sandbag or a hardwood block.

128

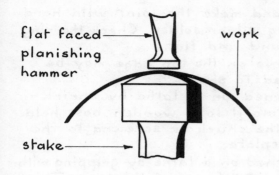

flat faced planishing hammer

work

stake

4. Anneal and pickle ready for planishing.

Planish on a round head stake with a curvature near to that of the bowl using a flat-faced planishing hammer.

Start from the centre, working outwards with light, well-placed blows. Ensure that the metal is trapped between the stake and the hammer and rotate the metal slowly during the process. Overlap the hammer facets to make certain that the complete surface is covered.

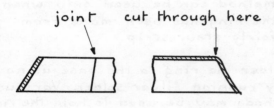

joint   cut through here

Developed Base   Raised Base

5. The shape for the base may be obtained in one of two ways —
a. By developing a truncated cone, bending up the shape on a funnel stake and making the joint with hard running silver solder.
or b. By raising the shape from a circular blank and then cutting out the top with a piercing saw.

6. To obtain the finished shape for the base, stretch it over a suitable stake or bar with a collet hammer.
If the shape has been made from a truncated cone, be careful when hammering near the joint area. Prolonged or heavy hammering at that point will crack the solder.

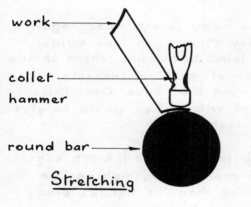

work

collet hammer

round bar

Stretching

7. Anneal, pickle and planish, using a collet hammer and a round stake or length of round bar.

8. Level off the lower edge of the base If much waste has to be removed cut it off with a pair of curved snips or file it off.
Strike a height line with a surface gauge. Trim off any waste and scour the edges on a sheet of emery cloth.

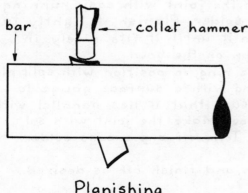

bar   collet hammer

Planishing

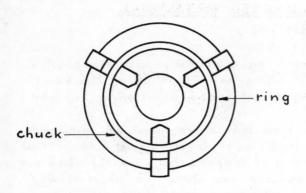

Base Ring Chucked for Turning

ring

chuck

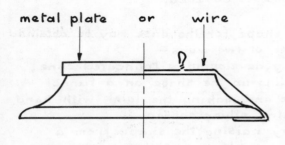

metal plate   or   wire

Base Ring in Place for Soldering

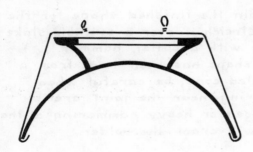

Base Wired to Bowl

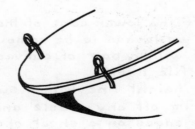

Half-round Wire in Position

9. Bend up the base ring from strip metal and make the joint with hard running silver solder. Check the ring for round and flat.
The curve on the top edge may be
a. Filed to shape.
or b. Turned on a lathe by shrink-fitting it to a wooden boss held in the chuck or screwed to the faceplate.
or c. Turned on a lathe by gripping with the outer faces of the jaws. This method can be used only when the ring has been made from fairly stout strip.

10. Solder the ring to the base using easy running silver solder. Various methods may be used to hold the ring in position depending on the shape and size of the work, e.g. cotter pins, binding wire, or it can be weighted with a strip of plate.

11. Wire the body to the base; again using easy running silver solder, make the joint. With care, there should be no fear of melting the joint between ring and base. Coat this first joint with rouge paste to give some protection.

12. Bend up the ring for the top edge from half-round wire, making it a little smaller than the needed size. Solder the joint with easy running silver solder. Planish it lightly to stretch it until it fits nicely in position on the bowl.
Fix the ring in position with split pins, checking with a surface gauge to make sure that it lies parallel with the base. Make the joint with soft solder. Trim off any excess solder.

13. Polish and finish off as desired.

SOLDERED JOINTS FOR HAMMERED METALWORK

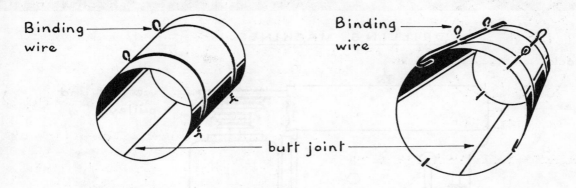

Binding wire

Binding wire

butt joint

__Cylinder Wired for Soldering__   __Truncated Cone Wired for Soldering__

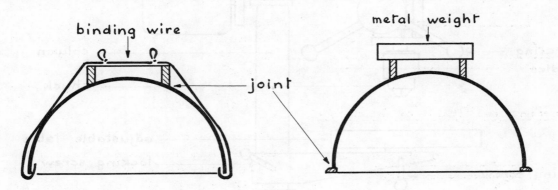

binding wire

joint

metal weight

__Base Wired to a Bowl for Soldering__   __Joint Held in Position by a Weight__

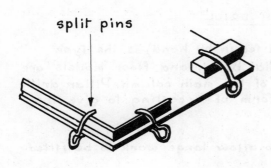

split pins

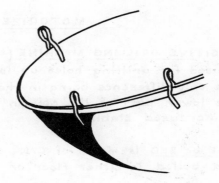

__Using Split Pins for Feet, Edges, etc.__   __Using Split Pins to Hold Wire in Position__

12. DRILLS AND DRILLING

DRILLING MACHINES

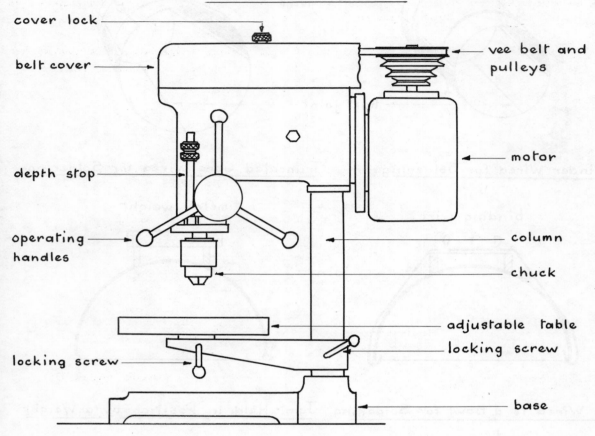

cover lock

belt cover

depth stop

operating handles

locking screw

vee belt and pulleys

motor

column

chuck

adjustable table

locking screw

base

MOTORIZED BENCH DRILL

THE SENSITIVE DRILLING MACHINE (with drill fed in by hand) is the type usually used for drilling holes up to 19 mm dia. Bench and floor models are made, the only difference being in the length of the main column. Pillar drills have the lower part of the column in the form of a casting to give the column increased stability.

THE BASE or BED is made of C.I., slotted to allow large work to be fitted to it and bolted to either floor or bench.

THE COLUMN, of tubular steel, supports the motor and operating mechanism.

THE TABLE, of C.I., may be circular or rectangular in shape and is provided with slots to allow for the bolting down of the vice or workpiece. The table may be locked at any position on the column and is sometimes capable of being swung round and locked at any desired angle.

DRIVE. An electric motor provides the drive through belt and pulleys to the spindle. The range of speeds will vary with different sizes and makes of machines from 4 to 10, a typical speed range being 300 r.p.m to 2000 r.p.m. Some machines are provided with a geared head in addition to belt drive in order to increase the speed range.

FEED on sensitive drills is by hand, i.e. the drill is fed into the metal by hand pressure. Large size machines are fitted with automatic feed.

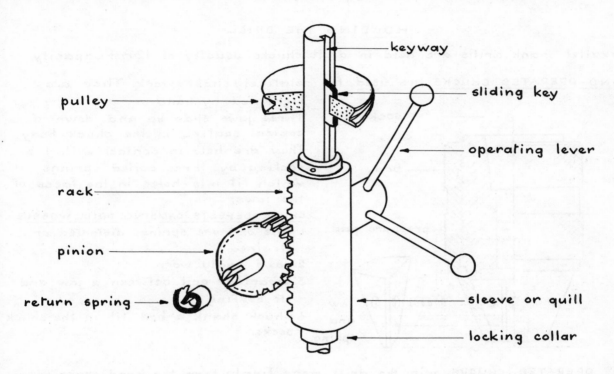

Pressure on the operating handle rotates the horizontal spindle. To this spindle is fixed a pinion (gear wheel) and a coiled return spring. When pressure is released on the handles the spring, slotted into the spindle, returns it to its original position.

Around the main vertical spindle is a round sleeve or quill which is cut along its length with teeth, called a rack. The pinion engages with the rack so that rotation of the pinion causes vertical movement of the quill. The pulleys are keyed to the top of the spindle in such a way as to allow rotation and vertical movement of the spindle within the pulley.

DEPTH STOP. Most drills are fitted with adjustable depth stop by means of which holes of a predetermined depth can be drilled or any given number of holes of equal depth. If the machine is not fitted with a depth stop a collar can be drilled out equal to the drill diameter and locked in position on the drill with a suitable grub screw.

RADIAL DRILLS are larger than sensitive drills, are able to deal with larger work and are powerful enough to drive large dia. drills. The drill head itself moves along the radial arm for positioning the drill whereas with bench and pillar drills it is necessary to move the work. They are fitted with automatic power feed and are used for heavy engineering.

HOLDING THE DRILL

Parallel shank drills are held in drill chucks usually of 12mm capacity.

HAND OPERATED CHUCKS are used for relatively light work. They are tightened by hand.

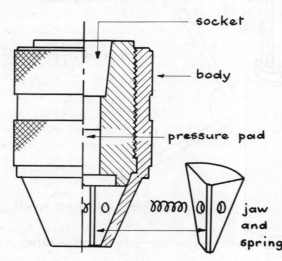

Three jaws slide up and down a conical seating in the chuck body. They are held in contact with the seating by three coiled springs which fit into holes in the faces of the jaws.

CHUCK DEFECTS CAUSING DRILL WOBBLE
1. One or more springs distorted or strained.
2. Jaws badly worn.
3. Swarf or grit between a jaw and its seating
4. Chuck shank a bad fit in the chuck socket.

KEY OPERATED CHUCKS grip the drill more firmly than the hand operated chucks. They are tightened by means of a key which engages with a rack on the chuck sleeve.

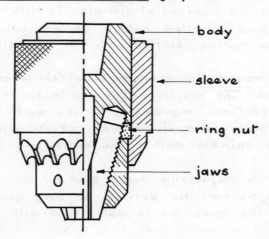

Both types of chuck are made with a tapered female socket which may
1. Fit directly onto a similar male taper on the machine spindle.
or 2. Have a morse taper shank fitted into it.

Drills up to 12mm diameter are usually chuck held. Drills above this size are usually supplied with morse taper shanks.

TAPER SHANK DRILLS fit directly into a female socket on the machine spindle. The tapers are called morse tapers and are usually used on drills above 12mm diameter because they are far more costly than parallel shank drills and breakages are frequent with drills of small diameter.

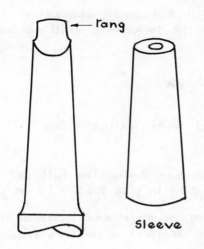

tang

Sleeve

Morse tapers have a taper of approx. 15 mm in 300 and run in sizes from 0 to 7, small drills having a smaller shank size than large drills.

Morse taper sleeves enable a drill with a small dia. morse taper to be fitted in a machine carrying a large morse taper.

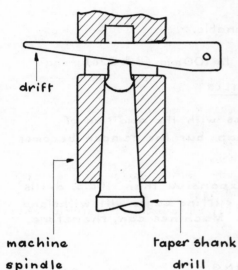

drift

machine spindle

taper shank drill

The drive is frictional by means of the taper and the tang serves no purpose other than for ejection. The tang fits into a slot in the machine spindle and the drill is ejected by means of a steel drift. Remember to support the drill by hand when using the drift. To fit the drill firmly in the socket, it is pushed in by hand and the drill then brought down onto a block of wood or soft metal resting on the drill table.

Morse taper shanks and sockets have to be treated with care at all times. They should be wiped clean before assembly and stored away properly when not in use. Any treatment causing bruising, etc. will affect, not only the accuracy of rotation but the efficiency of the frictional drive.

ADVANTAGES OF PARALLEL SHANK DRILLS
1. Cheaper than taper shank drills.
2. Can be used in a wide range of drilling machine, hand or power operated.

ADVANTAGES OF TAPER SHANK DRILLS
1. Positive drive is given by the shank, the frictional grip increasing with the feed pressure. If shank and socket are well maintained there will be no risk of the drill slipping.
2. More accurate than a chuck fitting.
3. Quicker to assemble than a parallel shank drill.

SQUARE SHANK DRILLS are used in a drill brace fitted with a pair of jaws.

with a vee seating, e.g. a woodworker's brace.

THE LATHE CHUCK is occasionally used for holding a drill. Awkwardly shaped or bulky workpieces are sometimes bolted to the saddle of the lathe and drilling done by rotating the drill in the head of the machine.

SIZES OF TWIST DRILLS

1. Fractional sizes from $\frac{1}{64}$ in. to 3 in. by $\frac{1}{64}$.

2. Number drills in sizes corresponding to the steel wire gauge sizes. No. 1 (0·228 in.) to No. 80 (0·0135 in.)

3. Letter drills which follow on in size from the number drills. The full set contains all the letters of the alphabet, from A (0·234 in.) to Z (0·413 in.)

British Standards (No. 328, 1959) recommended that number and letter drills be replaced by a range of B.S. drills expressed in decimal diameters from 0·0126 in. to 0·3228 in.

All the above sizes are now obsolete but still obtainable.

4. Metric sizes replace the above. Sizes from 0·20 to 100mm (B.S. 328).

STEEL FOR TWIST DRILLS

CARBON STEEL, usually 1% carbon and sometimes with the addition of chromium and tungsten. They are relatively cheap but the temper becomes drawn when they are overheated.

HIGH SPEED STEEL. Drills of H.S.S. are more expensive than H.C.S. drills but they have the property of "red hardness", ie. the cutting edges will withstand considerable heat before its hardness is affected. Machines can, therefore, be run at a faster speed.

MARKING OUT FOR DRILLING

A CENTREPUNCH MARK must be made in order to position the drill. This mark must be -
1. Accurate in position.

2. Large enough to take the chisel edge of the drill.

PILOT DRILLS, ie. a small drill used prior to a large one, are used for the following reasons -

1. Large drills have such a large chisel edge that the centrepunch mark would have to be so large that it could not possibly be positioned accurately enough even if it could be made large enough.

2. The chisel edge is inefficient in cutting and considerable pressure is needed to force it through the metal. The larger the drill the larger the chisel edge and, consequently, the greater the pressure needed. This pressure can be relieved by drilling a pilot hole.

The position for the hole is marked by intersecting lines, usually at right angles and the point of intersection centrepunched.

If the hole need not be very accurate for position it may now be drilled.

For accurate work and large holes better methods are necessary because a drill started in a centrepunch mark will not necessarily drill a hole truly concentric with its original centre

METHOD I. Scribe a circle the exact diameter of the drill and centrepunch the centre. Dot punch where the two lines intersect the circumference

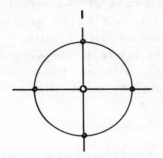 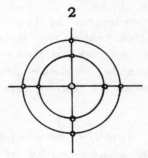

of the circle. These marks (pop marks) accurately fix the circumference of the circle, particularly as, during drilling, the circumference may be masked or obliterated with soluble oil, etc.

METHOD 2. Use two circles, one the diameter of the finished hole and one smaller; both with pop marks. This is more accurate than method I.

Drilling is started and the work inspected before the drill has cut in very far. If the drill is running off true it will be evident by its relative position to the intersecting lines and, if marked out by method 2, by its position in relation to the inner circle as well. If it is off true one or more grooves should be cut with a centrepunch, halfround chisel or diamond point chisel in the opposite direction to which the drill has run. Drilling is restarted and the work again checked. If the hole is now concentric with the marking out, the drilling can be continued and a further check made when drilling approaches the circle. A further adjustment can then be made if necessary.

ONCE THE DRILL HAS STARTED CUTTING ITS FULL DIAMETER IT IS IMPOSSIBLE TO MAKE ANY CORRECTION.

All adjustments must be made before the drill is cutting its full diameter.

FLAT DRILL Although in general use no longer this drill is useful when one of special size is needed quickly or when an odd countersunk angle is needed or when a hard piece of material has to be drilled.

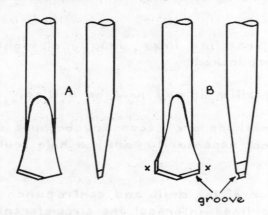

Type A is the common pattern.

Type B is an improved pattern with parallel portions xx to give guidance in the hole and a groove ground above the cutting edge to provide rake.

Usually made from a length of silver steel or H.C.S. of the required diameter, forged out at one end, shaped and hardened and tempered according to the hardness of the metal to be cut.

DISADVANTAGES
1. The effective diameter of type A becomes reduced with grinding.
2. Due to negative rake the drill scrapes rather than cuts.
3. Chips are not extracted from the hole. This leads to clogging and overheating.
4. The drill tends to wander and not produce a true hole, due to the shank of the drill being smaller in diameter than the effective cutting diameter.

ADVANTAGES
1. It is easily, quickly and cheaply made.
2. Stout cutting edges make it suitable for cutting hard materials and it can easily be resharpened when blunted. The grinding does not alter the diameter of type B.

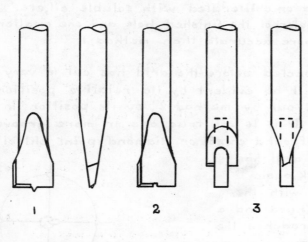

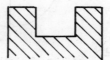

FLAT BOTTOM DRILLS are made from silver steel rod or H.C.S. and are useful for squaring off the bottoms of holes drilled with a twist drill.

A standard twist drill can also be modified for the same purpose by grinding.

PIN OR PEG DRILLS again are made from silver steel rod and are used for counterboring holes to receive a cheesehead screw. The projecting pin needs to be the same diameter as the hole to be counterbored and the shank the same diameter as the head of the screw to be flushed in.

WASHER CUTTERS OR TANK DRILLS AND HOLE SAWS are used for cutting

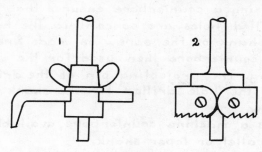

washers or holes in thin plate and made with round or square shanks. Both need pilot holes to be drilled first.

1. The washer cutter is adjustable for size, the cutter being locked in any desired position by means of a wing nut.
2. The hole saw is non-adjustable and consists of a blade like a hacksaw blade wrapped round and screwed to a body.

CENTRE DRILL OR COMBINATION DRILL OR SLOCOMBE DRILL This drill is a twist

drill and countersink combined. It is used for —
1. Preparing work for mounting between lathe centres.
2. Spotting the centre for drilling in the lathe.

Size ranges from 3mm diameter upwards. The drill is always double-ended with an angle of 60° to correspond with the 60° angle of the lathe centres. The small pilot hole keeps the weight off the point of the centre and acts as a reservoir for grease.

USAGE

Speed – as for twist drills. Feed – relatively light. Heavy feeds result in drill breakage.

When centre holes are required to a depth which uses half or more of the diameter of the countersink, ie. deep centring, the drill should be withdrawn frequently to prevent chips choking the flutes.

Always start the cut slowly. If the drill is bumped into the work the pilot drill will fracture.

Make sure the drill is securely held. Any slight movement will cause intermittent feed and subsequent breakage.

COUNTERSINK DRILLS are used to set flush countersunk screws and for

countersinking prior to riveting. They are made with an included angle of 60° or 90°, the latter being necessary for setting in screws.

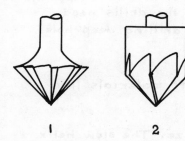

1. The rose countersink is usually made of H.C.S. and is used chiefly for soft materials, e.g. wood. Made with a square or round shank.

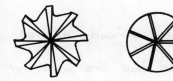
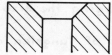

2. The machine countersink is usually made of high speed steel and is the type usually used on drilling machines and lathes.

Care is needed in their use because they cannot normally be sharpened.

COUNTERBORES are used to make a recess for a cheese-headed screw or cap screw. Using a counterbore ensures that both drilled holes are concentric. The hole for the shank of the screw is made first and the counterbore then used for the recessing. The projecting pin of the drill must fit the hole drilled for the shank of the screw.

Fig. 1 is a machine counterbore, available with parallel or taper shank.

Fig. 2 is a counterbore that can be made up for any special work from silversteel rod. The pin is made a push-in fit in the body. Both types can be used for spot-facing, ie. machining the surface of a rough casting around a hole in order to provide a flat seating for nuts and washers as at S-S.

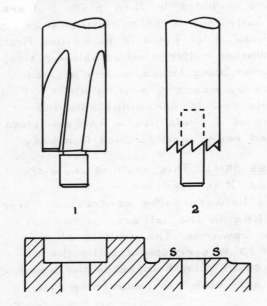

STRAIGHT-FLUTED DRILLS, instead of having spiral flutes like a twist drill have straight flutes. These give the drill zero rake, and so the drill scrapes rather than cuts freely.

Twist drills, when used for brass and, in particular, thin brass sheet, tend to bite excessively, screw themselves into the hole (due to a right hand helix on the drill), and possibly jam.

Because of the straight flutes these drills will drill brass more efficiently.

The straight flutes do not clear the chippings as well as helical flutes and the drills need frequent withdrawal when drilling deep holes.

SPECIAL DRILLS

QUICK HELIX DRILLS are designed for drilling very soft materials like aluminium. The quick helix gives increased rake.

SLOW HELIX DRILLS are designed for brass and bronze. The slow helix reduces the rake angle.

MULTI-FLUTE DRILLS are used for enlarging the size of holes already drilled.

MASONRY DRILLS have brazed in tips of tungsten carbide and are used for the drilling of brick, stone, etc.

TWIST DRILL DETAILS

The **TANG** is used for ejection of the drill.

The **SHANK** provides the drive.

The **BODY** tapers slightly in diameter from tip to shank to provide clearance in deep holes.

The **FLUTES** provide room for the escape of chippings, give the drill its fixed rake angle and allow coolant to get to the cutting edges.

The **LAND** is the narrow part of the body left at its full diameter. The metal behind the land is ground away to give body clearance.

The **WEB** increases in thickness from tip to shank to give added strength. This means that the flutes become shallower in depth as they near the shank. Consequently, when a drill breaks and is reground the size of the chisel edge is considerably increased.

The **CHISEL EDGE** is on the axis of the drill and considerable pressure is needed to force it through the metal being cut.

WEB THINNING reduces the size of the chisel edge.

1. On large drills it lessens the pressure necessary to force the drill through the work.
2. The depth of flute decreases from tip to shank to give strength and rigidity and therefore the web increases in thickness. When a drill gets shortened by constant grinding or breakage, the chisel edge becomes thick and the drill should be web thinned. If it is not done the drill will not centralize itself properly and as considerable force is needed to feed in the drill, the hole may be ou of round or oversize.

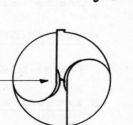

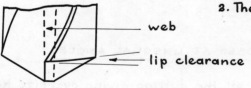

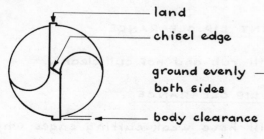

- tang
- morse taper
- land
- flute
- helix angle
- point angle
- lip
- chisel edge
- web
- lip clearance
- land
- chisel edge
- ground evenly both sides
- body clearance

Shank

Body

THE GRINDING OF TWIST DRILLS

To ensure correct cutting the following rules need to be observed —

1. The point angle needs to be correct – 118° included angle.

2. The chisel edge must be at the right angle – 130°.

3. The lip clearance must be correct for the size of drill. It is larger on small drills. The average clearance is 10° to 12°.

4. The two cutting edges should be the same length.

5. The two cutting edges should be at the same angle to the drill axis.

EFFECTS OF INACCURATE GRINDING

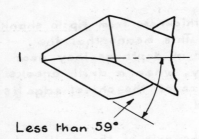 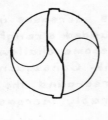

Less than 59°

1. POINT ANGLE TOO ACUTE

The lips become convex with loss of cutting efficiency.

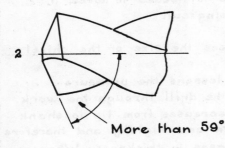 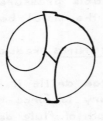

More than 59°

2. POINT ANGLE TOO OBTUSE

The lips become concave with much loss of strength.

3. CUTTING EDGES AT UNEQUAL ANGLES

One lip does all the cutting giving oversize holes.

4. INSUFFICIENT LIP CLEARANCE

The drill will rub and not cut cleanly.

5. EXCESSIVE LIP CLEARANCE

The drill will have weak cutting edges which will chip and break easily.

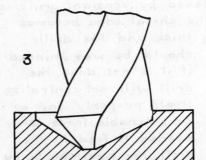

AIDS TO CORRECT GRINDING

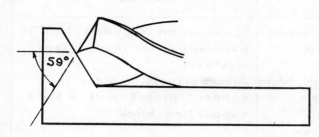

It is extremely difficult to grind a drill by hand to ensure that all the angles are correct.

A DRILL GAUGE can be made from steel plate and is a useful gauge for checking that the grinding of the point angle is correct.

DRILL GRINDING ATTACHMENTS fit onto pedestal grinding machines. These are essential for the accurate grinding of twist drills.

TWIST DRILL FAULTS, CAUSES AND REMEDIES		
DEFECT	**CAUSE**	**REMEDY**
BROKEN OR TWISTED TANGS Morse taper shanks are "self-driving", ie. they are made to drive off the taper not the tang. The tang is for ejection purposes only.	A bad fit between the shank and the socket, thus causing a drive off the tang and not the taper.	Make sure the shank is a good fit in the socket. Shanks and sockets must be free of bruises, clean of dirt and not badly worn. Always wipe clean before inserting and store away carefully when not in use.
SPLITTING OF THE WEB	1. Striking the drill on the point with a hard object to ensure that it fits tightly into its socket. 2. Too much feed. 3. Careless ejection of the drill. 4. Excessive web thinning. 5. Too little lip clearance necessitating excessive feed.	Use a soft-faced hammer or bring down the drill onto a block of wood. Reduce the feed. Hold the drill when ejecting to prevent it falling. Reduce the web thinning. Increase the lip clearance.
WORN OUTER CORNERS OF CUTTING EDGES	1. Excessive speed for the material being cut. 2. Lack of a suitable cutting solution.	Reduce the speed. Use the correct cutting solution.

DEFECT	CAUSE	REMEDY
FLAKED OUTER CORNERS OF CUTTING EDGES	This usually occurs when drilling thin-sectioned material which is not supported firmly enough. When the chisel edge breaks through, the material springs back and then snatches at the outer corners of the drill causing them to chip.	Examine the supports. If it is necessary, fix them closer together. Alternatively, replace the support pieces with a solid supporting block.
CHIPPED CUTTING LIPS	1. Excessive lip clearance angles 2. Too heavy a feed.	Regrind and reduce the clearance angles. Reduce the feed.
LARGE CHIP FROM ONE FLUTE, LITTLE OR NONE FROM OTHER	Unequal cutting edges causing one lip to do all the cutting.	Regrind, making cutting edges of equal length.
WALLS OF DRILLED HOLE LEFT ROUGH	1. Drill is blunt. 2. Drill is badly ground. 3. No cutting solution. 4. Too much feed.	Regrind. Regrind. Use a cutting solution. Reduce the feed.
DRILL BREAKAGE	1. Incorrect grinding. 2. Too much feed. 3. Worn lands. 4. Flutes choked with chips.	Regrind. Reduce feed. No remedy. Replace drill. Frequent withdrawal of the drill is necessary to clear the flutes especially with small drills and deep holes.
DRILL COLOURED BLUE	1. Speed too fast. 2. No cutting solution. 3. Worn lands. 4 No lip clearance. 5. Blunt drill.	Reduce speed. Use cutting sol. where needed. Replace drill. Regrind. Regrind.

DEFECT	CAUSE	REMEDY
HOLE TOO LARGE	1. Unequal cutting angles. 2. Unequal length of cutting edges. 3. Loose machine spindle.	Regrind. Regrind. Check the spindle bearings.
DRILL BINDS IN THE HOLE AND SQUEAKS	Lands worn due to speed being too high or lack of cutting solution.	Use a new drill. Reduce speed and use a cutting solution if the metal demands it.

DRILLING THIN SHEET

All thin sheet, but in particular thin brass sheet, is difficult to drill with a standard twist drill.
1. The holes are often out of round and roughly triangular in shape.
2. The underside of the holes are heavily burred.
3. The drill tends to catch up badly and screw into the metal.

A flat drill or straight fluted drill will make these holes more efficiently, particularly in brass sheet, because the rake angles are better suited to the material than the rake angle given by the helix of a standard twist drill.

If neither of these drills is available, then modification of a standard drill is necessary.

1. ALTERATION OF POINT ANGLE

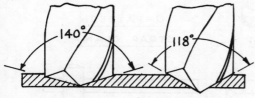

Modified Drill   Standard Drill

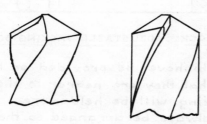

Grinding in the Flutes

Heavy burring will occur and the drill will tend to screw itself into the metal if the point of the drill breaks through on the underside before the full diameter of the drill has entered the work. This can be minimized if the point angle is altered to 140°, making it more obtuse.

2. ALTERATION OF HELIX ANGLE

The angle of the helix gives a tool angle that is much too acute for drilling brass. This angle can be altered by grinding in the flute to produce a rake angle of 15° or less. The cutting action then becomes similar to that of a straight fluted drill.

3. WEB OR POINT THINNING

will help in producing a hole that is round.

HOLDING WORK FOR DRILLING

Whenever metal parts have to be drilled they should always be clamped securely to the bed or table, where possible. When the work is held by hand there is danger of —
1. Damage to the hand or drill if the drill should catch up.
2. Drill breakage. As the drill breaks through on the underside of the metal it tends to catch up with consequent lifting of the metal.
3. Drill breakage due to lack of rigidity.

1. HOLDING BY HAND

For the above reasons, holding the work by hand should be avoided but it is sometimes convenient to drill small holes in long strip metal that is being held by hand. It is then advisable to use an end stop, which is a block of metal bolted to the drill table through one of the bolting slots. The stop prevents rotation of the work but does not prevent lifting of the work when the drill breaks through.

2. MACHINE VICE

The machine vice and hand vice are used for holding standard stock sections, particularly when extreme accuracy is not required. The machine vice should be bolted to the drill table except for the drilling of small holes. Machine vices vary in shape, size and cost, some having provision for swivelling the jaws to any desired angle. (See drawing under "HOLDING TOOLS".)

3. CLAMPING PLATES

These are bolted to the workpiece and held parallel to the drill table by means of packing pieces or adjustable stops. The clamping bolts

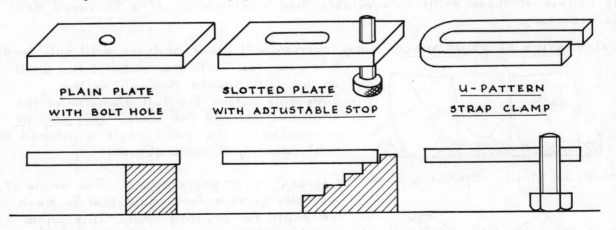

PLAIN PLATE
WITH BOLT HOLE

SLOTTED PLATE
WITH ADJUSTABLE STOP

U-PATTERN
STRAP CLAMP

PLAIN PACKING BLOCK   STEPPED PACKING BLOCK   ADJUSTABLE PACKING BOLT

fit either into T-slots or through bolting slots, whichever is provided on the drill table. The bolts must always be fitted so that they are nearer to the workpiece than the packing or otherwise the packing will be held more securely than the workpiece. The packing must always be arranged so that the plate gives a parallel grip. The clamping plates can be made from rectangular steel strip but drop-forged plates are stiffer with less likelihood of bending under pressure of the bolt.

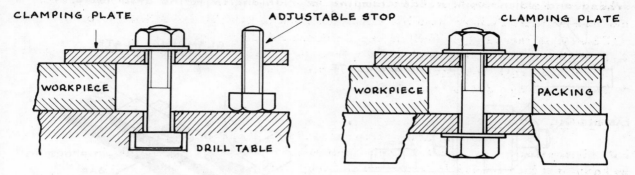

4. VEE BLOCKS

These are used for supporting round stock that has to be drilled, marked out or checked. When drilling rod diametrically, the set-up must be firm with no possibility of movement because—

a. The drill might wander off its centre on the curved surface and
b. The drill is inclined to bite fiercely when breaking through a curved surface.

For diametric drilling a centre line is needed on the end of the rod which must be in a vertical position for drilling. Clamping plates are

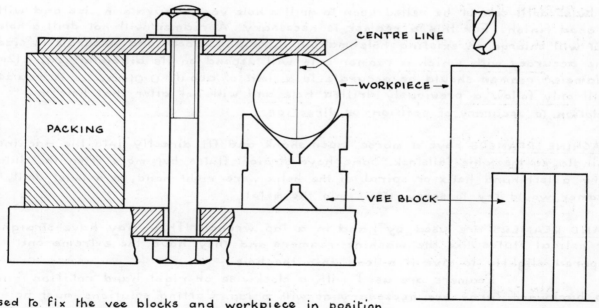

used to fix the vee blocks and workpiece in position on the drill table.

A vee block resting on its end is used for supporting rod vertically for drilling. For light drilling the rod and block may be held by hand but for heavy and accurate drilling the block and work will need to be clamped to the side face of the drill table.

5. ANGLE PLATES

These are useful when awkward shapes or castings have to be drilled and when work needs clamping at right angles to the drill table.

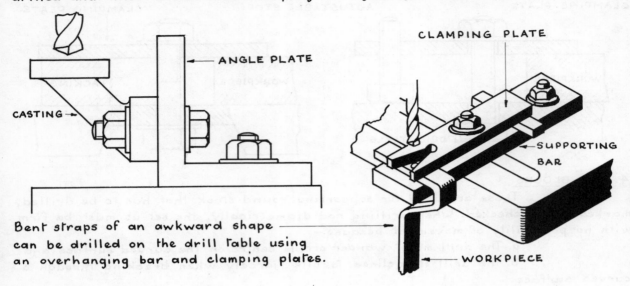

Bent straps of an awkward shape can be drilled on the drill table using an overhanging bar and clamping plates.

REAMERS

A twist drill cannot be relied upon to drill a hole very accurate in size and with a good finish. For this a reamer is necessary. A reamer will not drill a hole but will enlarge an existing hole making it round, smooth and accurate in size. The accuracy with which a reamer cuts will depend on its diameter, eg. a 12mm diameter reamer should be accurate to a limit of about 0.01mm. A reamer will only follow a previously drilled hole and will not alter that hole in relation to accuracy of position or direction.

MACHINE REAMERS have a morse taper shank and fit directly into the machine spindle, eg. the lathe tailstock. Some have straight flutes but more often the flutes form a left hand helix or spiral. If the helix were right hand, as a twist drill, the reamer would try to screw itself into the metal.

HAND REAMERS are used by hand in a tap wrench. They may have straight or helical flutes like the machine reamers and they have the extreme end tapered slightly to give it a lead into the hole.

Reamers are used with a clockwise or right hand rotation and no backward turns are necessary as with a tap. Cutting solutions must be used as for drilling.

ALLOWANCES FOR REAMING. The amount of metal removed by the reamer is small. If too much is left for reaming, the reamer will cut inefficiently and will deteriorate through excessive wear. The allowance for reaming will depend on the size of hole and type of metal being used. For holes up to 12mm dia. the allowance should be about 0·10mm.   For holes above 12mm dia. the allowance should be correspondingly larger.

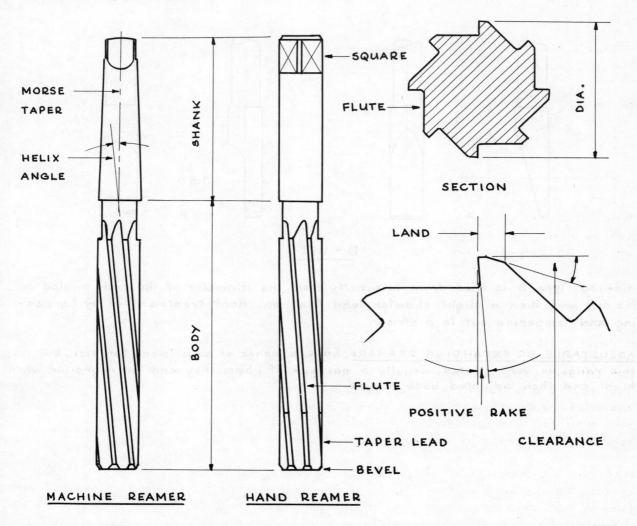

MACHINE REAMER   HAND REAMER

TAPER REAMERS have a taper over their whole length and are used only for the reaming of taper holes, eg. for fitting taper pins or cotters.

CARE OF REAMERS. Reamers are expensive, high precision cutting tools and need to be treated with extreme care. When blunted they can be sharpened only by grinding in the flutes. For this a special tool and cutter grinder is needed and the number of regrinds possible before the reamer becomes undersize is limited. Hence, always ensure that the reamer is used correctly and that the drilled hole gives the correct allowance for reaming.

D-BITS. When the correct size reamer is unavailable a D-bit can be made which will produce a hole of fair accuracy with a good finish, provided the tool is well made. Two types are shown, A being the quicker and easier to produce and B being the more efficient. Both are made from silver steel of the correct

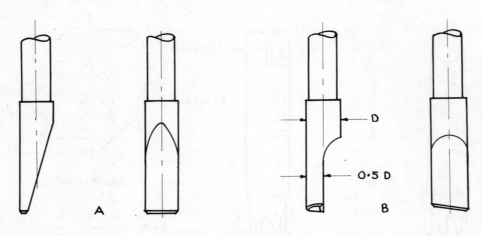

D - BITS

diameter. Type B is filed down to exactly half the diameter of the rod, angled on the end and then a slight chamfer lead filed on. Heat treatment is by harden-ing and tempering out to a straw.

ADJUSTABLE OR EXPANDING REAMERS have a range of adjustment for size but this range is very limited, usually a maximum of 1·5mm. They can be reground when blunt and then adjusted back to size.

MAKING USE OF IMPERIAL SIZE DRILLS

The chart gives the imperial equivalent of metric drills. This will enable stocks of imperial drills to be used in place of metric drills.

Metric	Imperial	Metric	Imperial
1·00	60	5·00	9
1·20	$\frac{3}{64}$	5·20	6
1·40	54	5·40	3
1·60	$\frac{1}{16}$	5·60	2
1·80	50	5·80	1
2·00	47	6·00	B
2·20	44	6·20	D
2·40	$\frac{3}{32}$	6·40	$\frac{1}{4}$ or E
2·60	38	6·60	G
2·80	35	6·80	H
3·00	31	7·00	J
3·20	$\frac{1}{8}$	7·20	$\frac{9}{32}$
3·40	29	7·40	L
3·60	$\frac{9}{64}$	7·60	N
3·80	25	7·80	$\frac{5}{16}$
4·00	22	8·00	O
4·20	19	8·20	P
4·40	17	8·40	Q or $\frac{21}{64}$
4·60	14	8·60	R
4·80	12	8·80	S

Metric	Imperial
9·00	T
9·20	$\frac{23}{64}$
9·40	U
9·60	V
9·80	W
10·00	X or $\frac{25}{64}$
10·20	Y
10·40	Z
10·60	-
10·80	$\frac{27}{64}$
11·00	$\frac{7}{16}$
11·20	-
11·40	-
11·60	$\frac{29}{64}$
11·80	$\frac{15}{32}$
12·00	-
12·20	$\frac{31}{64}$
12·80	$\frac{1}{2}$

13   GRINDING

GRINDING

Electric or power grinders are used for the removal of waste metal and the sharpening of small tools. "Off-hand" grinders, as they are sometimes called, are of two types — bench models and pedestal (or floor) models, these differing only in their method of mounting. Both are available with belt or direct motor drive.

GRINDING WHEELS

When ordering a wheel, the following details have to be specified — shape, diameter, width, arbor hole size, abrasive material, grain or grit size, grade and bond.

SHAPE   For ordinary tool grinding purposes a plain wheel is used but if much grinding is to be done on the side of the wheel then a plain cup wheel is better. A wide range of shaped wheels is available for special work.

DIAMETER refers to the outside diameter of the wheel, which, for ordinary off-hand grinding, may be from 150 to 300 mm.

WIDTH is the measure of the thickness of the wheel.

ARBOR HOLE SIZE is the diameter of hole that runs through the lead bush. For some sizes of wheel, two or more arbor hole diameters are offered. For any particular grinder no change must be made from the original design. The lead bush in the centre must not be turned out to suit a larger arbor, neither must a wheel be mounted which has an arbor hole larger than the spindle diameter. If this were done, it would be quite easy for the wheel to move and become out of balance, with the possibility of subsequent breakage.

ABRASIVE MATERIAL OR GRIT is the element in the stone that does the actual cutting. The sharp particles of the abrasive project beyond the face of

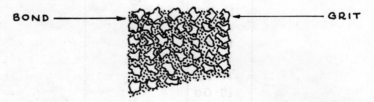

BOND ——————➤   ◄—————— GRIT

the bond producing a series of cutting edges. An examination with a magnifying glass of the small cuttings of metal taken off by the wheel will show that they differ very little from cuttings produced by edge tools. When a stone becomes glazed, the abrasive projections become blunted. When the stone is used for grinding unsuitable materials the small spaces between the particles of abrasive become filled up with the material being ground. (Compare file "pinning".) The stone then needs to be dressed. There are two kinds of abrasive in common use.

1. Aluminium Oxide – used for grinding high tensile materials, eg. tool steels.
2. Silicon Carbide – used for grinding low tensile and non-ferrous metals.

For grinding cemented carbide tools a special grit is used with vitrified bond.

GRAIN OR GRIT SIZE. The size of the abrasive grains determines the coarseness or fineness of the grinding wheel. The grain is graded by means of screens or sieves and the grain size is denoted by a number, which is equal to the number of holes per 25^2 mm of sieve, eg. 10 = very coarse and 150 = very fine. The size of the holes in sieves is measured in microns.

GRADE denotes the strength with which the bond holds the grit in place. The grade is indicated by the letters of the alphabet, soft wheels having letters at the beginning of the alphabet and very hard wheels letters at the end of the alphabet.

BOND is the material or matrix that holds the grit together. It may be one of the following types – vitrified, silicate, rubber, shellac or synthetic resin. A vitrified bond is the one commonly used for wheels for tool sharpening. Soft wheels, i.e. soft bond – the grit readily breaks away under grinding pressure, thus exposing fresh grit. Used for grinding hard materials.
Hard wheels, i.e. hard bond – the grit is retained under grinding pressure. Used for grinding soft materials.
The combination of bond and grit should be such that the grit breaks away when blunted under the pressure of cutting, thus exposing a fresh layer of sharp grit. If a stone is used for cutting the wrong material it will either become blunt, i.e. the grit loses its sharpness, or become glazed, i.e. particles of the ground metal stick between the grit of the wheel. If either of these things happens or if the wheel becomes worn out of shape, then dressing of the wheel is necessary.

DRESSING. For efficient cutting, the wheel must be free of glaze, run true and have a flat face. To maintain this condition frequent dressing is necessary with a wheel dresser, which may be one of three types
1. The Huntington or star-wheel dresser consists of a set of star-shaped wheels and washers, made of hardened steel, which rotate in a heavy holder. The wheels and washers are replaceable when worn. The complete unit is relatively cheap.
2. The diamond dresser consists of an industrial diamond brazed into a steel body. This tool is comparatively expensive but long-lasting. It is usually used for trueing the wheels of precision grinders.
3. The coarse abrasive stick is a cheap method.

In use dressers are held firmly on the tool rest and in contact with the wheel while it is rotating. Goggles must be worn and preferably some nose and mouth covering as well. Cuts are taken over the whole face of the wheel until the original shape has been restored or a fresh layer of sharp

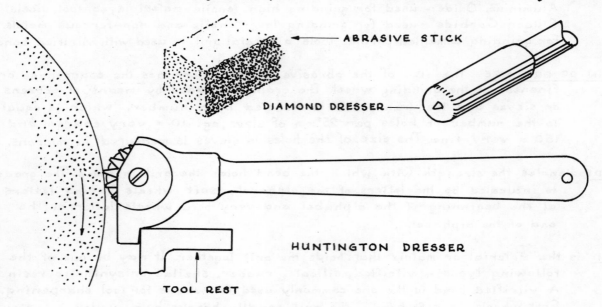

ABRASIVE STICK

DIAMOND DRESSER

HUNTINGTON DRESSER

TOOL REST

grit exposed. Mounting of the Huntington dresser is as shown, with the tool rest moved away from the stone to allow the step of the dresser to move in contact with it.

MOUNTING A WHEEL   Several precautions are necessary before mounting.

1. Examine for any obvious surface defects.
2. Test the wheel for cracks by suspending by its centre and tapping with a light bar. A clear ring indicates a flawless wheel, whilst a dull sound indicates a flaw. The wheel will have been factory tested but damage is always possible during delivery.
3. Examine the lead bush for burrs and for fit on the machine spindle. It should be an easy sliding fit. Do not force it on if too tight but ease the bush to a fit with a bearing (half-round) scraper.
4. After mounting, run the wheel for some minutes without load and without standing near. If the wheel has an undetected flaw it will disintegrate during the early stages of running.

① WHEEL. Thickness, diameter, grit and bond varying according to the type of the work.

② COLLARS or FLANGES should be of equal diameter, machined true and an outside diameter equal to half the diameter of the wheel. The inside surfaces are slightly recessed to reduce the bearing surfaces. The inner flange is keyed to the spindle.

③ WASHERS of thin card or paper, usually supplied attached to the wheel reduce the harshness of grip between flanges and wheel.

④ LEAD BUSH integral with the wheel and an easy fit on the spindle.

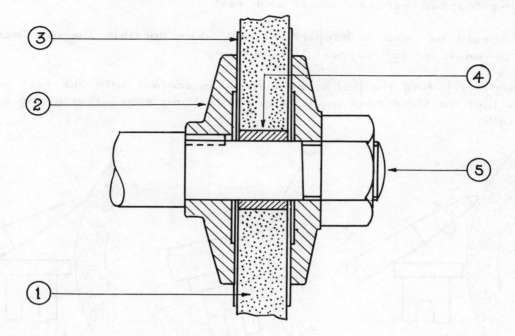

⑤ SPINDLE screwed with a right-hand thread on the right of the machine and a left-hand thread on the left in order to prevent the tendency to unscrew under rotation.

AIDS TO CORRECT GRINDING

Because of the abrasive nature of the dust thrown off by grinding, the machine should be sited well away from other machine tools.

If possible the whole face of the wheel should be used in order to maintain its flatness and prevent uneven wear.

The face and not the side of the wheel should be used because the wheel is best able to withstand the cutting stresses on its face rather than its side. If the curvature produced by the face of the wheel is too great and reduces the efficiency of the tool, then a light finish grinding on the side of the wheel is permissible.

Dipping the tool in water to cool it should be avoided. The alternate heating and cooling causes fine hair cracks to develop on the surface of the tool. Break-down of the tool follows.

155

Goggles should be worn unless the machine is provided with an eye shield or fixed visor.

The rest must be adjusted so that it is close enough to the wheel to prevent work being trapped between wheel and rest.

The rest should be used to support the tool when possible, the rest being tilted at an angle for full support if necessary.

For off-hand grinding the tool is held firmly in contact with the rest in such a position that the stone runs away from the cutting edge, thus giving maximum tool strength.

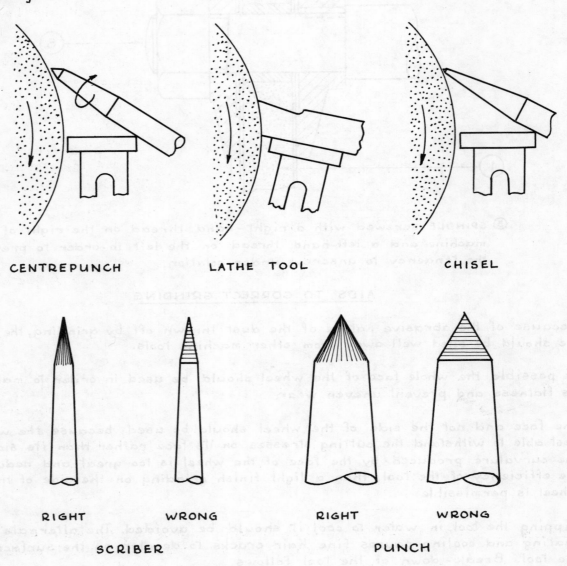

CENTREPUNCH   LATHE TOOL   CHISEL

RIGHT   WRONG   RIGHT   WRONG

SCRIBER   PUNCH

THE SHAPING MACHINE

Flat surfaces can be machined by means of milling, planing or shaping machines. Planing machines are used only for heavy machining operations. Shaping machines are cheaper than millers, will remove metal more quickly but are not capable of such a wide range of work.

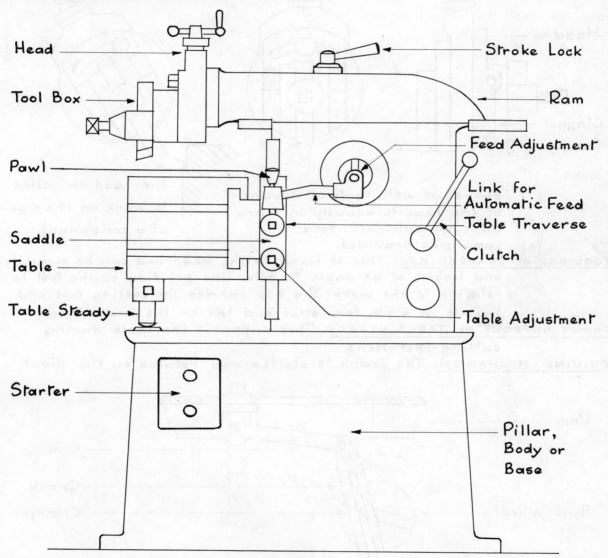

BASE or BODY. This is a heavy hollow casting supporting the main parts. The ram-operating mechanism and often the motor drive is contained within the casting.

THE SADDLE is fixed to the front vertical face of the body. It can be raised and lowered by hand and locked in position.

157

__THE TABLE__ is of machined cast iron, slotted on top, bottom and sides for the bolting on of work. It is sometimes made to swivel and can be traversed sideways by hand or power feed.

__RAM__. The base casting has slideways machined on its top face to take the ram which moves horizontally across it.

__THE HEAD__ can be moved vertically and is usually arranged so that it can

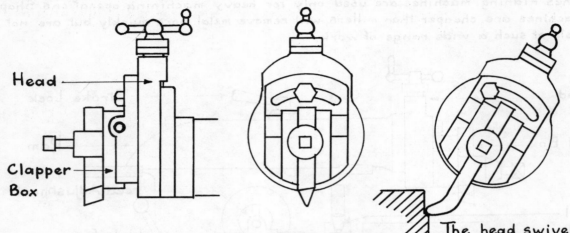

Head

Clapper Box

Swivel as well. Vertical movement of the head is usually by hand although automatic feed is sometimes provided.

The head swivelled to work on the side of a component.

__TOOL BOX or CLAPPER BOX__. This is fixed to the head and can be swivelled and locked at an angle to alter the position of the tool in relation to the work. The box carries the cutting tool and swivels on a pin for relief and lift on the back stroke.

__FRONT SUPPORT or TABLE STEADY__. This supports the table during cutting operations.

__DRIVING MECHANISM__. The crank is slotted and rotates on the pivot.

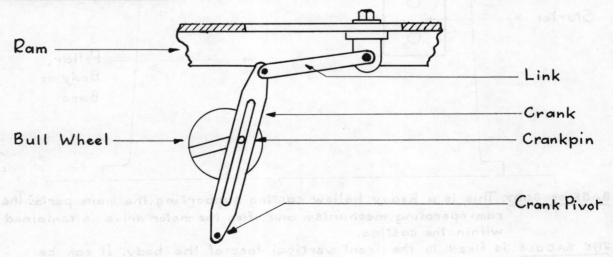

Ram

Bull Wheel

Link

Crank

Crankpin

Crank Pivot

158

It is connected to the bull wheel or crank gear by means of the crank pin. The link connects the crank to the ram. The length of stroke of the ram is decided by the position of the crank pin in the slot of the bull wheel. The further it is from the centre the longer the stroke. This same mechanism ensures that the idle return stroke is quicker than the forward cutting stroke.

TABLE FEED MECHANISM. The feed is arranged so that the table is moved a set amount after each stroke. The driving disc is slotted and attached

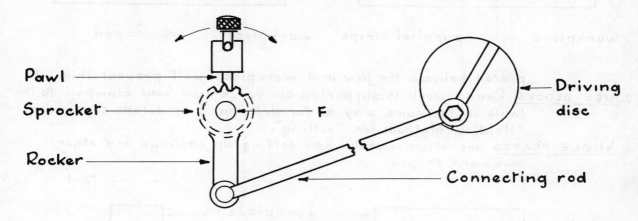

to it is the connecting rod, the latter being adjustable for position in the disc slot. The connecting rod is linked to a fulcrum F through a rocker arm in such a way that rotation of the disc causes the rocker arm to reciprocate. The reversible pawl is fixed to the top end of the rocker arm, its lower end engaging with a sprocket on the feed screw. Clockwise and anticlockwise movement of the sprocket is possible by rotating the pawl through 180°. A neutral position is provided. The amount of feed is governed by the position of the pin in the slot of the driving disc.

CUTTING TOOLS are basically the same shape as lathe tools but they are often deeper and therefore stronger.

HOLDING THE WORK

1. VICE. Shaper vices are relatively large and usually of the swivelling type. They bolt down to the shaper table by means of the Tee slots provided in the table.

    The work to be machined must be firmly fixed because of the extra strain imposed by the intermittent cutting. Therefore, it is much better practice to bolt down the vice with the jaws at right angles to the stroke, so that the cutting forces are taken against the vice jaws.

    If two opposite faces of the component have to be machined parallel to each other, the component should be supported with parallel strips.

When machining two surfaces at right angles, the movable jaw of the vice often lifts throwing the work off square. A piece of rod

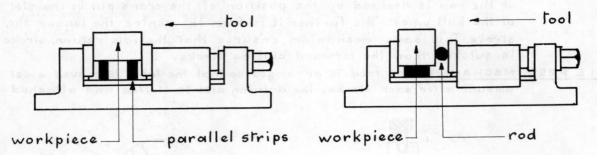

workpiece — parallel strips   workpiece — rod

placed between the jaw and workpiece will prevent this lift.

2. **VEE BLOCKS.** Round work is supported on vee blocks and clamped to the table in the same way as for drilling. For details see under "Holding Methods for Drilling".

3. **ANGLE PLATES** are often useful when setting up castings and other awkward shapes.

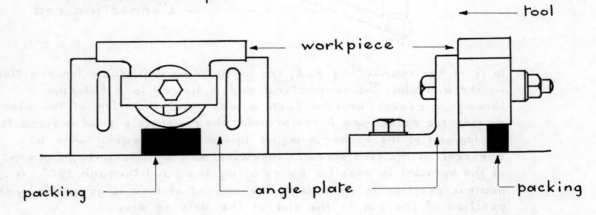

packing — angle plate — packing

4. **CLAMPING TO THE TABLE.** Bolting the work directly to the top or side of the table is often better than using a vice or fitting.

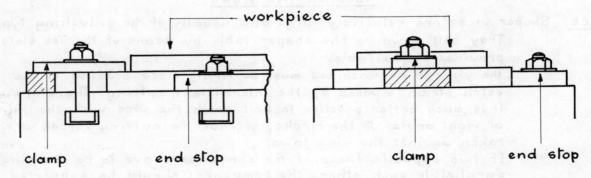

clamp   end stop   clamp   end stop

Use of an end stop to take the thrust is often advisable

THE SHAPING OPERATION

During shaping the tool moves horizontally along a line A-B while the work moves horizontally along a line C-D, thus producing a flat surface. The length

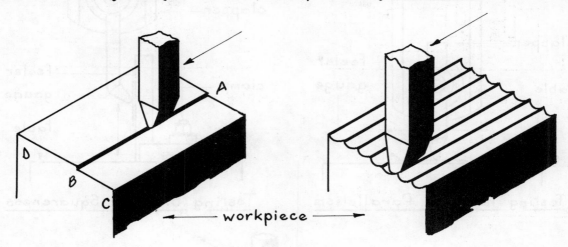

← workpiece →

of the stroke is adjusted so that the tool clears the workpiece at the start and end of each stroke.
The quality of finished surface will depend on —
      1. The width and convexity of the cutting edge of the tool.
      2. The speed of the machine.
      3. The rate of feed.
      4. To some extent, the use of a cutting solution.
A round-nosed tool fed across the work will produce a series of grooves. The depth and pitch of these will depend on the curvature of the tool and rate of feed. To obtain a fine finish a tool with shallow curvature is needed and the feed wants to be relatively fine.

PRECAUTIONS IN USE

1. Always try to arrange the work so that it is just below the lower face of the ram. Never arrange the table and work low down and then screw down the tool head to reach it.
2. Make sure, before switching on, that the tool and the ram clear the workpiece.
3. When adjusting the height of the work table ensure that any bolts locking the table are slackened off. When the table has been positioned correctly, make sure that the locking bolts are retightened.
4. The table support must be re-adjusted for position and locked once the table has been positioned correctly.

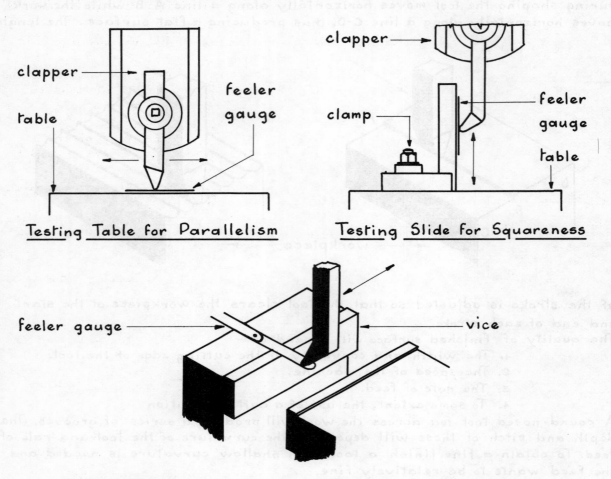

clapper

feeler gauge

table

Testing Table for Parallelism

clapper

clamp

feeler gauge

table

Testing Slide for Squareness

feeler gauge

vice

Testing Parallelism of Tool Travel and Vice Jaw

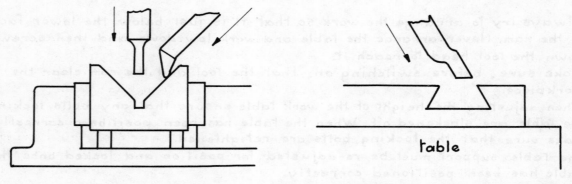

Shaping a Vee Block

table

Use of Knife Tool for Undercutting

162

The lathe is a machine tool used for turning, the metal being held and rotated while a cutter is moved across or along it.

<u>TYPES OF LATHE</u>. 1. The centre lathe is the general purpose lathe. It can vary in size and complexity but the most useful kind is the sliding, surfacing and screwcutting lathe (S.S.SC.) which is the one generally used in schools.

2. Production work, ie., repetitive work, is more often confined to capstan, turret and automatic lathes which can be pre-set with a wide range of tools.

3. Large components are turned on heavy duty lathes, often especially designed for a specific purpose.

<u>SIZE OF CENTRE LATHES</u>. English lathes were specified by the height of the centre from the bed. A lathe specified as 150mm x 1m has a bed 1m long

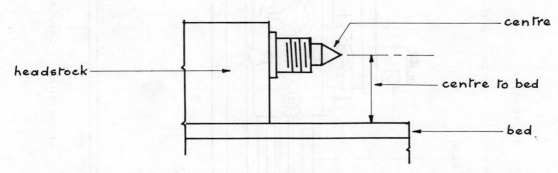

and the centre is 150mm above the bed. A lathe this size is capable of turning a diameter of 300mm over the bed but less over the carriage and a length of something less than 1m. The Machine Tool Trades Association recommends (1970) that lathe size be specified by the swing, i.e. the diameter that can be turned over the bed.

PARTS OF THE LATHE

<u>THE BED</u> is a casting, supported on rigid legs and very accurately machined on the top faces. Different lathes have differently shaped beds, two common forms of which are shown overleaf. The vee form of bed is more expensive to produce but provides a better seating and guide for the tailstock and carriage.

The bed must be treated with great care. The slideways should be kept lightly oiled always and also kept free of grit and fine swarf. Fine brass and cast iron turnings, in particular, can cause trouble. Small felt pads are usually fixed to the sides of the carriage to trap fine particles and prevent them getting between the mating faces of the bed and carriage.

To prevent accidental damage when changing chucks etc., it is a wise precaution to put a piece of flat wood on the bed under the chuck.

THE CENTRE LATHE

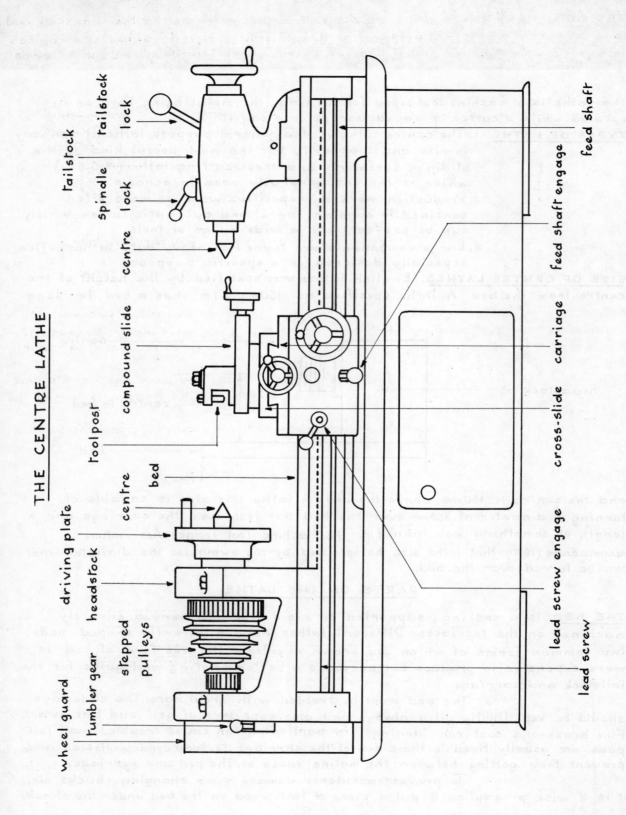

wheel guard
tumbler gear
headstock
driving plate
stepped pulleys
centre
bed
toolpost
compound slide
cross-slide
carriage
feed shaft engage
feed shaft
tailstock
tailstock lock
spindle lock
centre lock
lead screw engage
lead screw

GAP BED. Many lathes are provided with a gap in the bed at the headstock end to accommodate work that is short in length and larger in diameter than can be swung over the bed. Often, too, an extra, short length of the bed is made

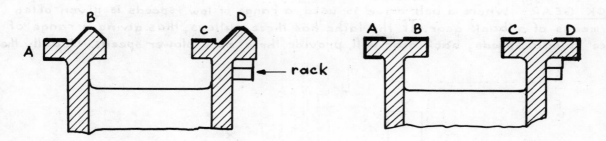

A and D guides for carriage, B and C guides for tailstock

VEE BED SECTION   FLAT BED SECTION

detachable so that slightly longer work of large diameter can be turned. The detachable piece should not be removed except when necessary, because it reduces the length of bearing surface for the carriage when working near the headstock.

THE RACK is fitted to the underside of the bed front. The carriage handle and spindle are linked to the rack by gears so that when the handle is turned the carriage moves along the bed.

THE HEADSTOCK is the casting fixed to the left-hand end of the bed. Through it

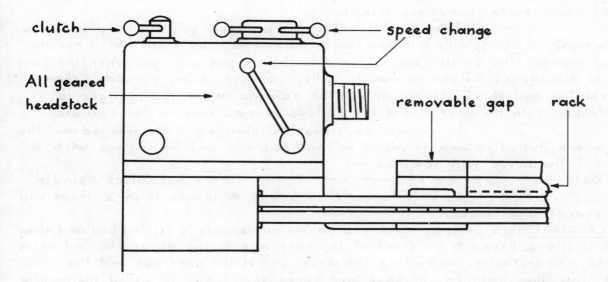

passes a hollow spindle supported on substantial bearings. The bearings may be two-piece bronze bearings or one-piece roller bearings. The spindle is hollow so that long bars can be passed right through it for machining. One end is threaded externally for the attachment of chucks, faceplates, etc., and is bored internally with a morse taper for accommodating the centre. The headstock spindle may be driven from a motor by means of belt and stepped pulleys or through a gear box.

BACK GEAR. Where a belt drive is used, a range of low speeds is given often by means of a back gear. If the lathe has three pulleys, thus giving a range of three spindle speeds, back gear will provide three more slower speeds. Usually the

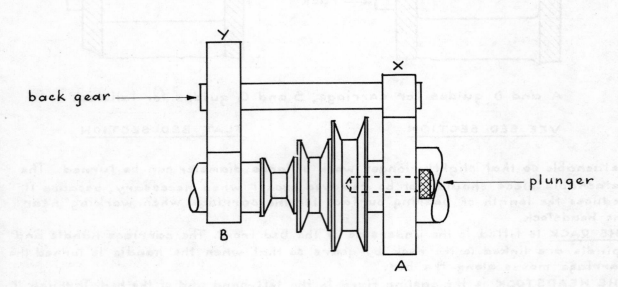

back gear is mounted behind the main spindle and can be swung to engage with the two gears on the headstock spindle.

Gear A is fixed to the headstock spindle. The pulleys are free to rotate on the spindle but they can be locked to A by means of a spring-loaded plunger. The small gear is fixed to the stepped pulleys. When the back gear is disengaged, the belt drives the pulleys. Gear A, being pinned to them, also rotates and this, in turn, drives the spindle. When the plunger is withdrawn, both the gear A and the pulleys become free on the spindle.

To operate back gear, the plunger is disengaged and the back gears pulled up and forward so that gears X and Y engage with A and B. The drive will now run —

Belt ——→ S ——→ Y ——→ X ——→ A ——→ headstock spindle.

As Y is larger than B and A larger than X there will be a reduction in speed.

THE CARRIAGE is a casting machined on the underside to fit the bed and along which it slides. Fixed to the front of the carriage is the apron, behind which lies the mechanism for controlling the movement of the carriage and the cross slide. The combined carriage and apron sometimes is called the saddle. There is always some form of locking device to lock the carriage to the bed and so prevent any unwanted movement of the carriage. This is useful when taking heavy facing cuts.

THE CROSS SLIDE is mounted on the carriage and can be moved at right-angles to the bed by means of a handwheel at the front. The handwheel may be graduated on its rim, a movement of one graduation giving a tool advance of 0.02mm. Remember that an advance of 0.02mm on the cross slide will reduce the diameter of the stock by 0.04mm. Dial graduations may be in 0.02mm, 0.05mm or 0.10mm.

The underside of the cross slide engages with vee slides machined on the carriage. A hardened steel slip or key is fitted, adjusted and locked

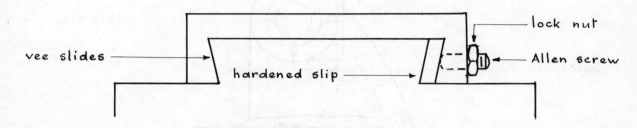

vee slides

hardened slip

lock nut

Allen screw

in position to give the correct "feel" to the cross slide movement without there being any slack. Most machine slides have the same, or similar, means of adjustment to take up wear and provide correct fit.

COMPOUND SLIDE or TOPSLIDE. Mounted on the cross slide is the compound slide. It is located by a heavy dowel pin, on which it swivels. The top of the cross slide is marked in degrees so that the compound slide can be turned and locked at any desired angle. The cutting tool, when fed by the compound slide handle, will then move at a corresponding angle, thus allowing short tapers to be machined.

TAILSTOCK or LOOSE HEADSTOCK

This is a casting that can be moved along the bed and locked in any desired position by means of a locking nut or lever. Through the casting runs a splined spindle which is keyed to prevent it rotating but it can be moved horizontally by means of a handwheel. The end of the spindle is bored out with a morse taper. Various fittings can be located in the socket, such as tailstock centre, drill chuck, taper shank drill etc. On some lathes these fittings are automatically ejected by moving the spindle back through the casting. Otherwise, the fittings have to be

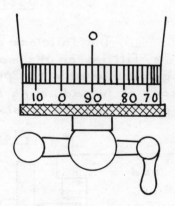

Slide Handle and Sleeve

ejected by placing a bar through the spindle bore and tapping them out. Care must be taken, while doing so, that the fittings are supported by hand to prevent them falling on the bed.

Normally, the tailstock is lined up so that the centre is in line with the centre of the spindle nose but adjustment is provided to enable the tailstock centre to be off-set from the head centre so that the lathe can be used for taper turning on centres. For details, see under "Taper Turning".

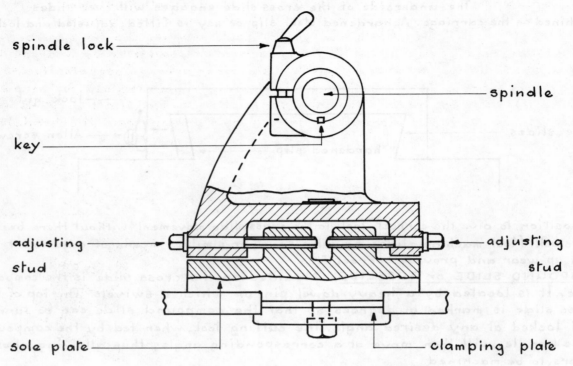

spindle lock

spindle

key

adjusting stud

adjusting stud

sole plate

clamping plate

Section through Tailstock

The tailstock casting is in two parts, the lower plate, called the sole plate, fitting on the machined slideways of the bed. The top part of the casting is adjustable for position on the sole plate, adjustment being made by means of two adjusting screws or studs. Long gradual tapers can be turned by off-setting the tailstock in this way.

View of Half-nut Mechanism

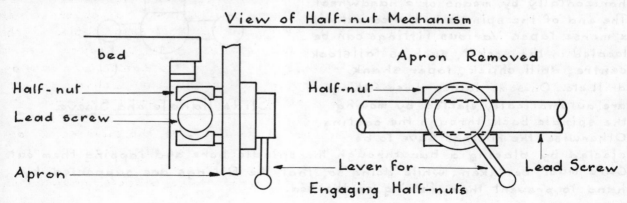

bed

Apron Removed

Half-nut

Half-nut

Lead screw

Lead Screw

Apron

Lever for Engaging Half-nuts

LEAD SCREW and FEED SHAFT. Running the length of the bed is the leadscrew, a threaded rod which can be turned at different speeds by means of a gear box or gear train. The carriage can be engaged with the leadscrew by means of two half nuts. (For sketch, see previous page.) Movement of a lever brings the two half nuts together on the leadscrew. The thread on the screw may be square or acme. Most modern lathes have the latter because the half nuts more easily engage and disengage on an acme thread than on a square thread.

The leadscrew on small lathes supplies the drive for both screwcutting and automatic feed. This arrangement can cause heavy wear on the screw, particularly near the headstock where the carriage operates for so much of the time. Larger lathes have a lead screw which is used for screwcutting only. To drive the carriage and cross slide, a feed shaft is fitted which has a keyway machined along its length and is driven from the headstock through a train of gears.

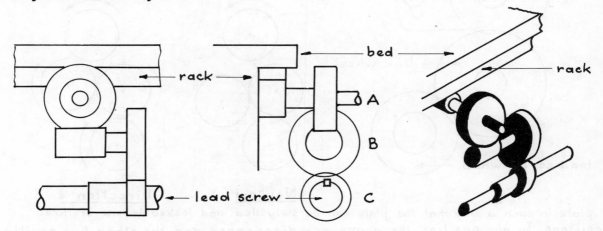

Engagement is by means of a lever on the front of the apron. The gears A link up with the rack and carriage handle. The worm wheel and gear B are permanently meshed with C, which is keyed to the feed shaft. When the lever is raised, the wheel unit BC rotates on the feed shaft so that the worm on B engages with A.

CHANGE WHEELS. The circular movement of the headstock spindle is transmitted to the lead screw through a set of gear wheels. Some lathes are fitted with a Norton gear box, by means of which the ratio of speed between the spindle and lead screw can be changed by moving a set of levers. On lathes that have no gear box, the change in speed ratio has to be made by changing the gear wheels. A range of gears of different sizes is always provided with these lathes. For details of screwcutting gear trains, see under "Screwcutting."

TUMBLER GEARS enable the direction of rotation of the lead screw and feed shaft to be altered. This, in turn, will change the direction of travel of the carriage when working on automatic feed.

The tumbler gears are a set of three wheels mounted on

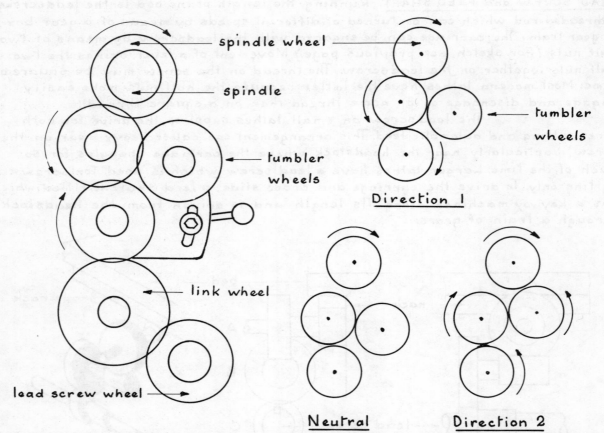

spindle wheel

spindle

tumbler wheels

tumbler wheels

link wheel

lead screw wheel

Direction 1

Neutral   Direction 2

a plate in such a way that the plate can be swivelled and locked in one of three positions. In one position the gears are disengaged and the other two positions give two directions of travel to the lead screw.

　　　　The tumbler gear mechanism must be moved only when the lathe is stationary.

　　　　All gear trains must not be meshed too tightly and must have grease applied occasionally.

HOLDING THE WORK

There are four main methods of holding work for turning —

　　　　　　　　1. Centres.
　　　　　　　　2. Three Jaw Concentric Chuck.
　　　　　　　　3. Four Jaw Independent Chuck.
　　　　　　　　4. Faceplate.

The method selected will depend on the size, length and shape of the work, the operations to be performed on it and the accuracy needed.

CENTRES, machined with a morse taper, fit into the morse taper sockets of the headstock and tailstock spindles. Work to be turned may be held between the two centres or with chuck and tailstock centre. They are usually made of H.C.S. but H.S.S, though expensive, is sometimes used for heavy work or high speed work.
DEAD and LIVE CENTRES. The dead centre (tailstock centre) fits into the tailstock and the live centre (headstock centre) fits into the headstock. Both have a 60°

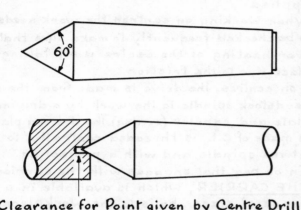

Clearance for Point given by Centre Drill

included angle at the point, although this is sometimes increased to 90° for heavy work. The metal to be fitted between centres is drilled at a corresponding angle with a centre (combination) drill. For details see under "Drills", "Centring" It is usual to leave the live centre soft so that it can be machined whilst in position. If this is done, it is wise to put a locating mark on the centre and on the headstock spindle so that it can be replaced in the same position always and so ensure true running.

The dead centre is always hardened to withstand wear.

All centres need treating with care. Any marking or bruising of their surfaces will not only reduce the frictional grip but the accuracy of rotation as well.

THE HALF CENTRE is used in the tailstock to allow the tool to clear the centre and give more room for facing up after the work has been mounted between centres.

THE BALL CENTRE, although not common, is sometimes used for taper turning by the "set-over tailstock" method. The standard centres cannot sit squarely in the centre hole when the tailstock is set over. The ball centre will always fit the centre hole regardless of the amount of set over.

THE RUNNING (REVOLVING) CENTRE is fitted with a ball race so that rotation takes place on the bearing and not on the centre itself. It is relatively expensive so it is used usually for high speed work only.

LUBRICATION OF CENTRES
When using all but the running centre

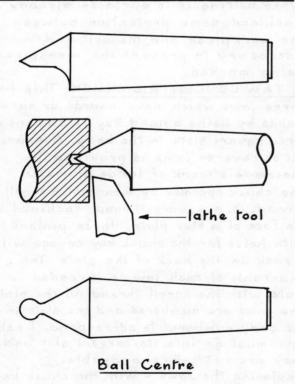

lathe tool

Ball Centre

friction takes place due to the work turning on a fixed point. If friction is allowed to continue, heat will develop causing expansion of the work. This increases the friction still further, with consequent inaccuracy when testing for size and possible damage to the centre itself. Suitable lubricants are tallow, tallow and graphite, and grease. When setting up the work, the tailstock centre must be adjusted with care. Too heavy a pressure will press out all the lubricant, while too light a pressure will allow movement of the work when the cut is applied.

When working on centres the work needs to be checked frequently to make sure that over-heating of the centre is not taking place due to the friction.

Ball races

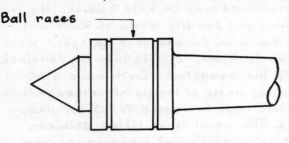

Revolving or Running Centre

DRIVING PLATE. When work is mounted on centres, the drive is made from the headstock spindle to the work by a driving plate and carrier (or dog). The driving plate is made of C.I., is threaded centrally to fit the spindle and with a projecting pin or peg that engages with the carrier.

THE CARRIER, which is available in a range of sizes, bolts to the workpiece. When bolting it to surfaces already machined, some protection between the workpiece and the bolt end is necessary to prevent the workpiece being marked.

3 JAW CONCENTRIC CHUCK. This has three jaws which move inwards or outwards by using a hand key in any one of three square slots in the body. A spare set of reverse jaws is provided to accommodate work of large diameter.

The chuck operates by means of a scroll thread, ie. a square thread machined on the face of a flat plate. Three pinions, with holes for the chuck key engage with a rack on the back of the plate. The underside of each jaw is threaded to mate with the scroll thread on the plate. The jaws are numbered and the slots in the body numbered to correspond. Each jaw must go into its correct slot and they are not interchangeable.

Replacing the Jaws – With the chuck key screw the scroll plate until the start of the thread is alongside Nº1 slot. Slide in Nº1 jaw and screw the scroll until the start of

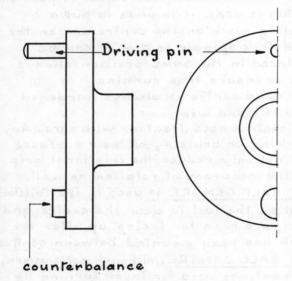

Driving pin

counterbalance

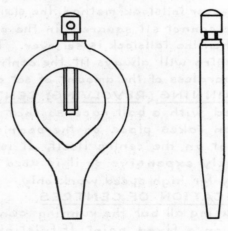

Carrier

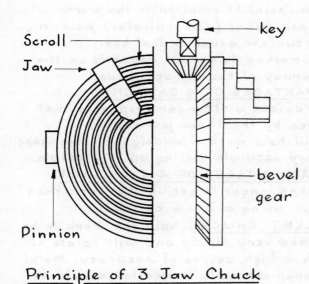

Scroll

Jaw

Pinnion

key

bevel gear

Principle of 3 Jaw Chuck

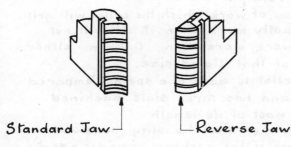

Standard Jaw   Reverse Jaw

4 Jaw Chuck

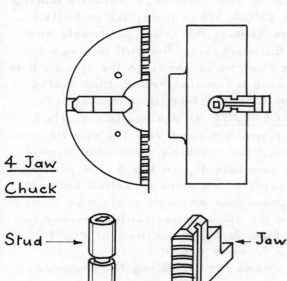

Stud   Jaw

the thread is alongside Nº2 slot. Slide in Nº2 jaw and repeat for Nº3 jaw.

ADVANTAGES OF 3 JAW CHUCK

1. Work can be quickly set up.

DISADVANTAGES OF 3 JAW CHUCK

1. As the jaws work concentrically, the chuck can be used only for holding round stock or stock which has sides a multiple of 3.

2. The tightening force from the key is distributed through three jaws. Therefore its gripping efficiency is comparatively low.

3. Even new 3 jaw chucks are not very accurate. With use they become more inaccurate still. Accurate work can be turned in them only when the work can be machined at one setting. For the same reason, it is bad practice to keep taking the work out of the chuck unnecessarily. The order of turning operations should be such as to allow as many operations as possible to be completed before having to move the work.

The 4 JAW INDEPENDENT CHUCK has 4 jaws which move independently. No extra set of jaws is needed because the jaws are reversible. The square slot to take the chuck key is set in a threaded stud. The underside of each jaw is threaded to match the stud. The stud has a recess machined on its surface which engages with projections on the chuck body in order to hold the stud in position.

    The four jaw chuck is used for holding square material, irregular shapes and work that has to be set up accurately.

    Care is needed when setting up to ensure that the work rotates truly. Various methods are used for checking the accuracy of the set-up.—

1. Use of chalk to mark the eccentricity.

2. The tool brought near to the work and the rotation of the work in relation to the tool noted.

3. Use of a surface gauge, on the bed or cross slide, the scriber acting as a

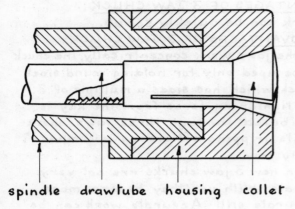

spindle   drawtube   housing   collet

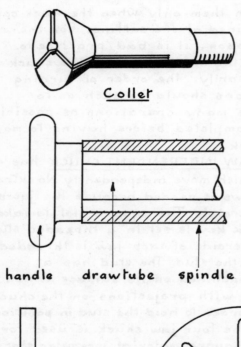

Collet

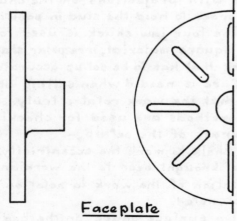

handle   drawtube   spindle

Faceplate

datum point in relation to the work.
4. Clock gauge (dial indicator) held in the surface gauge or tool box.
The method to choose depends on the accuracy of the set-up needed.

ADVANTAGES OF 4 JAW CHUCK.
1. Provides a stronger grip than that given by the three jaw chuck.
2. Will hold work of widely differing shape.
3. Very accurate setting up is possible.

DISADVANTAGES OF 4 JAW CHUCK.
1. Takes longer to set up the work than when using a 3 jaw chuck.

COLLET CHUCKS hold the work to be turned very firmly and will rotate it with a high degree of accuracy. Metal gripped correctly in a collet should be not more than 0·005 mm out of true when rotated.

The size of work which the collet will grip is usually marked on it. It will not grip work more than 0·1 mm either side of that stated size.

The collet is made of a spring-tempered steel and has three slots machined along most of its length.

A hardened steel housing, screwed on the nose of the machine, provides a seating for the collet. When the collet is pulled into this housing, the collet contracts and grips the workpiece. The pull is given by a tube that runs through the spindle bore and having a female thread that mates with an external thread on the collet.

The FACEPLATE is a circular slotted casting which screws onto the spindle nose. It is used for holding work that cannot be held conveniently in the 3 or 4 jaw chuck or by centres. The work is bolted onto its face. Sometimes an angle plate has to be used in the set-up, particularly when two faces have to be machined at right-angles to each other.

The methods for checking the accuracy of the position of the work on the plate are the same as when checking for the 4 jaw chuck.

THE TRAVELLING STEADY bolts to the cross slide or carriage of the lathe and is used to support long slender work to stop the metal bending under the pressure of cut. It makes two-point contact with the work at a point just behind the tool and travels along the work with the tool.

THE FIXED STEADY bolts to the lathe bed and is used to support work that projects a long way out of the chuck. It is often used as an end support for long bars, too big in diameter to go through the head of the machine, so that the end of the bar may be machined, eg. bored, drilled, etc. The work is supported by three jaws at 120° to one another. These jaws can be adjusted to fit different diameters and locked in position. Grease

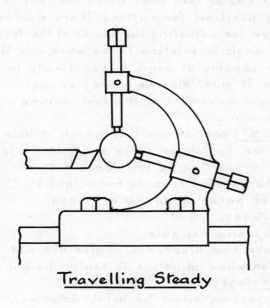

Travelling Steady

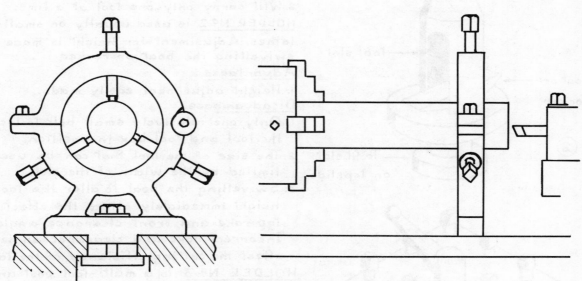

Fixed Steady

is necessary where the jaws make contact with the work. If the bar is rough or out of round on its surface, it may be necessary to chuck the work and use the tailstock centre for support, whilst taking a skim on the surface of the bar. This surface will then provide a true seating for the jaws of the steady.

TOOL HOLDERS.

The tool box or tool post holds the tool in correct position for cutting. There must be provision for adjusting the height of the tool and its angle in relation to the work and it must be capable of being locked firmly in position. It must also be sturdy enough to prevent movement of the tool during heavy cutting.

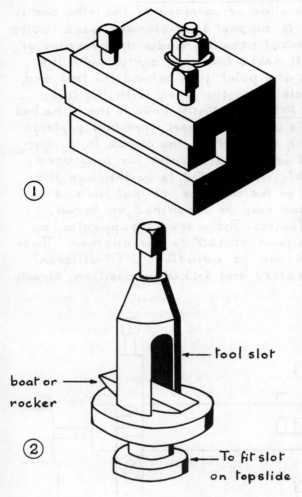

HOLDER Nº 1 carries one tool which is held in position by two or three set bolts. It is locked in position by one large nut or lever. Adjustment is made for height by means of parallel packing pieces.

Advantages.

1. Sturdy and reliable.
2. The rake and clearance angles are not affected when adjusting to centre height.

Disadvantages.

1. Needs packing pieces for height adjustment.
2. Will carry only one tool at a time.

HOLDER Nº 2 is used usually on small lathes. Adjustment for height is made by swivelling the boat or rocker.

Advantages.

1. Height adjustment easily made.

Disadvantages.

1. Only one relatively small bolt to lock the tool and tool box in position.
2. The size of the tool that can be used is limited by the width of the slot.
3. Swivelling the boat to alter the tool height immediately alters the effective top rake and front clearance angles. Incorrect rake and clearance angles affect the cutting efficiency of the tool.

HOLDER Nº 3 is a multi-tool post and holds four tools at the same time. It is locked in position by a single hand lever. The holder swivels about its centre bolt so that each tool in turn can be brought into position. This saves time on repetition work.

Advantages.

1. Carries four tools at the same time.
2. Height adjustment does not affect tool angles.

Disadvantages.

1. Needs packing for height adjustment.

← tool slot

boat or →
rocker

← To fit slot on topslide

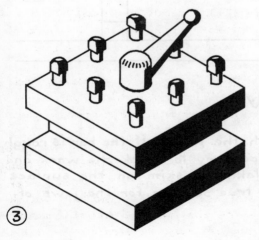

LATHE TOOLS

Lathe tools may be made of any of the following materials —

1. PLAIN CARBON STEEL

This is not used so much now as formerly. It suffers from the disadvantage of losing its hardness if overheated. Consequently, the turning speed has to be kept low and plenty of coolant applied. It is particularly useful when a tool has to made quickly or made especially for a particular machining operation, when, to use any other material, would either take too long or be too expensive.

2. HIGH SPEED STEEL

H.S.S. has the property of red-hardness, ie. it retains its hardness and cutting properties even at red heat. This enables greatly increased machine speeds to be used. It is more expensive and more brittle than high carbon steels and so is used often in the form of a tipped tool or a tool bit.

3. STELLITE

This is a non-ferrous alloy of chromium and cobalt, so hard that it cannot be forged or machined except by grinding. It is usually used in the form of a tipped tool.

4. CEMENTED CARBIDE

By compressing finely divided tungsten carbide with cobalt and subjecting it to an intense heat called sintering, an extremely hard brittle material is formed. The resulting carbide is almost as hard as diamond, but is very brittle and of low tensile strength. It can be shaped only by special grinding wheels and is always used in the form of a tipped tool.

5. DIAMOND

Tools tipped with diamond are used for high grade machining of hard metals and often plastics which blunt H.S.S. tools very quickly.

TOOL FORMS

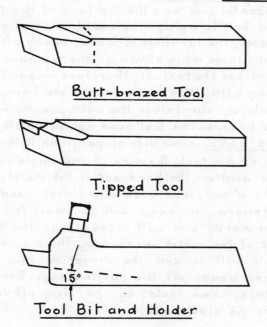

Butt-brazed Tool

Tipped Tool

Tool Bit and Holder

SOLID TOOLS are made throughout in one material, either H.C.S. or H.S.S.

BUTT-BRAZED (or butt-welded) TOOLS are made by brazing or welding a piece of H.S.S. to a high tensile steel shank.

TIPPED TOOLS have a tip of cemented carbide, etc, brazed to a blank of high tensile steel. They are very economical.

TOOL BITS fit in a special holder that grips the tool at an angle of 15°. This provides easy height adjustment. The angle must be taken into account when grinding the bits which are of square section and usually made of H.S.S. The holders may be straight or set over to the right or left for awkward positions.

TOOL ANGLES

The angles ground on a lathe tool to give the necessary shape for efficient cutting will depend on —

1. The hardness of the metal being cut.
2. The rigidity of the lathe.
3. The amount of metal to be removed.
4. The quality of finish required.

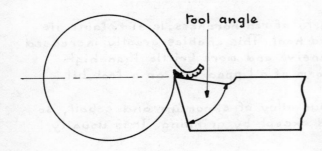

tool angle

A large tool angle
1. Gives maximum strength.
2. Helps heat dissipation.
3. Increases the power needed to force the tool into the work.

A small tool angle
1. Weakens the cutting edge.
2. Gives a good finish.
3. Gives little tearing.
4. Gives easy cutting.

front clearance   side clearance

front rake   side rake

profile angle

The affect of Side Rake and Clearance

The harder and tougher the material to be turned, the more difficult it will be for the cutting edge of the tool to penetrate the metal and, at the same time, retain its sharpness. Consequently, the harder the metal, the greater the tool angle must be.

THE TOOL ANGLE is formed by the top and front faces of the tool. It is fixed by the size of the rake and clearance angles.

TOP or FRONT RAKE is the angle between a horizontal line and the top face of the tool. Hard brittle metals like cast iron and some brasses, the turnings of which break off short impose a big strain on the top face (breast) of the tool. It, therefore, needs to be strong with little or no front rake. For soft metals, eg. aluminium, the rake can be made more because the tool need not be so strong.

SIDE RAKE is the side slope given to the top face of the tool. The size of the angle is dependent on the hardness of the metal, the depth of cut, feed used and finish needed. In general, the angle will be small for hard metals and will increase as the hardness of the metal increases. The side rake angle will govern the direction that the swarf moves off the cutting edge. Because of this, some tools, eg. parting off tools, have no side rake.

FRONT CLEARANCE is the angle formed by the front of the tool and a line at right angles to the base. The front clearance is reduced to a minimum for hard materials and large diameters. For soft metals and small diameters the clearance is increased.
SIDE CLEARANCE is the angle at the cutting side or leading face of the tool. Its size is governed by the hardness of the metal to be cut and the feed used. Coarse feeds need more clearance than fine feeds, but, at the same time, the tool becomes weaker.

EFFECT OF TOOL POSITION ON TOOL ANGLES

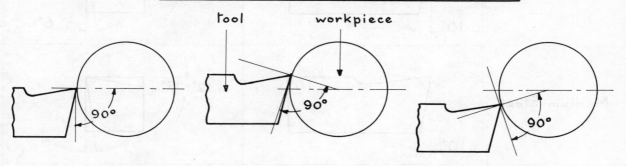

Tool on centre height giving correct tool angles.

Tool too high.
Top rake increased.
Clearance decreased.

Tool too low.
Top rake decreased.
Clearance increased.

THE EFFECT OF TOOL SWIVEL ON TOOL ANGLES

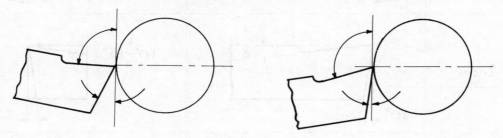

Small top rake, large clearance.

Large top rake, small clearance.

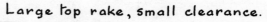

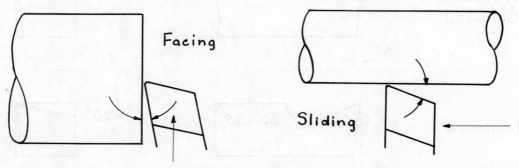

Facing

Sliding

The tool must be angled to the work to give clearance behind the tip.

LATHE TOOL ANGLES

METAL	TOOL – SIDE VIEW	TOOL – FRONT VIEW
Soft Steel	top Rake 20° 10° Front clearance	rake 20°-25° side clearance 6°
Medium Steel	10° 10°	12°-15° 6°
Hard Steel	5° 6°	6°-10° 6°
Cast Iron	8° 10°	10°-15° 6°
Brass and Gunmetal	1° 6°	0° 6°
Aluminium	35°-55° 6°	10°-20° 1°-3°

TOOL SHAPE

The shape of the tool and the angles of its ground faces will depend on —
1. The operation to be performed.
2. The material which has to be machined.
3. The power and rigidity of the lathe.
4. The amount of metal to be removed.
5. The quality of finish desired.

TYPICAL TOOL SHAPES

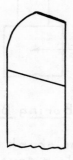

Round Nose Rougher

Used for turning off heavy waste.

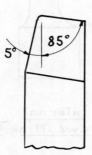

Str. Nose Rougher

Used for turning off heavy waste.

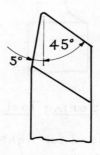

Fine Finishing

General purpose tool for light finishing cuts.

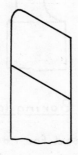

Side Finishing

Used for facing and finishing up to a shoulder.

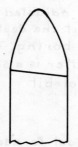

Round Nose

A general purpose tool used often for radiusing a shoulder or for recessing.

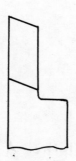

Knife Tool

Used for facing and finishing a square shoulder.

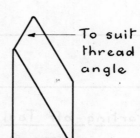

To suit thread angle

Screw cutting Tool

Used for machining external threads. The tool angle is ground according to thread angle.

Form Tool

Used for special contours. Ground to suit finished shape.

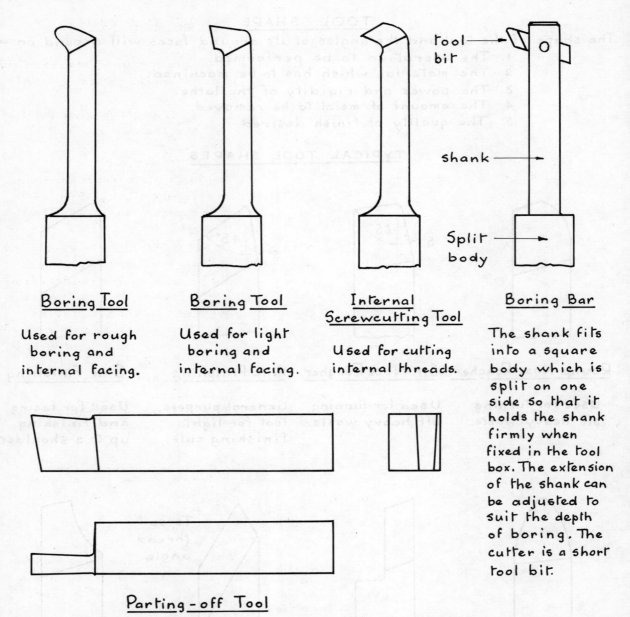

Boring Tool

Used for rough boring and internal facing.

Boring Tool

Used for light boring and internal facing.

Internal Screwcutting Tool

Used for cutting internal threads.

Boring Bar

The shank fits into a square body which is split on one side so that it holds the shank firmly when fixed in the tool box. The extension of the shank can be adjusted to suit the depth of boring. The cutter is a short tool bit.

Parting-off Tool

A tool used for cutting off metal in the lathe. A difficult tool to use. For details of parting-off, see under "Turning Operations."

The shapes of the tools shown are typical of those used for general work but they can vary considerably according to the work being done. Special tools often have to be made for specific purposes such as narrow recessing and odd shapes.

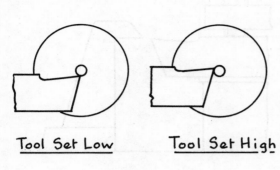

Tool Set Low   Tool Set High

The tool must be —
1. Set firmly in the toolpost and position-ed so as to allow the minimum amount of overhang.
2. Set at the correct angle to give the clearance behind the cutting tip.
3. Set at centre height.

SETTING TO CENTRE HEIGHT

The height adjustment is made by using packing pieces of metal or, when using the post type of holder, by swivelling the rocker (boat).

If the tool is set too high when working along the length of a bar, it will cut little, if at all, because of the reduced front clearance. If the tool is set too low, the effective rake and clearance angles become altered. (see "Tool Position")
In addition, the work will tend to roll over the top of the tool. This it will do if the metal is slender or the tool or work not fixed firmly.

When surfacing, if the tool is set too high or too low, a small pip will be left in the centre of the face.

CHECKING THE HEIGHT OF THE TOOL

1. Tighten the jaws of the three jaw chuck so that they meet. Set the tool to the centre of the jaws.
2. Set the tool to the head or tail centre.
3. Estimate the height of the tool. Take a trial facing cut. If the tool is set too high or too low, reset the tool to the centre of the pip left on the end face.
4. Position a steel rule between the tip of the tool and the work, using a slip of card to protect the tool tip. Correct-ness of setting will be indicated by the rule being vertical or not.
5. Use a centre height gauge. These can be made in a variety of shapes to suit individual taste. The one shown is made from a piece of plate slotted and brazed into a heavy base. It sits on the lathe bed and the tool is set to the underside of the finger.

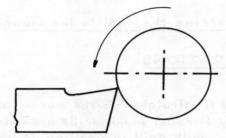

Tendency of Work to Roll Over the Top of the Tool

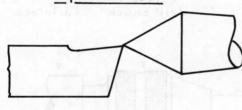

Tool Set to a Centre

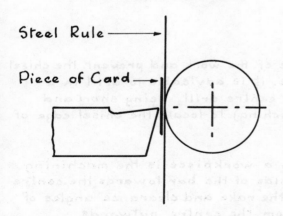

Steel Rule ⟶

Piece of Card ⟶

Tool Being Checked with a Steel Rule

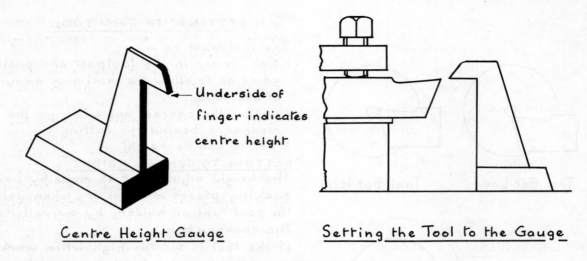

Underside of finger indicates centre height

Centre Height Gauge

Setting the Tool to the Gauge

TURNING OPERATIONS

DRILLING

The drill fits in the tailstock. Taper shank drills fit straight into the morse taper socket, using a morse taper sleeve where necessary. Parallel shank drills are held by a drill chuck fitted into the socket. The tailstock, with drill in position, is brought up near to the workpiece and locked in position on the bed. The spindle locking lever needs to be left loose. The drill is fed into the work by means of the tailstock

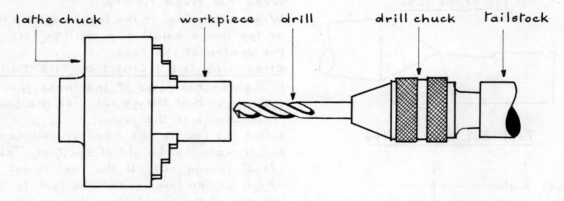

lathe chuck   workpiece   drill   drill chuck   tailstock

wheel. In order to spot the drill in the centre of the work and prevent the chisel edge sliding out of place on the work surface, it is advisable to drill in a short distance first with a centre drill. The centre drill, being short and stiff, will provide a centre mark (cf. centrepunching) to locate the chisel edge of the twist drill.

SURFACING or FACING UP

The first operation usually performed on a workpiece is the machining of the end. Cuts may be taken from the outside of the bar towards the centre or from the centre outwards depending on the rake and clearance angles of the tool. Finishing cuts are usually taken from the centre outwards.

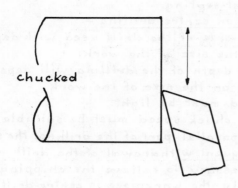

chucked

Cuts have to be relatively light because the cutting forces are at right angles to the headstock bearings.

When surfacing, it is advisable to lock the carriage to the bed and so prevent the carriage moving away from the work under the pressure of cut, leaving the end of the work with a convex face.

Work that projects too far out of the chuck to be surfaced without support, can be either 1. Centre drilled, supported with a half centre and then surfaced.

or 2. Supported by means of a fixed steady.

THREE JAW CHUCK WORK

When working with the three jaw chuck, too long a length must not project from the jaws without providing some form of support. The length that can project will depend on the diameter of the work, the metal being turned and the operation to be performed on it.

Often waste has to be provided as a chucking allowance so that the machining can be completed without moving the workpiece. It is then finally parted off.

FOUR JAW CHUCK WORK

A stronger grip is provided by the four jaw chuck than the three jaw, so heavier cutting is possible.

SETTING UP The workpiece is positioned between the jaws, the jaws being adjusted approximately in place by making use of the circular lines that are cut usually on the chuck face. Final positioning is accomplished by any one of the methods listed under "Four Jaw Chuck", the method chosen being dependent on the shape of the work and the accuracy of machining needed.

When using a surface gauge for checking, the gauge is rested on the bed or cross slide and the position of the scriber point adjusted so that it is either near to the work or near to any datum line, eg. a scribed circle that needs machining to. The chuck is pulled round by hand, the space between scriber and work being noted. If the space is not constant, the work has to be re-adjusted for position. A sheet of white paper on the bed under the work helps to give a clear view of the gap.

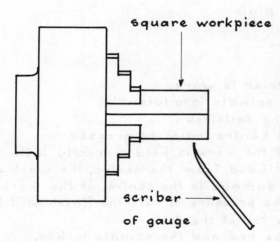

square workpiece

scriber
of gauge

WORKING ON CENTRES

When working between centres, two holes have to be drilled to act as a seating for the centres. When using a chuck and one centre, only one hole is necessary to accommodate the tailstock centre.

A centre or combination drill (for details see "Drills") is used to provide the correct seating.

Notes on centre drilling —
1. The size of the drill used will depend on the size of the work.
2. The depth of the drilling will depend also on the size of the work.
3. Feed must be light.
4. The chuck speed must be suitable for the parallel part of the drill, not the shank.
5. Frequent withdrawal of the drill is necessary to relieve the chippings.

Usually, the workpiece is centre-drilled in the lathe but a drilling machine may have to be used for work that is large or of awkward shape. In this instance, the centre of the bar will have to be found by means of surface gauge, centre square, bell punch or oddleg callipers.

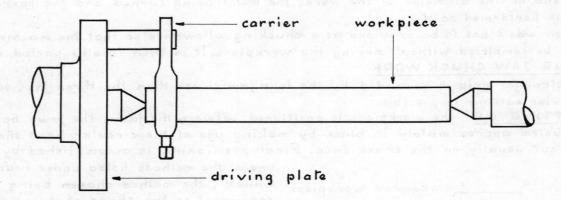
carrier   workpiece
driving plate

SETTING-UP ON CENTRES
The drive is from driving plate to carrier to work.
1. Minimum projection of the tailstock spindle is advisable.
2. Ensure that the hard centre is in the tailstock.
3. The centre hole, to take the tailstock centre, must be greased.
4. The tailstock must be adjusted so that the work is held correctly. If the work is held too tightly, grease will be excluded from the centre, the work and centre will overheat with consequent damage to the centre. If the work is held too loosely, it will move under the pressure of cut, the finish will be poor and the work may roll over the top of the tool.
5. The tailstock must be tightened to the bed and the spindle locked.

CHECKING FOR PARALLELISM
When turning work that has to be accurately parallel, the following procedure is necessary —
1. Take a light cut for the full length of the work.
2. With a micrometer measure the diameter at each end of the work.

3. If the diameters are the same, the lathe is turning parallel.
4. If the diameters are different the lathe is turning taper and the following
   checks have to be made —
      a. Check that both the centres are seating correctly in their
sockets, with no grit or swarf between the mating surfaces.
      b. Check that the head centre is not rotating off-true.
If so it will have to be machined true whilst in position.
      c. If the centres are not at fault, the tailstock must be out of
line with the head centre. If the work is tapered with the smaller diameter at the
headstock end, the tailstock is set too far back and will have to be moved forward.
If the larger diameter is at the headstock end, then the tailstock needs moving
backwards.

METHODS OF RESETTING THE TAILSTOCK

1. Usually, two guide lines are provided on the two halves of the tailstock casting. When these are lined up, the tailstock is in line with the headstock.
2. A much more accurate method of resetting is to mount a parallel test bar between centres and test with a clock gauge (dial indicator) set in the tool box. The attachment shown below is a good method of holding the indicator. When the gauge is moved along the bar, any deflection of the

sole plate   lathe bed

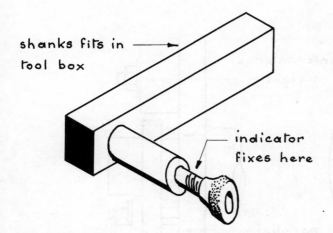

shanks fits in
tool box

indicator
fixes here

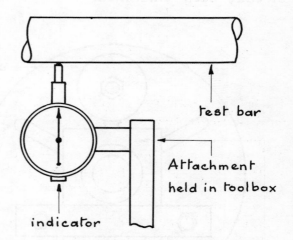

test bar

Attachment
held in toolbox

indicator

Attachment for Holding Dial Indicator in the Tool Box

Indicator in Position for Reading

pointer will indicate an error of tailstock setting and the amount it will have to be moved to correct it. Adjustments are made until the gauge reading remains constant when the indicator is moved along the length of the bar. If the gauge shows a deflection of 0.20 mm, the tailstock will have to be moved a distance of 0.10 mm.

FACEPLATE WORK

Irregularly shaped castings and forgings that cannot be held in the chuck are bolted to the faceplate with clamping plates. Often an angle plate has to be included in the set-up, particularly when faces have to be machined at right-angles to each other.

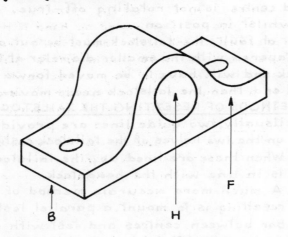

Bearing Block to be Machined

The hole H has to be parallel with base B. The face F has to be at rt. angles to B. It is assumed that the base has already been machined.

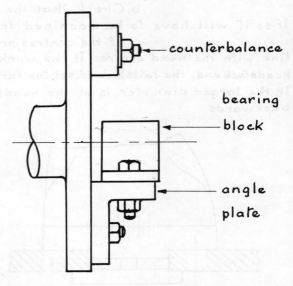

Bearing set up on base so that the hole H and face F may be machined at one setting.

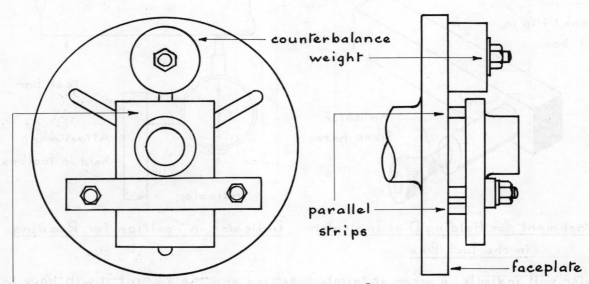

Extra clamps may be needed here, depending on the weight of work

A Casting Set Up for Boring.

188

The workpiece is fixed approximately in correct position by making use of the circular lines on the faceplate as a guide. The final checking for position is done in the same way as when using a four jaw chuck. Before work commences the set-up has to be checked for balance. The gears are disengaged so that the spindle runs free and can be spun round by hand. If the work comes to rest in the same position each time, a counterbalance weight will be needed opposite the heavy spot. Any convenient piece of large diameter rod can be used, its size being found by trial and error.

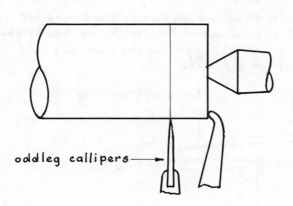

oddleg callipers ──▶

MARKING OUT LENGTHS

Lengths to be machined can be marked with oddlegs, pulling the work round by hand to give a scribed line around the circumference.

TAPER TURNING

There are four methods of turning a taper on a piece of work.

        1. Using the tool angle.
        2. Setting the angle on the compound slide.
        3. Setting over the tailstock.
        4. Using a taper turning attachment.

1. **USING THE TOOL ANGLE.** The cutting edge of the tool is set round to the angle required and the cut taken by feeding straight in. This method can be used only for short tapers, eg. chamfers.

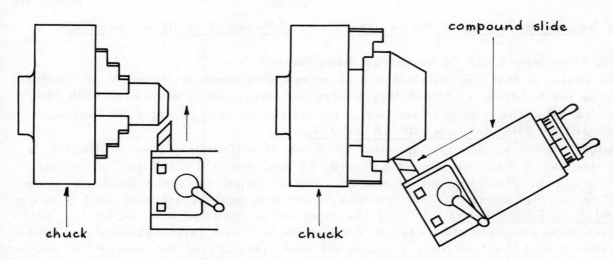

compound slide

chuck   chuck

<u>Plunge cutting with the edge
of tool at correct angle</u>
        <u>Cutting a taper with the
compound slide set at an angle</u>

2. <u>**SETTING THE COMPOUND SLIDE AT AN ANGLE.**</u> Here the compound slide is swivelled, locked at the required angle and the tool fed by hand, using the slide handle. Power feed cannot be used and the length of taper that can

be turned is restricted to the length of travel of the compound slide. Because of the hand feed, a good finish is obtained only with difficulty. This method therefore is used only for tapers of short length.

3. SETTING OVER THE TAILSTOCK. With this method, which can be used only for long gradual tapers, the tailstock is intentionally set out of line with the headstock. The work then becomes angled to the direction of movement of the carriage and will be tapered in proportion to the amount of set-over.

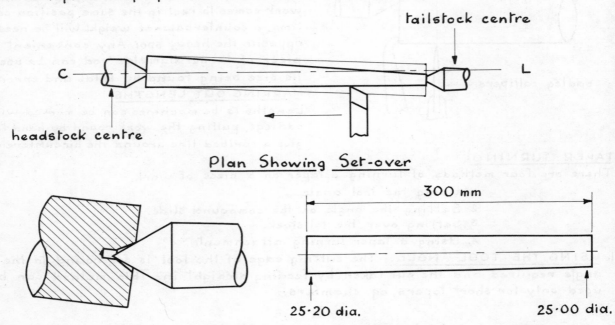

Plan Showing Set-over

The Inaccurate Seating of the Centre

A Taper of 0·20 mm per 300

Only slow tapers can be machined because —
1. The distance that the tailstock can be moved, backwards or forwards, is limited.
2. Once the tailstock is off-set, the centre becomes out of alignment with the centre hole. The misalignment increases as the amount of set-over increases.

MEASURING THE AMOUNT OF SET-OVER

Gradual tapers usually are specified in terms of a fraction of a millimetre to 300 mm, eg, a bar 300 mm long and 25 mm dia. with a taper of 0·20 mm in 300 will be 25·00 mm dia. at one end and 25·20 mm the other. The taper is in relation to the diameter. The tailstock, therefore, must be set over half 0·20 mm.

1. Tailstock Index Lines   [The taper can be expressed also as, eg. 1 in 50.]
Most lathes have these lines cut on the back of the tailstock casting. The distance that the two lines move apart is a measure of the amount of set-over. This method does not give great accuracy.

2. Dial Indicator
Turn the bar parallel in length or mount a test bar between centres. Fix the indicator in the tool box and adjust its position so that it touches the bar near the headstock end. Adjust the dial to read zero or take a note of the reading. Move the carriage along the bed a distance of 300 mm. If the bar is parallel, the indicator will still show the same reading. By means

190

of the tailstock adjusting screws, move the tailstock over until the needed deflection is shown on the indicator and relock the tailstock. Remember that if the taper is 0·20 mm per 300 , the set-over will be 0·10 mm.

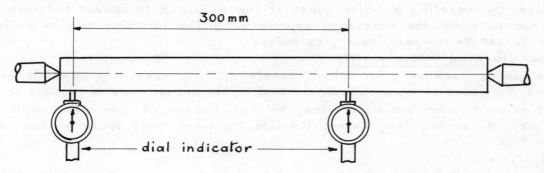

dial indicator

3. Cross-slide Graduations
Set a round nose tool at centre height and bring it up to the work. Place a slip of paper between the tip of the tool and the work so that the paper is just

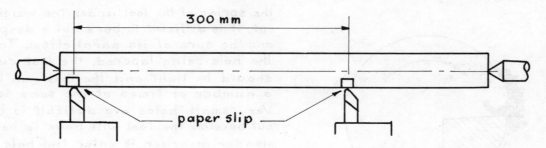

paper slip

nipped. This will give the necessary "feel". Take a note of the cross-slide reading. Move the carriage a distance of 300 mm and then set the cross-slide either backwards or forwards for the required distance by making use of the

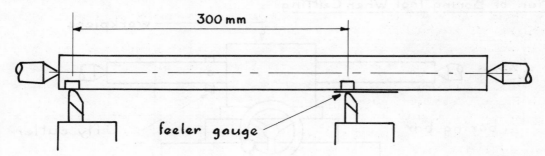

feeler gauge

cross-slide graduations. Adjust the tailstock position so that the slip of paper is nipped again between the tool and the work.
If the taper to be machined is not given as a taper per 300mm but as a taper on a stated length, the same steps are followed except that the carriage is moved a distance, not of 300mm, but a distance equal to the length of the taper given.

191

4. Feeler Gauges

Position a round nose tool at one end of the work with a piece of paper between the tool and the work. Move the carriage along the bed for the needed distance. By inserting a feeler gauge of the required thickness between the tool and the work, the necessary adjustment to the tailstock can be made. Use paper to get the correct "feel", as before.

5. Taper Turning Attachments

These can be used only on lathes constructed, or specially adapted for the purpose. By means of them automatic travel of the cross-slide is possible at the same time as the carriage moves along the bed. The use of such attachments is the best way of turning long tapers because the work runs truly on the centres all the time.

BORING

Shaping the metal internally is called boring. A hole has to be drilled first into which the tool is entered. The hole should be sufficiently large to allow the minimum waste for removal and as large a boring tool as possible used. Small boring tools lack strength and rigidity. The tool may have to be set above centre height to gain the needed clearance at the base of the tool. Because of the spring of the tool under the weight of cut, it is difficult to bore out a deep hole and be sure of its parallelism. To avoid the hole being tapered, the last cuts should be light and the tool run through a number of times at the same setting. Very small holes are difficult to bore out because the tool will have to be so slender in order to enter the hole. Small holes are reamed, usually, not bored. Awkwardly shaped castings are sometimes bored by fixing them on the cross slide of the lathe. A boring bar is set between

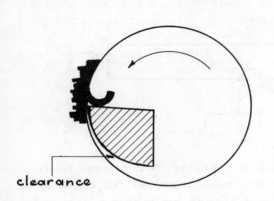

clearance

Position of Boring Tool When Cutting

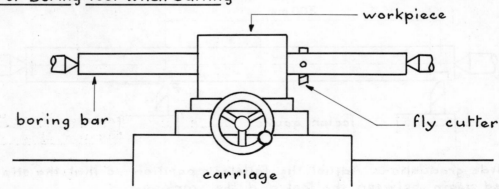

workpiece

boring bar

fly cutter

carriage

A Workpiece Bolted to the Carriage for Boring with a Boring Bar

chuck and centre or between two centres with a cutter fixed midway along its length. The bar passes through the hole to be bored, the cutter rotating while the work moves on the carriage along the bed.

PARTING OFF

Workpieces are often machined by being held in the chuck, with a chucking allowance, and then finally parted off by feeding a narrow tool into the work. Parting off is difficult and points to be noted are —

1. The lathe must be in good condition, with bearings and slideways fitting well.
2. The tool must be ground correctly with the right clearances.
3. The tool must be set square to the work, exactly at centre height and with the minimum of overhang.
4. The cut should be made close to the chuck to avoid chatter.
5. The machine should be run at a slower speed than is usual for ordinary turning.
6. The feed must be slow, steady and even, with a liberal amount of cutting solution applied.
7. Two cuts made alongside one another often help by increasing the clearance at the sides of the tool.
8. Immediately the tool stops cutting effectively, stop the machine and find out what is wrong. If cutting continues, the tool might jam and snap. If the tool cuts in jerks or is difficult to feed in, it is a sign that the tool is either blunt or set too high.
9. Chatter is an indication of something loose or the tool set too low.

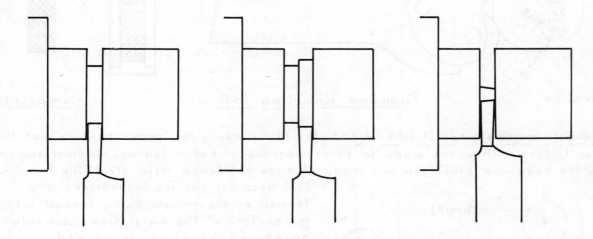

Parting Off in One Cut   Parting Off in Two Cuts   Parting Off with Tool
                                                     Ground at an Angle

10. To avoid a projecting pip being left on the face of the piece parted off, the tool often is ground on the end face at an angle.
11. Never try to saw off a component while it is being held in the lathe. If the saw slips, it will damage the bed. If a parting tool cannot be used, take the work out of the lathe and saw it in a vice.

KNURLING

A knurled surface is often put on components in order to provide suitable finger or hand grip.

A straight knurling tool has a single wheel with straight cuts on its surface that provide a similar pattern on the workpiece.

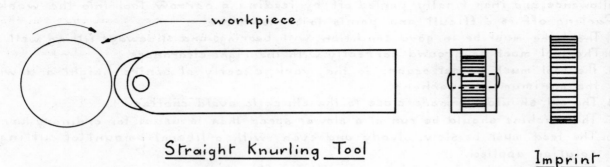

Straight Knurling Tool   Imprint

The diamond knurling tool has two wheels with the cuts on each wheel angled in different directions. This has the effect of forming a diamond pattern on the work.

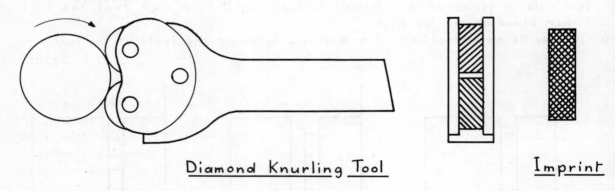

Diamond Knurling Tool   Imprint

The wheels may be made of H.C.S. or H.S.S., the latter being the more expensive but the longer lasting. They are made in three degrees of cut — coarse, medium and fine. Both the body and pivot pin are made of case-hardened mild steel. The knurling tool does not cut. The impressions are formed by the wheels being forced into the surface of the metal. Considerable pressure, therefore, is needed.

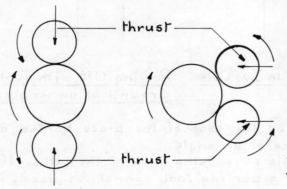

Improved Knurler   Standard Knurler

Points to Note.
1. The knurling tool must be set square to the work and at centre height.
2. There must be minimum overhang of the tool for rigidity.
3. A fairly slow lathe speed is needed.
4. The work must be securely held with a steady or centre giving additional support, if necessary.

An improved form of knurling tool has the wheels set apart and they can be adjusted so that the wheels meet the work on top and bottom. The thrust from the wheels, therefore, is directly opposed. Less strain is imposed on the lathe compared with the standard type knurling tool where the thrust is from one side and at right angles to the bearings of the machine head.

CUTTING CURVED PROFILES

Components having curved profiles, eg. knobs, studs with radiused ends, etc. should be cut with form tools. These are tools ground to the required profile. They are not easy tools to use because a broad surface of the tool is in contact with the work at

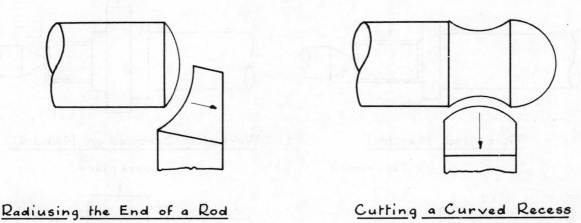

Radiusing the End of a Rod   Cutting a Curved Recess

all times. Low lathe speeds are advisable and a liberal supply of cutting solution applied. It is usual to use form tools only when a batch of items is required, because it would be uneconomical to make a special form tool for the shaping of one or few components. Very often the profile can be cut by manipulating the cross slide and compound slide at the same time. A file and emery cloth is used for the final shaping and finishing.

TURNING WORK ON MANDRELS

Some components, with a central hole, often cannot be held by means of centres or

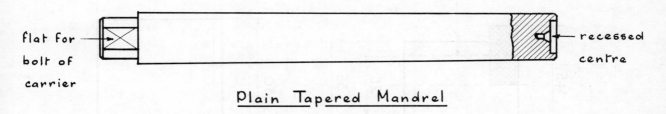

flat for
bolt of
carrier

recessed
centre

Plain Tapered Mandrel

chuck. These components are machined on mandrels. The hole in the centre of the component must be clean and true or threaded to enable it to be fitted to a screwed mandrel. Plain tapered mandrels are made from mild steel casehardened or high carbon steel, hardened, tempered and ground or even untreated mild steel, depending on the amount of use they have to withstand. They are tapered along their length with a taper of about 0·10 mm in 300 mm. The centre holes sometimes are recessed to prevent damage and a flat is provided as a positive drive for the carrier. The work is best pressed on the mandrel but if this is impossible, a lead or copper hammer can be used. The work should be arranged on the mandrel in such a way that the direction of feed tightens it on the mandrel. The turning procedure becomes the same as for turning on centres.

Although the plain tapered mandrel is the most common, other kinds are used for certain work, some of which are shown.

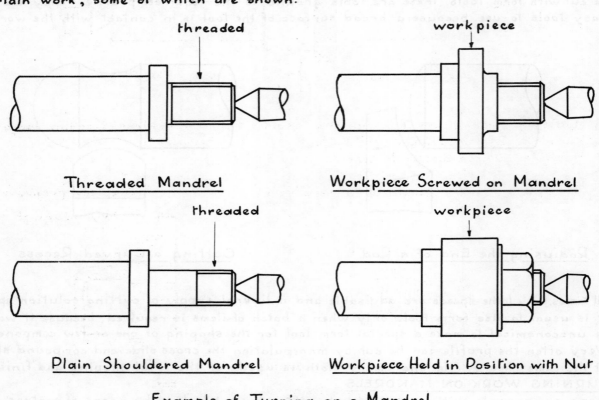

Threaded Mandrel

Workpiece Screwed on Mandrel

Plain Shouldered Mandrel

Workpiece Held in Position with Nut

Example of Turning on a Mandrel

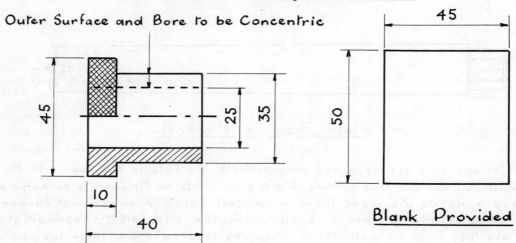

Outer Surface and Bore to be Concentric

Blank Provided

Procedure

1. Chuck the workpiece. Drill and machine the bore.
2. Face the ends. Alternatively, face the ends when the workpiece is on the mandrel.

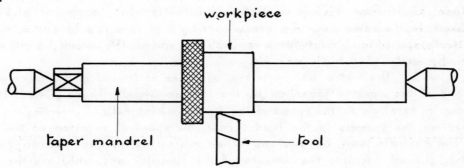

3. Mount the workpiece on a mandrel and fix between centres. Machine large dia.
4. Knurl with a medium knurling tool.
5. Machine outer diameter to size.

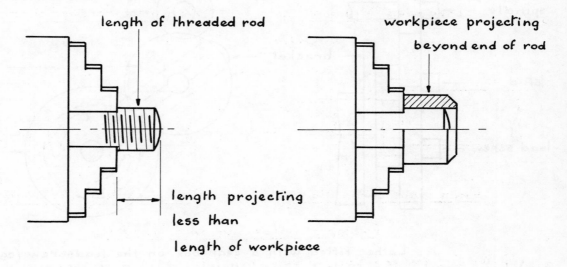

A Length of Threaded Rod in Use as a Mandrel

This method of holding is useful for finishing off small components that are threaded internally.

1. Thread a length of rod to match the thread on the workpiece. The length of thread needs to be sufficient for the workpiece to screw on comfortably.
2. Chuck the rod with a length projecting less than the finished length of the workpiece.
3. Screw on the workpiece until it meets the chuck jaws. Machine to shape. Holding it in this way, the workpiece becomes released as soon as the chuck is undone. Never screw the work onto the rod first. The pressure of cut will force it on so tightly that force will be needed to unscrew it.

SCREWCUTTING

When screwcutting in the lathe, the cutter, carried on the carriage, moves along a known distance at the same time as the work revolves a known number of times. With the cutter in contact with the work, a spiral is thus formed. If the work revolves 25 times and, at the same time, the cutter travels a distance of 25 mm, a spiral of 1mm pitch will be formed. In the same way, if a screwcutting tool is used to cut a thread and it travels a distance of 25 mm for every 25 turns of the work, a thread of 1mm pitch will be cut.

The ratio between the distance of travel of the carriage and number of revolutions of the work is governed by the change wheels. These control the speed of the leadscrew in relation to the speed of the headstock spindle. By changing the train of wheels connecting the spindle to the lead screw, the speed of rotation of the leadscrew in relation to the spindle can be varied. When calculating gear trains, the tumbler gears can be ignored because the wheels of the tumbler assembly are the same size always as the spindle wheel. Speed is not affected, only direction of travel.

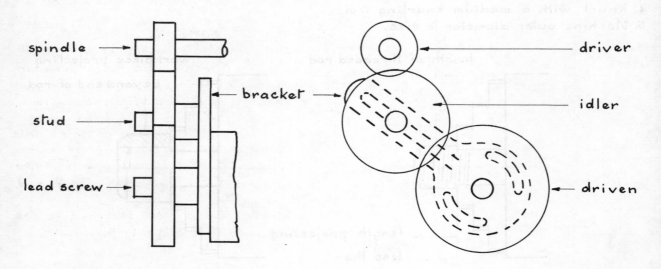

Lathes fitted with a gear box on the leadscrew (eg. a Norton Box) have no change wheels because all the speeds needed for the leadscrew can be derived from the box.

CHANGE WHEELS

Lathes not fitted with a gear box on the leadscrew are supplied with a set of change wheels so that a range of speeds between the spindle and the leadscrew can be obtained.

Some lathes are provided with a set of change wheels that range from 20 teeth to 120 teeth in steps of 5, always with one pair of wheels of the same size, usually two 20s. To cut 150 threads on an imperial lathe a 63 or 127 wheel is needed. More recent practice is for the set to range from 20 to 65 in steps of 5. This smaller range is more economical in price but the train of wheels that has to be set up very frequently becomes more complicated.

The gear wheels may be set up as a simple train using three wheels, a compound train using four wheels or a compound train using six wheels.

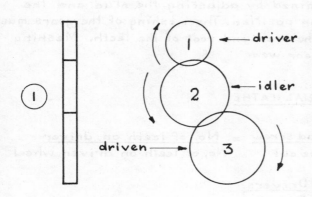

SIMPLE TRAIN ①

1. The driver Nº 1 is fixed to the spindle and rotates with it.
2. The idler or intermediate wheel Nº 2 rotates on a stud which is fixed to the swivelling bracket.
   The size of this wheel has no effect on the speed of the train. It is simply a connecting wheel and any convenient wheel may be used for it. However, it does affect the direction of rotation of the third wheel Nº 3.
3. The driven wheel Nº 3 is fastened to the lead screw and causes it to rotate.

COMPOUND TRAIN ②

Whenever possible, a simple train is used to give the required speed ratio between spindle and leadscrew, but if a simple train will not give the required ratio, a compound train has to be used.

1. The driver Nº 1 is fixed to the spindle and rotates with it.
2. Driven wheel Nº 2 and driver Nº 3 are linked together on the centre stud and rotate together on it.
3. The driven wheel Nº 4 is fixed to the leadscrew and causes it to rotate.

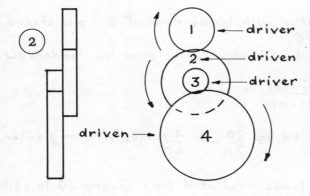

COMPOUND TRAIN ③

When the lathe is supplied with a set of gears ranging from 20 to 65, a more complicated gear system has to be used. Six wheels are used in place of four. Two studs are fixed on the bracket, each of them carrying two wheels. As before the first driver is fixed to the spindle and the last driven wheel is fixed to the leadscrew. The resulting drive is through all the gears in turn from Nº 1 to Nº 6.

Most lathes carry a chart listing the size of gears necessary for any speed ratio.

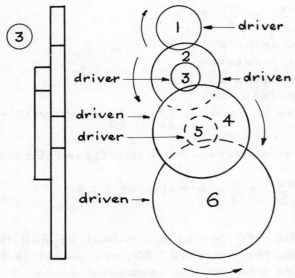

Care is needed when fitting the change wheels. The bracket rotates about the lead-screw and is slotted to enable wheels of different sizes to mesh properly. When assembling, the spindle and leadscrew wheels are fitted first. The idler then is fixed to the stud and correct meshing obtained by adjusting the stud and the bracket. Finally, the bracket is locked in position. The meshing of the gears must be such that there is a slight gap between the crest and root of the teeth. Meshing too tightly increases noise, friction and gear wear.

CALCULATION OF GEAR TRAINS

I. TO CUT IMPERIAL THREADS ON AN IMPERIAL LATHE

$$\frac{\text{No. of turns of lead screw}}{\text{No. of turns of spindle}} = \frac{\text{t.p.i. of lead screw}}{\text{t.p.i. to be cut}} = \frac{\text{No. of teeth on driver}}{\text{No. of teeth on driven wheel}}$$

$$\text{i.e.} \quad \frac{\text{t.p.i. of lead screw}}{\text{t.p.i. to be cut}} = \frac{\text{Drivers}}{\text{Driven}}$$

Eg. 1. To cut a thread of 6 t.p.i. on a lathe with leadscrew of 6 t.p.i. Gears run from 20 to 120 in steps of 5.

Here, the ratio is 6:6 or 1:1. When the spindle turns once the leadscrew must turn once.

$$\frac{\text{t.p.i. of lead screw}}{\text{t.p.i. to be cut}} = \frac{\text{Drivers}}{\text{Driven}} = \frac{1}{1}$$

Any two wheels of the same size can be used, eg. $\frac{20}{20}$, or $\frac{40}{40}$ etc, with any idler.

Eg. 2. To cut a thread of 8 t.p.i. with a leadscrew of 4 t.p.i. Gears 20 to 120.

$$\frac{\text{t.p.i. of leadscrew}}{\text{t.p.i. to be cut}} = \frac{\text{Drivers}}{\text{Driven}} = \frac{4}{8} = \frac{1}{2}$$

$$\frac{1}{2} \times \frac{20}{20} = \frac{20 \text{ on spindle}}{40 \text{ on leadscrew}}$$

$$\text{or} \quad \frac{1}{2} \times \frac{30}{30} = \frac{30 \text{ on spindle}}{60 \text{ on leadscrew.}}$$

Any pair of wheels giving a 1:2 ratio may be used eg. $\frac{20}{40}$ or $\frac{30}{60}$ etc. Any idler.

Eg. 3. To cut a thread of 32 t.p.i. with a leadscrew of 4 t.p.i. Gears 20 to 120.

$$\frac{\text{t.p.i. of leadscrew}}{\text{t.p.i. to be cut}} = \frac{\text{Drivers}}{\text{Driven}} = \frac{4}{32} = \frac{1}{8} \text{, a ratio of 1 : 8}$$

If we multiply by 20 to make the ratio 20:160, we have a wheel beyond the range given. If we multiply by 10 to make the ratio 10:80, one wheel is too small. A simple train, therefore, cannot be used and a compound train is necessary. The required wheels are found by factorizing —

$$\frac{\text{t.p.i. of leadscrew}}{\text{t.p.i. to be cut}} = \frac{\text{drivers}}{\text{driven}} = \frac{4}{32} = \frac{2}{4} \times \frac{2}{8}$$

These two fractions now are treated as before.

$$\frac{2}{4} \times \frac{2}{8} \times \frac{10}{10} = \frac{20}{40} \times \frac{2}{8} \times \frac{10}{10} = \frac{20}{40} \times \frac{20}{80}$$

Driver on spindle = 20 teeth
Driven on stud = 40 teeth
Driver on stud = 20 teeth
Driven on leadscrew = 80 teeth

Eg. 4. To cut a thread of 28 t.p.i. with a leadscrew of 4 t.p.i. Gears 20 to 120.

$$\frac{\text{t.p.i. of leadscrew}}{\text{t.p.i. to be cut}} = \frac{4}{28} = \frac{2}{4} \times \frac{2}{7} = \frac{2}{4} \times \frac{2}{7} \times \frac{10}{10} = \frac{20}{40} \times \frac{2}{7} \times \frac{10}{10} = \frac{20}{40} \times \frac{20}{70}$$

Driver on spindle = 20 teeth
Driven on stud = 40 teeth
Driver on stud = 20 teeth
Driven on leadscrew = 70 teeth

For lathes provided with a range of wheels from 20 to 65 teeth in steps of 5, the procedure is similar. The factorization has to be taken one stage further.

Eg. 5. To cut a thread of 28 t.p.i. with a leadscrew of 4 t.p.i. Gears range from 20 to 65 in steps of 5.

$$\frac{\text{t.p.i. of leadscrew}}{\text{t.p.i. to be cut}} = \frac{4}{28} = \frac{2}{4} \times \frac{2}{7}$$

These fractions, multiplied by 5 or 10, will not bring them within the wheel range provided. The factorization has to be taken further —

$$\frac{4}{28} = \frac{2}{2} \times \frac{2}{2} \times \frac{1}{7} = \frac{20}{20} \times \frac{20}{20} \times \frac{5}{35} = \frac{20}{20} \times \frac{20}{40} \times \frac{10}{35} = \frac{20}{60} \times \frac{20}{40} \times \frac{30}{35}$$

Driver on spindle = 20 teeth
Driven on 1st stud = 60 teeth
Driver on 1st stud = 20 teeth
Driven on 2nd stud = 40 teeth
Driver on 2nd stud = 30 teeth
Driven on leadscrew = 35 teeth

2. TO CUT METRIC THREADS ON AN IMPERIAL LATHE

As before $\dfrac{\text{t.p.i. of leadscrew}}{\text{t.p.i. to be cut}} = \dfrac{\text{Drivers}}{\text{Driven}}$

1 inch = 25·4 mm   and   1mm pitch = 25·4 t.p.i.

Therefore to cut a thread of 25·4 t.p.i. with a leadscrew of 1 t.p.i

$$\frac{\text{Drivers}}{\text{Driven}} = \frac{1}{25\cdot4} = \frac{10}{254} = \frac{5}{127}$$

To cut a thread of "a" mm pitch with a leadscrew of 1 t.p.i.

$$\frac{\text{Drivers}}{\text{Driven}} = \frac{5a}{127}$$

To cut a thread of "a" mm pitch with a leadscrew of "b" t.p.i.

$$\frac{\text{Drivers}}{\text{Driven}} = \frac{5ab}{127}$$

Thus to cut a metric thread on an imperial lathe a gear wheel with 127 teeth is needed. A 63 wheel will give a near approximation.

Eg. 1. To cut a thread of 2mm pitch on a lathe with a leadscrew of 4 t.p.i. Gears range from 20 to 120 in steps of 5 plus a 127 wheel.

$$a = 2 \qquad b = 4$$

$$\frac{\text{Drivers}}{\text{Driven}} = \frac{2 \times 4 \times 5}{127} = \frac{40}{127}$$

This gives a simple train with a 40 gear on the spindle and a 127 gear on the leadscrew. Any idler.

Eg. 2. To cut a thread of 3·2 mm pitch on a lathe with a leadscrew of 6 t.p.i. Gears range from 20 to 120 in steps of 5 plus a 127 wheel.

$$a = 3\cdot2 \qquad b = 6$$

$$\frac{\text{Drivers}}{\text{Driven}} = \frac{3\cdot2 \times 6 \times 5}{127} = \frac{96}{127}$$

There is no 96 gear so a compound train will be needed.

$$\frac{96}{127} = \frac{4 \times 24}{127} = \frac{4 \times 24}{127} \times \frac{5}{5} = \frac{4 \times 120}{127 \times 5} = \frac{4 \times 120}{127 \times 5} \times \frac{10}{10} = \frac{40 \times 120}{127 \times 50}$$

$$\text{Driver on spindle} = 40$$
$$\text{Driven on stud} = 50$$
$$\text{Driver on stud} = 120$$
$$\text{Driven on leadscrew} = 127$$

Eg. 3. To cut a thread of 2·4mm pitch on a lathe with a leadscrew of 4 t.p.i. Gears range from 20 to 120 in steps of 5 plus a 127 wheel.

$$\frac{\text{Drivers}}{\text{Driven}} = \frac{5ab}{127} = \frac{5 \times 2·4 \times 4}{127} = \frac{48}{127}$$

There is no 48 wheel so the compound train is found by factorizing –

$$\frac{4 \times 12}{127} \times \frac{5}{5} = \frac{4 \times 60}{127 \times 5} = \frac{4 \times 60}{127 \times 5} \times \frac{10}{10} = \frac{40 \times 60}{127 \times 50}$$

$$\text{Driver on spindle} = 40$$
$$\text{Driven on stud} = 50$$
$$\text{Driver on stud} = 60$$
$$\text{Driven on leadscrew} = 127$$

3. TO CUT METRIC THREADS ON A METRIC LATHE   *

$$\frac{\text{Drivers}}{\text{Driven}} = \frac{\text{t.p.i. of leadscrew}}{\text{t.p.i to be cut}} = \frac{\text{pitch to be cut}}{\text{pitch of leadscrew}}$$

Eg. I. To cut a thread of 2mm pitch on a lathe with a leadscrew of 4mm pitch. Gears range from 20 to 120 in steps of 5.

$$\frac{\text{pitch to be cut}}{\text{pitch of leadscrew}} = \frac{2}{4} = \frac{1}{2}$$

Any pair of wheels giving a 1:2 ratio may be used – a simple train with any idler.

$$\begin{aligned}
20 \quad &\text{on spindle} \\
40 \quad &\text{on leadscrew} \\
\text{or } 40 \quad &\text{on spindle} \\
80 \quad &\text{on leadscrew}
\end{aligned}$$

Eg. 2. To cut a thread of 2·5mm pitch on a lathe with a leadscrew of 4mm pitch. Gears range from 20 to 120 in steps of 5.

$$\frac{\text{pitch to be cut}}{\text{pitch of leadscrew}} = \frac{2·5}{4} = \frac{2·5}{4} \times \frac{10}{10} = \frac{25}{40}$$

A simple train with any idler, a 25 wheel on the spindle and a 40 on the leadscrew.

Eg. 3. To cut a thread of 3·2mm pitch on a lathe with a leadscrew of 4mm pitch. Gears range from 20 to 120 in steps of 5.

$$\frac{\text{pitch to be cut}}{\text{pitch of leadscrew}} = \frac{3·2}{4}$$

$$\frac{3·2}{4} \times \frac{5}{5} = \frac{16·0}{20} = \frac{16}{20} \times \frac{5}{5} = \frac{80}{100}$$

A simple train with any idler, a 80 wheel on the spindle and a 100 on the leadscrew.

Examination questions on gear trains usually specify a range of gear wheels from 20 to 120 although in practice few, if any, lathes are now produced with this range of gears.

The question of the range of change wheels is under consideration by a standards panel of the Machine Tool Trades Association (Nov. 1970) with a view to proposing a draft British Standard which will be circulated to industry for approval.

THE SCREWCUTTING TOOL

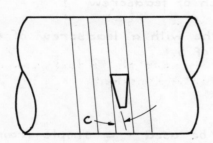

1. The tool is ground to match the thread form using a thread gauge to check the thread angle.

2. The tip of the tool is radiused according to the size of the thread to be cut. A screw pitch gauge can be used to check the amount of curvature.

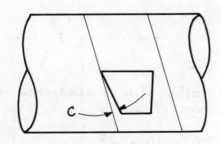

Side Clearance and Helix Angle

3. The side clearance angle of the tool is dependent on the pitch of the thread to be cut.
   The coarser the pitch of the thread, the greater its helix angle will be. The clearance C between the leading face of the tool and the flank of the thread must be maintained. When cutting a coarse thread, the side clearance of the tool has to be relatively large in order to maintain the angle C.

4. The tool must be set at centre height and also set square to the work by means of a thread gauge.

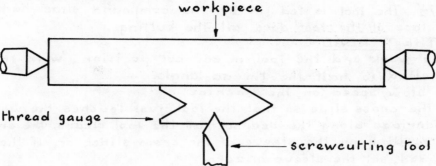

workpiece

thread gauge

screwcutting tool

FEEDING THE TOOL INTO THE WORK
1. By Means of the Cross-slide Screw.
Here the point does a lot of the cutting and the point is the weakest part of

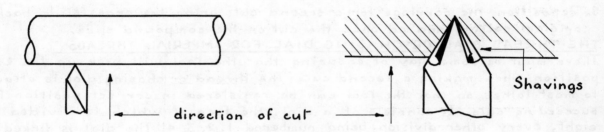

direction of cut

Shavings

the tool. In addition, the chips come off both side faces of the tool, converge and foul each other. This is not a very satisfactory method.
2. By Means of the Compound Slide Screw.

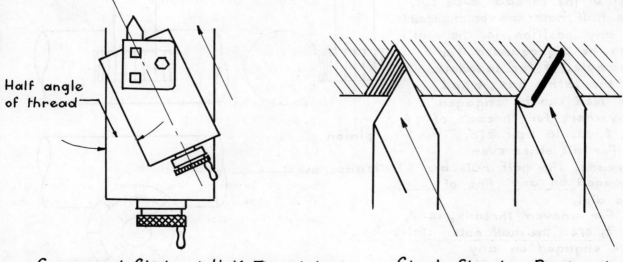

Half angle of thread

Compound Slide at Half Thread Angle

Single Shaving Produced

The compound slide is set to half the included angle of the thread to be cut. For ISO metric threads of 60°, the set-over angle is 30°, for imperial threads eg. B.S.W. $27\frac{1}{2}°$. The tool is fed in by the compound slide handle so that the leading face of the tool does all the cutting.

CUTTING THE THREAD

1. Set up the work and the tool in correct position, with the compound slide swivelled to half the thread angle.
2. Engage a slow speed on the machine.
3. Advance the cross slide so that the tool just touches the work and then take the carriage along the bed so that the tool clears the end of the work.
4. Note the reading on the sleeve of the cross slide, or, if the sleeve is spring-loaded, set the sleeve at zero.
5. Advance the compound slide a small amount for the depth of cut.
6. Start the lathe and engage the half nuts. The tool now will move along the work cutting a spiral, the pitch of which will be dependent on the gear train that has been set up.
7. At the end of the cut, disengage the half nuts and bring the cross slide forward at the same time.
8. Reposition the carriage for a second cut, bring the cross slide back to its original setting and advance the cut on the compound slide.

THE THREAD DIAL OR CHASING DIAL FOR IMPERIAL THREADS

There must be some way of ensuring that the tool will pick up the exact position when making a second cut. The thread or chasing dial is attached to most lathes so that the tool can be registered in correct position for succeeding cuts. It consists of a dial, the face of which is divided into eight, every other division being numbered 1, 2, 3, 4. The dial is linked to the leadscrew by means of a pinion (small gear wheel).

RULES FOR ENGAGEMENT

1. If the t.p.i. of the leadscrew will divide exactly into the t.p.i. of the thread to be cut, the half nuts can be engaged in any position, ie. the dial can be disregarded. For example, if the leadscrew of the lathe has 4 t.p.i the feed can be engaged anywhere for threads of 4, 8, 12, 16 t.p.i. etc.
2. For all other even threads, the half nuts are engaged on any line of the dial.
3. For uneven threads, ie. 3, 5, 7, etc. the half nuts are engaged on any numbered line of the dial.

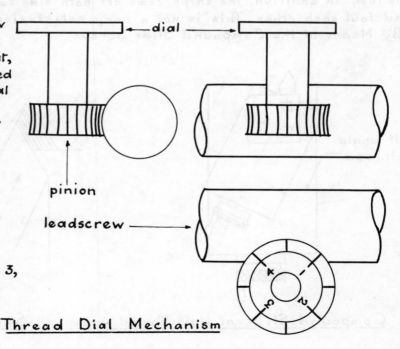

Thread Dial Mechanism

THREAD DIALS AND METRIC LATHES

Thread dials, "which are almost standard equipment on British screwcutting lathes, are very difficult to design for use with a metric feed screw." (Machine Tools for Metric Production - Ministry of Technology)

If no dial is fitted -

1. Between cuts, reverse the lathe and return the carriage to the start without disengaging the half nuts from the leadscrew.

2. To cut a thread, the pitch of which will divide exactly into the pitch of the leadscrew, the half nuts can be engaged in any position on the leadscrew, eg. when cutting threads of 0·5, 1, 1·25, 2·5 mm pitch etc. with a 5mm pitch leadscrew.

CHASERS are used to provide -

1. A good finish.
2. An accurate fitting of the thread.
3. An accurate thread form.

Standard imperial vee threads have a rounded crest and root. When a thread is cut on the lathe, the tool cuts a thread root of correct radius but leaves the crest flat. A chaser will radius off the crest, thus giving correct thread form.

Crest left flat from tool

Crest rounded off with chaser

Hand and machine chasers are obtainable. Hand chasers, made of either H.S.S. or H.C.S, are available for all standard pitches. The correct pitch of chaser must be used for the thread being cut. They may be sharpened by grinding on the top face only.

Hand chasers are held by hand and hand fed along the thread.

Machine chasers are held in the tool box and power fed along the thread in the same way as the screwcutting tool is used.

tang
for
wooden handle

External Chaser   Internal Chaser

USING THE CHASER

1. Set a bar rest in the tool box so that, when resting on it, the top face of the chaser is at centre height.
2. Position the rest so that it is near to the work.
3. Engage the lathe on a fairly fast speed and press the chaser firmly into the thread, starting at the beginning of the thread length. Repeat until a fit is obtained,

using a screw ring gauge or a standard nut for checking. The use of soluble oil will improve the surface finish.

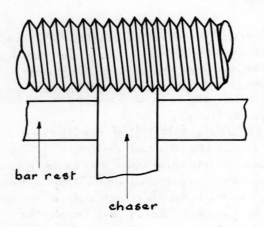

bar rest

chaser

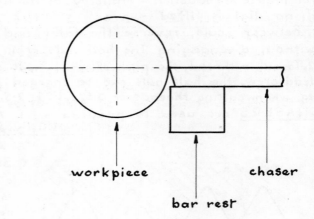

workpiece

bar rest

chaser

OBTAINING CORRECT THREAD SIZE

If the thread being cut is not a standard one, no screw ring gauge or nut will be available to use for checking. Some other method of checking size must be used.

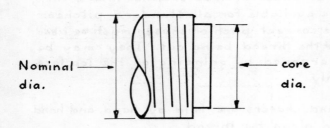

Nominal dia.

core dia.

Nominal Diameter and Core Diameter

As for any thread, the rod must be turned to the correct thread diameter, ie. nominal diameter.
The end of the bar is then turned down for a short length to a size equal to the core diameter of the thread.

Core Dia. = nd − 2 x d, where
 nd = nominal diameter and
  d = depth of thread.

The depth of thread may be obtained from either a. reference tables.
        or b. the formula d = 0.54 x p,
where p = pitch and d = depth of thread, for 150 metric threads.
Cutting of the thread can continue until the tip of the tool just touches the core diameter.

INTERNAL THREADS

The procedure for cutting internal threads is the same as for cutting external threads except that a hole has to be bored first that is equal to the core

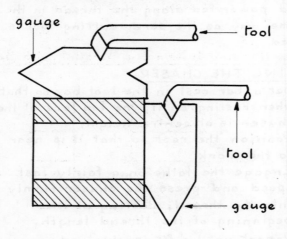

gauge

tool

tool

gauge

Two Ways of Setting the Boring Tool

208

diameter of the thread, the core diameter being found by either of the two methods explained before.

The internal screwcutting tool has to be set square to the work as shown overleaf.

CUTTING SQUARE AND ACME THREADS

These are more difficult to cut than vee threads. There is no standard pitch for a given diameter. Small threads of square or acme shape may be cut by using a tool ground to the correct thread shape and following the same procedure as for vee threads. Threads of large pitch are cut by using two or even three tools to obtain the required shape.

SIX BASIC PRINCIPLES OF METAL TURNING

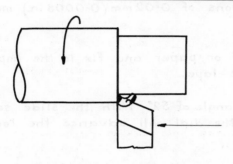
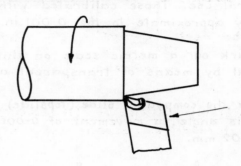

Tool Moving Parallel with the Bed   Tool Moving at an Angle to the Bed

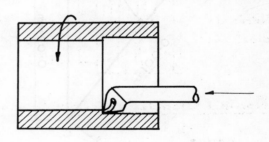

Tool Moving at Rt. Angles to the Bed   Tool Moving Internally Parallel with Bed

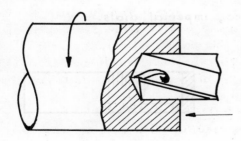
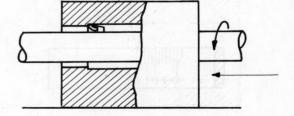

Drilling in the Lathe   Work Moving Along Bed, Tool Rotating

METHODS OF MODIFYING AN IMPERIAL LATHE TO CUT METRIC

The unit for precise imperial measurement is 0·001 in. and the collars on machine tools are usually graduated on this basis.

Existing metric machine tools cannot be relied upon to have a particular unit as a base. The cross slide and topslide might have graduations of 0·3 and 0·6mm respectively, but this is not standard and different machines might have different graduations, eg. 0·02mm, 0·05mm, 0·1mm.

Metric dials calibrated with divisions of 0·01mm (0·0004 in.) are too fine for general use. Those calibrated with divisions of 0·02mm (0·0008 in.) most nearly approximate to the 0·001 in. unit.

1. Mark out a metric scale on thin card or paper and fix to the imperial dial by means of transparent adhesive tape.

2. Set the compound slide (topslide) to an angle of 52°. With the slide set at this angle, a movement of 0·001 in. on the dial will advance the tool by 0·02 mm.

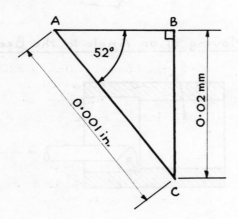

$$\text{Sine A} = \frac{0·02}{0·001 \times 25·4}$$

$$= \frac{20}{25·4}$$

$$= 0·7874$$

$$A = 52° \text{ approx.}$$

For surfacing, the set-over angle will be 38° (the complement of 52°).

3. Make new collars to add to, or replace, imperial dials.

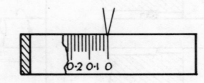
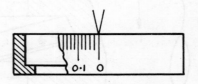

a. Sleeves to fit over imperial machine dials

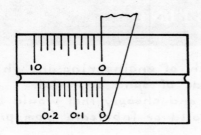

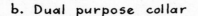

b. Dual purpose collar

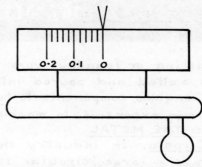

c. Metric replacement collar

4. Manufactured geared dials are available. These are marked in imperial and, or, metric but they are costly.

5. Most manufacturers sell conversion sets. Leadscrew, half-nuts, cross-slide and compound slide screws, nuts and dials are replaced with metric components. The lathe then is fully metric. These conversion sets are expensive.

THE PROBLEM OF DIAL CALIBRATION

"The internationally - agreed conversion factor of 1 in. = 25·4 mm exactly results, however, in some inconvenience in operation as, eg. a single rotation of the handwheel of a 5 t.p.i. screw would produce 5·08 mm axial movement. An exact division of the dial into an integral number of units of a millimetre is not possible". (Machine Tools for Metric Production – Ministry of Technology)

Using a conversion factor of 1 in. = 25·0 mm gives an error of approx. 1·6%. For most practical purpose this degree of error is acceptable and an exact division of the dial into an integral number of units of a millimetre is then possible.

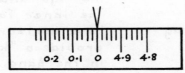

The t.p.i. of the feed screw has to be found, eg. 5. One revolution of the dial will feed in the tool by this amount, i.e. $\frac{1}{5}$ in. or 0·2 in. If the dial is marked with spaces of 0·001 in. there will, therefore, be 200 x 0·001 in. divisions. Using a conversion factor of 1 in. = 25 mm, a metric replacement dial will have 250 divisions, each of 0·02 mm.

211

Metal casting or foundry work is that branch of engineering in which metal is melted and poured into moulds made of sand or metal. Casting enables components to be made easily and cheaply that would be difficult and expensive to machine from the solid or fabricate from pieces.

MELTING THE METAL

1. By Cupola. In industry the ferrous metals are melted in a cupola which is a large, circular furnace lined with firebrick, and charged with metal, coke and limestone.

2. By Crucible Furnace. Non-ferrous metals are melted in a crucible furnace which may be fired by gas, coke or oil. These furnaces house one or more crucibles made of plumbago.

Furnaces used in schools and colleges are usually of the crucible type, fired by gas.

CASTING EQUIPMENT

FLASK Large castings are made straight into a mould formed in a bed of sand or a sand pit in the floor. Smaller castings are formed in moulding boxes called flasks. They may be made of wood, steel or cast iron and are in two parts.

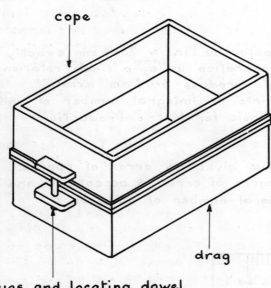

cope

lugs and locating dowel

drag

The cope is the top half of the box. The drag is the bottom half of the box. Both these halves are open top and bottom. The two halves must be assembled always in the same position. To register and locate the two parts the boxes have projecting lugs and a pair, or more, of locating pins. To prevent wrong assembly, the pins may be of different size or section or the lugs and pins may be off-set. The inner faces of the flask may have horizontal grooves or ribs to provide a "key" and so help to hold in the sand.

SPRUE PINS and RISERS

These are used to form the runners and risers.

They can be made from any close-grained wood by turning a long gradual taper along the length.

A range of sizes is needed from 12mm dia. to 35mm dia. at the small end and a length to suit the moulding boxes in which they will be used.

Shape for Sprue Pins
and Risers

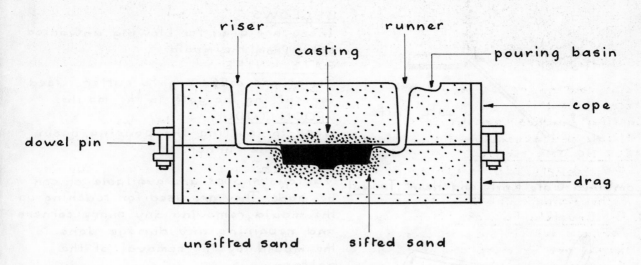

riser   casting   runner   pouring basin   cope

dowel pin

drag

unsifted sand   sifted sand

Parts of the Mould

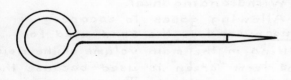

Draw Spike

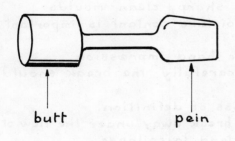

butt   pein

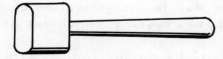

Rammers

DRAW SPIKE
This is used for driving into the pattern to withdraw it. It may be made from 6mm dia. H.C.S. hardened and tempered to a straw. One end is pointed and the other ringed for easy withdrawal. A length of about 200mm is suitable.

RAPPING IRON
To allow the pattern to be easily withdrawn, the flask is tapped or rapped with a rapping iron. This can be a length of mild steel rod about 12 or 16mm diameter.

RAMMERS
The sand needs to be packed firmly in the flask and around the pattern with rammers. They can be made of hardwood in a range of shapes. The head of the rammer is called the butt and the shaped handle, also used for ramming, called the pein.

RIDDLE
Some form of sieve or riddle is necessary to sift the sand.

CRUCIBLE TONGS
Tongs, which fit snugly around the crucible, are used to lift it out of the furnace and to hold it while pouring.

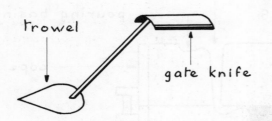

trowel

gate knife

Combined Gate Knife and Heart Trowel

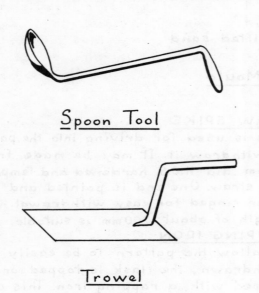

Spoon Tool

Trowel

BELLOWS
These are used for blowing unwanted sand from the mould.
GATE KNIFE
Sometimes called a gate cutter. Used for cutting the gate in the mould.
SPOON TOOL
Used for cutting the pouring basin around the runner.
TROWELS
Various shapes are available or can be made. They are used for touching up the mould, removing any sharp corners and repairing any damage done to the mould by the removal of the pattern.
MOULDING SAND
Moulding sand must be capable of —
1. Maintaining the shape of the pattern.
2. Withstanding heat.
3. Allowing gases to escape.
Green sand is the sand used for filling in the main volume of the mould. The term "green" is used because the sand is used damp. The sand is bonded together with a small proportion of clay which may be combined with the sand when dug or added separately. The sand, with clay, when moistened, makes sharp, clean moulds.
The moisture content is important.

Tests for correct moisture content are —
1. Squeezed in the hand it should retain the hand impression.
2. When squeezed in the hand and broken carefully, the break should be firm, with no sign of crumble.

If the sand is too dry
1. There will be loss of definition.
2. The corners will break away under the flow of metal.
3. The mould will tend to collapse.

If the sand is too wet
1. There is danger that molten metal will spurt out of the runner due to the generation of steam.
2. Gases will be trapped, causing blowholes in the finished casting.

When the sand is too dry, it must be "tempered" by sprinkling it with water and turning it well over with a spade or trowel.
Facing Sand. To obtain a good finish on the casting, the sand in contact with the pattern should be of good quality. This facing sand is riddled, sprinkled or brushed onto the mould when the pattern has been

removed. The depth of facing sand and its fineness will depend on the quality of work desired and its weight.

<u>Parting Sand</u> (or dust or powder) is a fine, dry sand, brick dust or burnt clay which is dusted over the surface of the moulding sand so that cope and drag can be separated easily and so that the pattern can be withdrawn easily. The sand or dust can be dusted on with a cotton bag.

MOULDING OPERATIONS

RAMMING

The sand is packed into the flask with a rammer. The pein of the rammer is used for most of the ramming so that each layer of sand "keys" itself to the previous layer. Using the butt will give too even and flat a surface to "key." The main use of the butt is to flatten off the surface before strickling.

<u>If the ramming is too hard,</u> the porosity of the sand is lost, resulting in trapped gases and blowholes.

<u>If the ramming is too soft,</u> the mould becomes weak and the flow of the metal will break off particles of the mould causing sand inclusions in the finished casting.

FORMING RUNNERS

Runners are formed by inserting a sprue pin in the cope and ramming sand around it. A depression is scooped out around the pin before its removal to form a pouring basin. The bottom end of the runner should be cut deeper than the gate to receive the force of the pour without causing damage to the mould.

The size and position of the sprue pin is important. The volume of the runner should never be more than the cast. One function of the sprue is to feed the casting as it shrinks. If the sprue is too big, the reverse action takes place. Also, the sprue should be positioned on the casting where it can be broken off easily and the break cleaned up with no difficulty.

FORMING RISERS

The riser is made in the same way as the runner, i.e. by inserting a taper pin in the mould. It is located at the opposite end of the mould from the runner or where the highest part of the casting will come. The riser acts as a vent for gases and also indicates when the mould is full.

GATING

The gates are the channels that are cut between the runner, riser and casting cavity. Sometimes, the term is used to include runner, riser and the channels to the casting cavity.

VENTING

When the molten metal is poured, the gases must have some means of exit. Much will escape through the riser but additional ventilation must be provided by means of vent holes.

The gases that need to be removed are -

1. The air filling the mould cavity.

2. Steam that is formed when the hot metal meets the moist sand.

3. Gases formed by the burning of the facing sand, etc.

If these gases are not removed the casting will be pitted with blowholes. Vent holes are made, with the pattern in place, by pushing a fine pointed rod into the sand, stopping it a little short of the pattern. The number of vent holes made depends on the size of the casting, the vent holes increasing in number as the casting increases in size.

CORES

Often, castings have holes or cavities in them in order to take some working part or to make the casting lighter. These holes or cavities are formed by using cores. The cores are held in position in the mould by means of –

a. <u>Core prints</u>. These are extensions of the core itself and rest in the mould outside the casting cavity.

or b. <u>Chaplets</u>. The simplest form of chaplet is like a nail, the head of it being used to support the core. The chaplet should be made of a metal similar to that being cast.

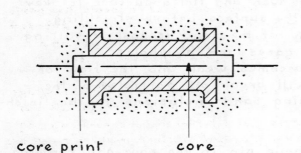

core print   core

Plain cylindrical cores can be bought ready made from a foundry. They are quite cheap and available in a wide range of diameters.

Cores are made from sand (core sand) and mixed with a binder, often raw linseed oil. The mixture is rammed into a suitably shaped core box, carefully removed and then baked in order to harden it. Small cores may be baked on a sheet of steel supported over a gas stove or ring.

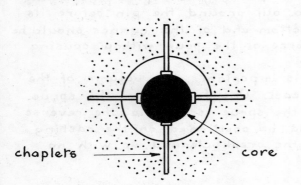

chaplets   core

Core Held Centrally By Chaplets

The core box is a simple form of two-piece mould, usually of wood and fitted with dowel pins to locate the two halves.

TEMPERATURE CONTROL

Many castings are defective or spoilt completely because the casting metal is brought to the wrong temperature. One satisfactory way to make sure that the temperature is correct is to use a <u>pyrometer</u> – an instrument that is capable of reading temperatures above the thermometer scales.

PATTERNS

The shape and size of the finished casting is largely dependent on the shape and size of the pattern. This is made of wood unless a very large

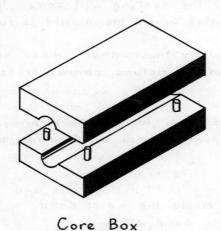

Core Box

number of castings is required, when they are made of metal.

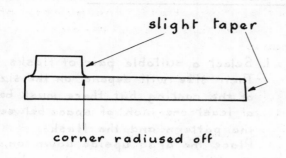

slight taper

corner radiused off

Pattern for Drilling Machine Base

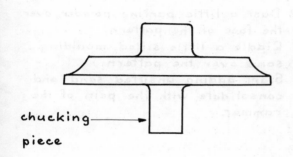

chucking piece

Base for a Table Lamp

IMPORTANT POINTS CONCERNING PATTERNS

1. The pattern must have a good surface.
2. It must be of such a form that it can be withdrawn easily from the mould.
3. It must have draft, i.e. a slight taper, to make withdrawal easier.
4. To enable the pattern to be taken from the mould without damage to the mould it might have to be made in two or more parts. Dowels are used to locate the parts.
5. Sharp internal angles must be avoided. They are a source of weakness. Any sharp angles are filled with leather fillets, plastic wood or beeswax.
6. Allowance has to be made for shrinkage of the casting during cooling. Metals vary in the amount that they shrink during cooling. Special pattern-makers' rules are made, which have scales compensated for the shrinkage rates of the common metals. Direct measurement is taken from the rules, avoiding the need for repeated calculation.
7. Consideration must be given to any machining allowances and the method by which the metal can be held for any machining. Holding lugs may have to be provided.

USE OF CHILLS

If the casting varies in section to any large extent, the thin part of the casting will cool far more rapidly than the thick parts causing stresses and possible fracture. Chills are pieces of metal shaped to fit in the mould and positioned alongside the thick part of the casting. The embedded chills cause rapid cooling when the metal comes in contact with them, resulting in more even cooling over the casting.

DIE CASTING

This is a form of casting using metal dies or moulds instead of sand moulds. The process is used only for large quantity production because the dies are very expensive to produce. To make them for casting small quantities would be uneconomical. Zinz and aluminium alloys are used very often for die-casting because they melt at a low temperature, give good, sharp castings and are moderately cheap. Typical die-cast components are car door handles and hinges, toys, pump and carburetter bodies, etc.

The molten metal may be gravity fed or pressure fed into the die and the finished casting needs little, if any, further treatment.

MAKING A MOULD WITH A ONE-PIECE PATTERN

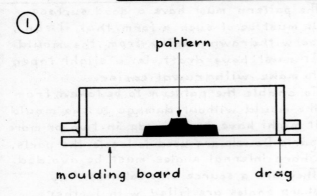

(1) pattern

moulding board   drag

1. Select a suitable pair of flasks. Their size will depend on the size of the casting but there must be at least one inch of space between the pattern and the flask.
Place the drag upside down on a moulding board or moulding bench and position the casting centrally.

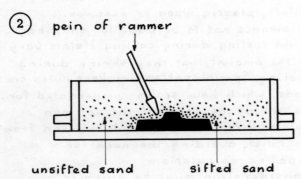

(2) pein of rammer

unsifted sand   sifted sand

2. Dust a little parting powder over the face of the pattern.
Riddle a little sifted moulding sand over the pattern.
Start adding unsifted sand and consolidate with the pein of the rammer.

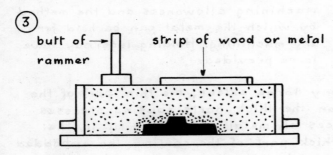

(3) butt of → rammer   strip of wood or metal

3. Continue packing, using the butt of the rammer when nearing the top of the drag.
Strickle off (ie. flatten it off) using a straight strip of wood or metal. Make sure the sand is level with the top of the drag.

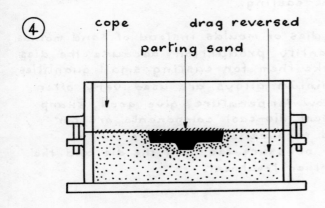

(4) cope   drag reversed
parting sand

4. Turn over the drag and dust the face with parting powder.
Place the cope in position, locating it on the drag by means of the dowel pins. Fix or lock the cope and drag together, if there is means of doing so.

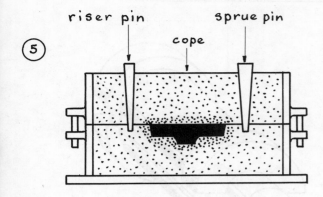

5. Position the sprue and riser pins and riddle a layer of sand over the pattern.
Pack with unsifted sand, using the pein of the rammer. When approaching the top of the cope use the butt of the rammer.
Strickle flat.

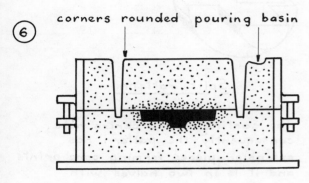

6. Prick vent holes if ventilation in addition to the riser is needed.
Cut the pouring basin with a spoon tool.
Loosen the pattern and pins by rapping with a rapping iron.
Remove the sprue pins and round off the sharp corners by rubbing the fingers round the top of the holes.

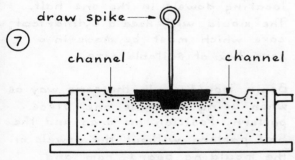

7. Separate the flasks and cut the channels from the sprue holes to the pattern using a gate knife. Make sure that the bottom of the runner is deeper than the channel. Using a soft brush moisten the sand around the pattern. Drive the draw spike into the pattern and carefully withdraw.

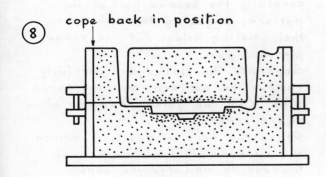

8. Remove the sharp edges around the channels using the fingers.
Make good any slight flaws in the surfaces.
With a bellows, blow out any loosened sand.
Replace the cope.

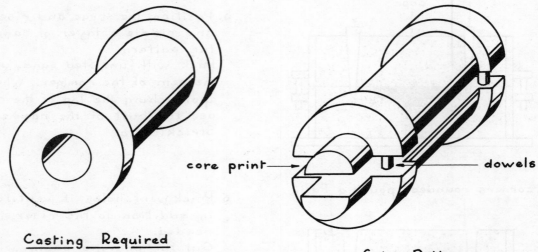

Casting Required

core print → ← dowels

Split Pattern

The casting has a centre hole, consequently the pattern has extension pieces forming core prints and it is in two halves with locating dowels in the one half. The mould will need a cylindrical core which must be made in a core box of suitable size.

Begin moulding in the same way as when using a simple one-piece pattern. Position the drag and the half pattern without the dowels on the moulding board, ram and strickle off.

Turn over the drag and locate carefully the second half of the pattern, engaging the dowels in their mating holes. Fit the sprue pins and ram.

Separate the flasks and carefully remove the pattern and the sprue pins. Cut the gates and trim off sharp corners.

Place the core in position where the core prints have made their impression and fix the cope.

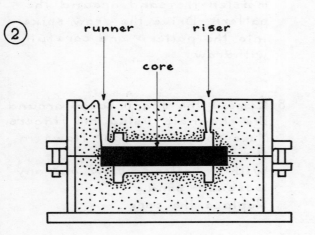

① drag   sifted sand   unsifted sand   half pattern

② runner   core   riser

MELTING AND POURING

1. Preheat the furnace and crucible to avoid cracking the refractory linings.
2. Tools used must be brushed over with a refractory wash to prevent the metals of which they are made contaminating the melt.
   The chief tools are — a. Crucible tongs, for lifting and carrying the crucible.
                                 b. Skimmer, for removing dross from the top of the melt.
                                 c. Plunger for stirring, etc.
3. Place the metal to be melted in the crucible and cover with a protective layer of flux.
4. Heat the metal by raising the temperature steadily in order to avoid any local overheating.
5. When molten, the metal has to be freed of impurities. Aluminium needs degassing and brass de-oxidizing. Preparations for these purposes, usually in tablet form, are obtainable from foundry suppliers.
6. Reduce the heat and allow the metal to settle.
7. Pre-heat the tongs to prevent chilling the crucible. Remove the crucible from the furnace and place on a tray of sand.
8. Skim off the dross and pour out steadily.
9. Clean the crucible immediately after use.

SAFETY PRECAUTIONS

1. Control of the pour should be in the hands of the teacher.
2. During the melt and the pour suitable clothing must be worn, ie. goggles, spats, leather aprons and gauntlets.
3. Only the operator and his helper should be near at hand when a pour is being made.
4. Adequate ventilation must be provided to carry away fumes.
5. Care is needed when adding fresh metal to the melt. Such metal should be preheated.
6. Skimmers, plungers, etc. should be heated before immersing in the melt.
7. The casting apparatus, furnace and moulds, should stand on a tray of dry sand in order to catch any spills.
8. Blowbacks are dangerous. Make sure the sand is not too moist.
9. Pouring must be done at floor level.
10. To prevent the cope and drag from separating during the pour they should be fastened together or weighted down.
11. Make sure the metal has solidified before opening up.

When metal is cut the action is tearing rather than cutting. The metal breaks away and tears ahead of the cutting tip. The chip, as it comes off, is compressed and causes severe pressure on the tool just behind the cutting tip – the pressure point. The extreme tip of the tool follows behind the break and trims off irregularities. Proof of the forces exerted at the pressure point often can be seen as a mark on the tool after heavy cutting. With brittle materials the chips shear off at this point but with

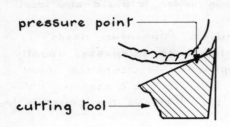
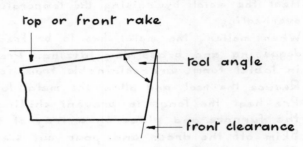

ductile materials the chips bend at this point and curl away.

The FRONT CLEARANCE is the clearance at the front of the tool behind the tip. Without it the tool would rub. It varies little for any one tool and is usually between 5° and 10°.

The TOP RAKE is the angle ground on the top or leading face of the tool and helps the tool to cut efficiently.

The TOOL ANGLE is what remains after top rake and front clearance have been ground away.

As the top rake increases the tearing or wedging action becomes less and the cutting easier. At the same time, the tool angle becomes less and the tool, consequently, weaker. When shaping a cutting tool it is always a problem to balance ease of cutting (with a heavy top rake and small tool angle) and strength of tool angle (with small top rake and less efficient cutting).

Tools for cutting soft materials can afford to have considerable rake because the tool can be relatively weak (a small tool angle).

Tools for cutting hard materials need to have little or no rake because the tool needs to be relatively strong (a large tool angle).

SIDE CLEARANCE is the slight clearance ground on the leading side of the tool. Many tools will rub without side clearance.

SIDE RAKE is the angle ground on the top face away from the leading edge.

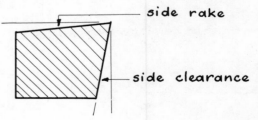

Many tools have no side clearance or side rake.

TOOL	DETAILS OF CUTTING ACTION
CHISEL 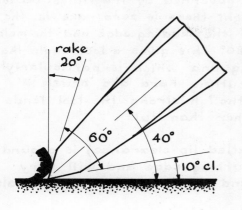	For cutting med. hard metals the cutting angles are 　　　　RAKE ANGLE 20° 　　　　TOOL ANGLE 60° 　　　　CLEARANCE ANGLE 10° For cutting hard metals the cutting angles are 　　　　RAKE ANGLE 10° 　　　　TOOL ANGLE 70° 　　　　CLEARANCE ANGLE 10° For cutting soft metals the cutting angles are 　　　　RAKE ANGLE 50° 　　　　TOOL ANGLE 30° 　　　　CLEARANCE ANGLE 10° There is no side rake or side clearance unless the chisel is used on a skew, ie., a shearing cut.
HACKSAW 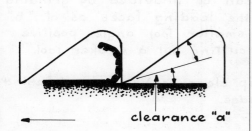 clearance "b" for chippings clearance "a"	The leading face of the tooth is at right-angles to the metal (or nearly so). Therefore there is no (or little) front rake. The primary clearance "a" is to give extra strength to the tooth. The secondary clearance "b" provides clearance for the chippings and prevents clogging. This double clearance and little or no rake gives a tooth that is strong and, at the same time, there is plenty of clearance for waste.
FILE 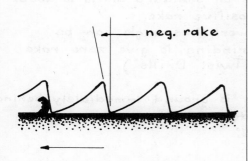 neg. rake	Basically the same tooth form as the saw. The leading face of each tooth lies at an angle less than 90° to the material being cut so that there is negative rake. The file teeth are cut at an angle across the face of the file and this provides side rake. Using the file obliquely over the face of the metal also has the effect of providing side rake.

TOOL	DETAILS OF CUTTING ACTION
STR. FLUTED DRILL 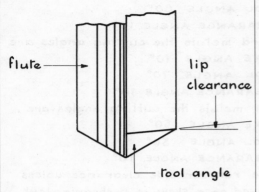	Front rake is governed by the flutes. Because these are straight there is zero rake, ie. the angle between the leading edge and the metal being cut is 90° This gives a tool angle that is very strong and which is particularly suitable for cutting hard and brittle materials. Although strong the tool tends to scrape rather than cut. Clearance (called lip clearance) is ground behind the cutting edge and will vary between 5° and 10° for different materials.
FLAT DRILL 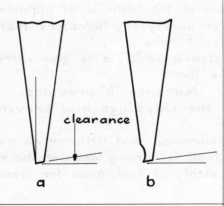	The angle between the leading face and the material being cut is less than 90°. This gives a large, strong tool angle with negative rake, but the tool scrapes rather than cuts. Front rake can be provided by grinding a groove in the leading faces as at " b." This gives a smaller tool angle, positive rake, easier cutting but a weaker tool. Clearance (lip clearance) is ground behind the cutting edge.
TWIST DRILL 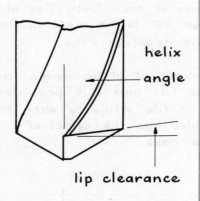	The helix angle governs the front rake and under normal circumstances is unalterable. The helix angle on standard drills is about 25°, giving positive rake. For special work this angle can be altered by grinding to give zero rake (see under "Twist Drills"). Lip clearance is ground immediately behind the cutting edge, the clearance angle being 10° - 12°

CUTTING SPEED AND FEED

__CUTTING SPEED__ is the speed with which the cutting tool passes over the surface of the metal or, conversely, the speed with which the metal passes over the cutting tool. It is commonly expressed in metres per min. Cutting speed depends on –
1. The material being cut and the type of work being done on it.
2. Condition and strength of tools or machinery.
3. Depth of cut.
4. Rate of feed.
5. Material of which the tool is made.
6. Whether or not a cutting solution is being used.

__FEED__ governs the thickness of the metal shaving that is removed. The rate of feed depends on –
1. Smoothness of finish required.
2. The condition and power of tools and machinery being used.
3. Depth of cut.
4. Whether or not a cutting solution is being used.
5. Material being cut.

__FILING__ The file enters and passes over the work by a combination of vertical pressure and forward push. Exact speeds cannot be given because they will vary with the strength of the worker, condition of the file, and type of metal being cut. Most novices file far too fast.

__SAWING__ The action is similar to filing and the same general rules apply. The speed recommended for general work by the blade manufacturers is 50 strokes per minute.

__DRILLING__ The speed of drilling depends on the circumferential (i.e. peripheral) speed of the drill. In one revolution a large drill will take off more metal than a small drill, the exact amount depending on the diameter of the drill. A large drill, consequently, should travel at a slower speed than a small one. The actual cutting speeds for drilling with H.S.S. drills are the same as for turning.
Feed in drilling is the movement of the drill downwards into the metal. The feed rate increases for soft materials.

__TURNING__ The cutting speed is the speed at which the material passes over the cutting tool. This speed will depend on the circumference of the bar and the material being cut.
Large diameters are turned at a slow speed.
Hard materials are turned at a slow speed.
Feed during turning is the movement of the cutting tool along the face that is being cut. Feed rate increases for soft materials but will be dependent on the finish required and all the other conditions listed above.

Because of the number of factors that have to be taken into account in relation to cutting speed any formula from which to calculate speed can be only approximate.

CALCULATING CUTTING SPEED AND R.P.M.

Cutting speed is chiefly dependent on the circumference of the bar or drill.

The circumference of the bar in mm = $\Pi \times d$, where d = dia. of work in mm.

$$\text{Cutting Speed, S, in metres per min.} = \frac{\Pi \times d \times R.P.M.}{1000}$$

$$\therefore R.P.M. = \frac{S \times 1000}{\Pi \times d}$$

CUTTING SPEEDS
using H.S.S. Tools

MATERIAL to be CUT	CUTTING SPEED in METRES per MIN.		
	DRILLING	TURNING	SHAPING
MILD STEEL	25	30	20
HIGH CARBON STEEL	10	15	10
CAST IRON	15	15	10
STAINLESS STEEL	20	20	15
BRASS	50	60	30
COPPER	55	60	30
BRONZE	20	20	15
ALUMINIUM ALLOY	60	100	40
ZINC ALLOY	30	40	30
PLASTIC	50	50	35

The cutting speed for turning mild steel is 30 metres per minute.

$\therefore$ the R.P.M. for a 75 mm dia. bar of B.D.M.S.

$$= \frac{S \times 1000}{\Pi \times d}$$

$$= \frac{30 \times 1000}{3 \cdot 14 \times 75} = 128 \text{ approx.}$$

The speed of the machine would be set at the nearest speed to 128.

The same formula can be used for calculating the speed for drilling if "d" is allowed to represent the drill diameter instead of the work diameter.

A cutting solution or lubricant –

1. Keeps the tool cool. Excessive heat causes rapid wear of the tool and, consequently, results in the need for slower cutting speeds.

2. Prevents overheating of the work due to friction from the tool. Excessive heat causes expansion of the work resulting in inaccuracy when work is checked for size and causing undue pressure on the lathe centres.

3. Permits the use of higher cutting speeds.

4. Washes away chips or turnings.

5. Imparts a good finish.

6. Serves as a lubricant between the cutting edge of the tool and the work and between the tool face and the chip which is being removed.

A cutting solution should possess the following qualities:

1. It preferably should be clear to allow an easy view of the work being tooled. This is one disadvantage of soluble oil.

2. It should not rust the machine.

3. It must not be expensive.

4. It should not smell unpleasantly or go stale with age.

5. It must be harmless to the operator. Suitable antiseptics are available which can be added.

There are two main groups of cutting solutions.

1. STRAIGHT OILS

These are vegetable, animal or mineral oils, used either singly or mixed and sometimes with sulphur added to improve the "wetting" properties. They are usually clear and are of particular advantage where lubrication is more important than cooling effect. They are generally expensive and are often used for complex machine set-ups, eg. gear cutting where maximum life between regrinds is an advantage.

2. SOLUBLE OILS

These are usually mineral oils which can be emulsified with water. Most soluble oils or "suds" are milky white which is a disadvantage (hides the work). They are very effective as coolants, much cheaper than straight oils and allow higher cutting speeds, but they are not such good lubricants.

APPLICATION

The solution should be directed upon the cutting edge of the tool which is the place where the friction starts. Application may be by means of –
1. Brush.
2. Oilcan.
3. Drip can. This is a can attached to, and above, the carriage of a lathe and fitted with tap and feed pipe.
4. Pump. This is the most efficient method. The solution is contained in a sump and pumped directly onto the work through an adjustable pipe.

THE USE OF CUTTING SOLUTIONS ON PARTICULAR METALS

CAST IRON When C.I. is being tooled the metal breaks off in short chips which are only a short time in contact with the surface of the tool. Therefore there is less heat generated than when cutting mild steel when the shaving slides over the face of the tool and is in contact with it for a relatively long time.
A cutting solution is not usually used on C.I. because the tool will retain its cutting edge for a reasonable time without it. If a solution is used it mixes with the free carbon and tends to dull the cutting edge of the tool and spoil the surface finish.
In addition the graphite content of the C.I. acts as a lubricant itself.
Application of a cutting solution when using hand tools, eg. taps and dies, impedes the free flow of chips from the cutting edges.

BRASS and BRONZE These metals, too, when tooled, break off in small chips and, for the same reason as with C.I., there is no need for the use of a cutting solution.

ALUMINIUM is soft, has a low melting point and "pins" on the cutting edge of a tool due to friction and heat. Very often it builds up a false cutting edge that prevents efficient cutting and spoils surface finish. Very thin cutting solutions, eg. turpentine, are found to be the most effective.

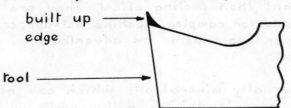

built up edge

tool

OPERATION	C.I.	M.S. and W.I	COPPER
TURNING	Dry	Soluble Oil	Soluble Oil
DRILLING	Dry	Soluble Oil	Soluble Oil
THREADING	Dry	Soluble Oil	Soluble Oil
REAMING	Dry	Soluble Oil	Soluble Oil
KNURLING	Dry	Soluble Oil	Dry or Sol. Oil

OPERATION	BRASS	ALUMINIUM	LEAD and BABBIT
TURNING	Dry	Turpentine	Dry
DRILLING	Dry	Turpentine	Soluble Oil
THREADING	Dry	Turps. or Paraffin	—
REAMING	Dry	Turps. or Paraffin	Dry
KNURLING	Dry	Turpentine	—

General Rules

The general tidiness and cleanliness of a workshop not only reflects the character of the person using it, but also helps in the prevention of accidents. Safety depends on an attitude of mind rather than a set of rules.

Workshop and personal cleanliness are "musts", e.g. patches of oil or bits of metal rod left on the floor are always a source of danger and might cause a fall onto moving parts of a machine.

Barrier cream should be used before starting any very dirty work and hands should be well washed on completion.

Minor cuts and scratches should be properly treated to prevent infection.

It is reported that many more accidents are caused by carelessness, thoughtlessness and failure to appreciate possible danger than faults in machinery, absence of guards, etc. Because of this, occasional talks on the danger of accidents are useful, particularly when it is felt that a class is getting over-confident in the use of machine tools.

Clothing

Suitable protective clothing should be worn with well-fitting sleeves and no loose cuffs. Ties should be tucked in and not allowed to flop about. Hair should be short and tidy and kept away from all moving parts of a machine.

Hand Tools

Worn spanners and worn nuts, especially on machine parts, are dangerous.

Bench shears should have some means of locking the lever to prevent the jaws operating accidentally.

Files need good handles and hammers should have secure heads.

Chisel heads must be free of burrs and, when chiselling, care is needed to ensure that chips do not fly.

Make sure that the work is securely fixed in the vice before doing any cutting.

Tools should be laid out on the bench methodically and not thrown on top of one another.

Use the correct tool for the purpose.

Machine Tools

Remember that a machine operator must know not only how to switch on a machine but also how to switch off quickly in an emergency. This action should be automatic.

Starters for machines should be fitted with a no-volt release. This is necessary to prevent the machines restarting when power is restored after a power failure.

Make no adjustments to a machine while it is running. Stop the machine first.

Guards for gear trains, belting, chucks, etc. must be in correct position before starting the machine.

Make sure the machine is set at the right speed. Too fast a speed on a long length of metal can be dangerous.

Never lean on a machine when it is running.

Beware of swarf. Never remove it while the machine is running and never pull it away by hand. Always stop the machine and brush it away. Remember it may be hot and very sharp

See that the work and cutting tool are securely fixed.

Make sure that the chuck and work clear the tool and machine before starting the machine, especially with awkward "set-ups". Pull the machine round by hand first before starting.

Never put tools on the bed or slideways of a machine.

Never leave a machine unattended while it is running.

Never leave a chuck key in a chuck.

When work is completed, put the machine in neutral with all feeds, etc., disengaged.

Grinding and Polishing

If a grindstone is not fitted with a transparent screen then goggles must be worn.

The gap between tool rest and stone must be kept small so that the work cannot be trapped between the two.

Stones, other than special ones, are not intended to take any side pressure, therefore grinding should be confined to the front face.

Always make use of the rest to support the tool.

Polishing spindles should be covered with protective sleeves when the machine is not being used. The threaded ends of the spindles are a particular source of danger.

Work must not be held in a cloth or apron when being ground or polished. There is a temptation to do this when the work gets hot, but it is most dangerous. Nothing gets caught more easily on moving parts than cloth.

WHEN WORKING ON A MACHINE, IF ANYTHING GOES WRONG, DO NOT GET FLUSTERED BUT SWITCH OFF IMMEDIATELY

Casting

Control of the pour must be in the hands of the teacher.

Pouring always should be done over sand. Any hot metal coming into contact with a cold concrete floor is liable to spit.

Pouring into a wet mould is extremely dangerous because of blow backs.

Protective clothing must be worn during the pour—asbestos gloves, goggles, aprons and spats.

Avoid using scrap metal containing magnesium. It is highly inflammable.

A high concentration of zinc fumes is dangerous.

Be sure that adequate ventilation is provided.

Forging

There should be some place in the room where hot metal can be laid to cool off. Providing a shallow sand tray is better than putting the metal on the concrete floor, ringing it with chalk and marking it "HOT". A suitable place for it is under the forge. Be sure that the air blast on the forge is not set too high or hot coke may be blown out of the hearth. Well-fitting tongs are essential for holding the metal securely and safely. Rings fitted on the reins makes holding easier.

When using oil for quenching, care is needed. A high flash point oil like whale oil should be used, not a lubricating oil. The container must be such that all the work can be immersed to prevent the oil catching fire.

Soldering, Brazing, Pickling

The acid pickle bath must be on floor level.

When mixing the fresh pickle remember that the acid must be added to the water. The bath should be provided with a lid and clearly marked "ACID".

It is not wise to dip the work when it is very hot because of the danger of spitting.

The bath should be near a sink with a supply of running water so that the work has not to be carried far for washing.

If zinc chloride is used as a flux, care is needed, particularly when cleaning the bit because it is an acid flux. A block of sal-ammonia is a less messy and safer means of cleaning the bit.

The soldering bench should not be covered with sheet metal. The fluxes cause corrosion and heavy scaling of the surface. Heating of the surface in this condition will cause particles of scale to fly.

Hard asbestos is equally dangerous because it, too, cracks and flies under localized heat.

Soft asbestos is safe but not long-lasting. The best surface is given by a special grade of asbestos, which will withstand localized heating e.g. "Sindanyo".

This same asbestos can be used to back the brazing hearth.

Notes on the Working of Stainless Steels

These notes are based on information supplied by: British Steel Corporation, Special Steels Division, Stocksbridge and Tinsley Park Works, Stocksbridge, Sheffield.

Commercial stainless steels can be ordered hot or cold-rolled and with a dull, satin or bright polish.

DESIGN CONSIDERATIONS

Cleanliness and care in handling are essential to avoid subsequent corrosion and to maintain surface finish. Unnecessary marks are slow and difficult to remove. Design the component with the minimum of corners and crevices for ease of cleaning. Avoid sharp bends and make them radiused.

BENDING AND FORMING

Bending procedure is the same as for mild steel but because of the higher mechanical properties about twice the power is needed. The austenitic forms of stainless steel bend most easily. When in a soft condition these can be bent through 180° over a radius equal to their thickness, but the metal quickly work-hardens.

CUTTING

All stainless steels can be cut in the same way as mild steel.

SAWING

Use H.S.S. blades at 50 strokes per minute and lift the blade clear on the return stroke to stop rubbing.

SPINNING

Because the metal work-hardens quickly spinning is slow and considerable power is needed. Use a hard brass tool with soap as a lubricant.

ANNEALING AND DESCALING

After work-hardening the ductility of the steel needs to be restored by annealing before further shaping can take place. Before annealing clean the surface of the metal. Dirt or grease on the surface can produce heavy local scaling. The annealing temperature is approximately 1050 °C. Soak at this temperature for a short time only and cool off quickly in cold water or an air blast. Remove the scale of iron oxide by pickling in a 10% nitric acid bath or by scouring with a suitable abrasive. Wash thoroughly afterwards.

WELDING

Stainless steel can be welded by all conventional methods except forge welding.

SOFT SOLDERING

Soft soldered joints on stainless steel are relatively weak and, where possible, should be used only as a seal. Riveting, seaming and spot welding will give added strength.

Before soldering, roughen the surfaces to be tinned with a file or abrasive paper. The flux can be a proprietary one, e.g. Frysol Stainless Steel Fluid or a workshop flux of zinc chloride in 50% hydrochloric acid or a 50% solution of phosphoric acid and water.

The solder can be standard 50-50 tinman's solder. Apply heat by means of a bit, bunsen, blowlamp or blowpipe. Pre-tinning of the surfaces is recommended. The thermal conductivity of stainless steel is low so the soldering must be done slowly. Scrub away the residual flux with soap and water or an alkaline wash.

SILVER SOLDERING AND BRAZING

When silver soldering or brazing, strong joints are obtained only with difficulty because of the formation of a tough oxide film. The oxide is most troublesome when heating is prolonged or the parts over-heated. Under these conditions borax begins to break down. Use a Johnson Matthey stainless steel flux or, better still, Tenacity No. 5. This has a higher melting temperature than Easy Flo and has the ability to act well at high temperatures as well as during long jointing operations.

MACHINING

Generally speaking stainless steels are more difficult to machine than carbon and low alloy steels. Special machining grades are manufactured having a small proportion of sulphur and molybdenum to improve their machining qualities. Tools must be kept sharp and must not rub on the surface of the workpiece. This causes work-hardening of the surface. Tools must be well supported with the minimum amount of overhang and side clearance angles kept small. For general machining a nose radius of about 1 millimetre is recommended.

Turning Speeds using H.S.S. Tools.
Roughing—18 metres/min.
Finishing—24 metres/min.

HAND TAPPING

H.S.S. taps are much more effective than H.C.S. and they must be sharp. Drill a hole as large as possible to give not more than 75% depth of thread. Avoid blind holes and use a sulphurized oil diluted with paraffin as a cutting solution.

DRILLING

Avoid heavy centre punching and use short H.S.S. drills. The point angle should be ground to approximately 130° and larger sizes web thinned. Mounting must be rigid and the cut uniform and continuous. Use soluble oil as a cutting solution and withdraw the drill frequently when drilling deep holes. Cutting speed should be 15 metres per minute.

POLISHING

Protect the surface of sheet with paper pasted on before starting work. This will enable marking out to be done more easily and the surface condition will be maintained.

The abrasive must be free of iron in order to avoid contamination and rusting of the surface. For the same reason, never use a mop that has previously been used for polishing mild steel. Start with a felt or stitched calico mop coated with glue and rolled in grit spread out on paper. The starting grit will depend on the surface condition of the metal. Avoid finishing in exactly the same direction. Arrange that successive grinding or polishing is made at an angle to the previous one. In this way the surface condition of the metal will more readily be seen. Unless the surface is badly marked, use 80 grit to start with, followed by 120. This will produce a dull polished finish. For finer finishes use 180 or 220 grit followed by polishing compositions such as Cannings SS White No. 1472 or "Steelax" Green No. 500 X.

APPENDIX 2

RECOMMENDED METRIC SIZES OF METAL

NON-FERROUS BARS, Aluminium; aluminium alloys; copper; copper alloys; nickel; nickel alloys.
B.S. 4229 1967

	3	3.2	4	5	5.5	6	7	8	9	10	11	12	13	14	16	17	18	19	20	22	24	25
●		•	•	•	•	•	•	•	•			•		•	•		•		•	•	•	•
■		•				•		•				•		•	•				•	•		•
⬡			•	•	•	•	•	•	•	•	•	•	•	•		•		•		•	•	•

FERROUS BARS

B.S. 4229 1969

TYPE		5	5.5	6	7	8	9	10	11	12	13	14	15	16	17	18	19	20	21	22	23	24	25
Hot rolled non-alloy steel	●			•		•		•		•								•					•
	■				•	•	•	•	•	•	•	•		•	•		•		•		•	•	
	⬡					•	•	•	•	•	•			•				•		•		•	•
Non-alloy bright steel	●	+		+		+		+	+		+	•	•	•	•	•	•	•	•	•	•	•	
	■	+		+		+		+	+	•	•	•		•		•		•		•		•	
	⬡					+		+		•	•	•		•				•		•		•	•
Stainless steel	●	•		•	•	•	•	•	•	•	•	•		•	•	•	•	•	•	•	•	•	
	■	•	•	•	•	•	•	•	•	•	•	•	•	•	•	•	•	•	•	•	•	•	•
	⬡					•	•	•	•	•	•	•		•				•		•		•	•

FERROUS and NON-FERROUS SHEET, WIRE and STRIP

B.S. 4391 1969
Wire sizes are customarily limited to those having diameter of 13.5 mm and below.

	0.020	0.025	0.030	0.032	0.040	0.050	0.060	0.063	0.080	0.100	0.120	0.125	0.165	0.200	0.250	0.300	0.315	0.400	0.500	0.600	0.630	0.800	1.00	1.25	1.60	2.00	2.50	3.15	4.00	5.00	6.30	8.00	10.00
Wire	•	•		•	•	•			•	•		•	•	•	•		•	•			•	•	•	•	•	•	•	•	•	•	•	•	•
Sheet Strip	•	•	•		•	•	•		•	•	•	•	•	•	•	•	•	•	•	•	•	•	•	•	•	•	•	•				•	•

+ Provisional

SILVER STEEL
B.S. 4391 1969

Round	0·5 mm dia. to 20·0 mm dia. in steps of 0·5 mm.
	20·0 mm dia to 40·0 mm dia. in steps of 1·0 mm.

Square	3·0 mm a/f to 20·0 mm a/f in steps of 1·0 mm.

ALUMINIUM and ALUMINIUM ALLOYS
B.S. 1470

Sheet   1000 x 2000 mm and 1250 x 2500 mm in thicknesses from 0·5 mm to 3 mm.
Definition - a cold rolled product of rectangular section supplied flat in all available conditions.

Strip   500 mm, 1000 mm and 1250 mm widths in thicknesses from 0·25 mm to 2·0 mm.
Definition - a cold rolled product of rectangular section supplied in coil over 0·2 mm thick but not exceeding 3 mm thick.

Hot rolled plate   3 mm to 16 mm thick and up in multiples of 10 or 100.
Definition - a hot rolled product of rectangular section over 3 mm thick supplied flat in a variety of conditions and with less control of surface finish and tolerances than applies to sheet.

Cold rolled plate   3 mm to 12 mm thick.
Definition - a cold rolled product of rectangular section supplied flat in a variety of conditions with better surface finish and normally to closer tolerances than the hot rolled plate.

COMPARISON of METRIC and IMPERIAL SIZES of WIRE and SHEET

Round sections	mm	3·15	4·00	5·00	6·30	8·00	10·0	11·2	12·5	16
	imperial unit	$\frac{1}{8}$	$\frac{5}{32}$	$\frac{3}{16}$	$\frac{1}{4}$	$\frac{5}{16}$	$\frac{3}{8}$	$\frac{7}{16}$	$\frac{1}{2}$	$\frac{5}{8}$

Round wire	mm	0·80	1·00	1·25	1·6	2·0	2·5	3·15
	I.S.W.G.	22	20	18	16	14	12	10

Sheet	mm	0·40	0·50	0·60	0·80	1·00	1·2	1·6	2·0	2·5	3
	I.S.W.G	28	26	24	22	20	18	16	14	12	10

The examination questions have been so selected and arranged that they more than cover the various G.C.E. syllabuses. If a pupil works through these questions during the course he will have completed the theory needed for these examinations. Questions that often give some trouble, *e.g.*, twist drill grinding angles, hardening and casehardening, etc., are intentionally repeated in varying forms for revision purposes.

The following abbreviations for the various Examining Boards have been used :

AEB	Associated Examining Board.	*SCE*	Scottish Certificate of Education.
CSE	Certificate of Secondary Education (Southern Regional Examinations Board)	*SUJB*	Southern Universities' Joint Board.
		UC	University of Cambridge
OCSEB	Oxford and Cambridge Schools Examination Board.	*UEI*	Union of Educational Institutions
		UL	University of London.
OLE	Oxford Local Examinations.	*WJEC*	Welsh Joint Education Committee.

Note: Imperial terms and quantities have been metricated.

Materials

1. (*a*) State, with reasons, the materials you would recommend for making the following: (*i*) a spanner, (*ii*) an oilcan, (*iii*) the body of a water tap, (*iv*) the bit of a soldering iron, (*v*) a marking out table.
   (*b*) Describe in detail how you would make No. (*i*) or No. (*ii*). (*AEB*)
2. Write a brief account of the manufacture of one of the following materials and state the forms in which it may be obtained for use in the workshop: (*a*) foundry cast iron (from pig iron), (*b*) mild steel, (*c*) carbon tool steel. (*AEB*)
3. (*a*) If the following materials were heated, in what order would they melt? Copper, aluminium, soft solder, zinc, tin and lead.
   (*b*) What happens when the following metals are brought to a red heat and hammered? Copper, mild steel, cast iron. (*UEI*)
4. What are the constituents of brass and bronze? Name the important differences and give uses for each alloy. (*UEI*)
5. You have been asked to sort out a heap of scrap metal containing cast iron, cast steel, mild steel, brass, lead, copper, bronze and aluminium. How would you identify each metal? (*UEI*)
6. (*a*) What is an element, a ferrous metal and a non-ferrous metal?
   (*b*) Name two metallic elements and two alloys and give their general properties. (*UEI*)
7. Write notes on the common properties of metals. What particular properties are desirable in metals for making rivets, wire and soldering irons?
8. How would you distinguish between the following types of irons and steels? Mild steel, high carbon steel, wrought iron, cast iron and high speed steel. (*AEB*)
9. Give brief descriptions of the properties and uses of any four of the following materials: malleable cast iron, mild steel, duralumin, carbon steel, brass, chilled cast iron. (*AEB*)
10. Describe one method of steel production from the 'pig iron' stage. Sketch the type of furnace used. (*AEB*)

11. (*a*) State the type of furnace used to produce each of the following materials: mild steel, pig iron, cast iron. Make a simple sectional sketch of one of these furnaces.
    (*b*) Make sketches of, and name, four bright rolled steel sections in common use. (*AEB*)
12. Describe the characteristics of (*a*) cast iron, (*b*) malleable cast iron. Show how malleable cast iron is produced and give the main reason for its manufacture. (*AEB*)
13. Give the composition of (*a*) soft solder, (*b*) silver solder, (*c*) brazing spelter. Explain a use for each, naming the metal and flux used. (*AEB*)
14. Explain clearly what is meant by each of the following terms applied to metals: tensile strength, shear strength, malleability and ductility.
    (*a*) Using these terms compare the mechanical properties of three of the following materials: grey cast iron, copper, hardened H.C.S. and annealed H.C.S.
    (*b*) Give three examples to show how the selection of a material for a specific workshop application is governed by the above properties. (*AEB*)
15. What are the differences in composition between:
    (*a*) phosphor bronze and brass,
    (*b*) wrought iron and cast iron,
    (*c*) tool steel and mild steel?
    Give one example of an article made from each of these metals with a reason for the choice. (*WJEC*)
16. Write down the name of the metal you would use to make: (*a*) a tap wrench, (*b*) a cold chisel, (*c*) a nut and bolt. (*CSE*)
17. Write down the metal you would use to make: (*a*) a scriber, (*b*) a small bowl to hold sweets or pins, (*c*) a poker, (*d*) the base of a scribing block or surface gauge. (*CSE*)
18. Name three alloys which contain two or more of the following metals: copper, tin, zinc, lead. (*CSE*)

Benchwork and tools

1. What is a piercing saw? How is it used? What precautions would you take in fitting the blade and using the saw? (*UEI*)

2. Sketch an adjustable hacksaw showing two different types of handle. What provision is usually made to enable long narrow strips to be cut? (*UEI*)

3. Describe the common types of hacksaw blades. How is the length of the blade measured? What kind of blade would you use for cutting (*a*) tool steel rod, (*b*) aluminium, (*c*) tube?

4. What is a tension file? How can it be fastened in a hacksaw frame?

5. What precautions should be observed when fitting a hacksaw blade to the frame? Explain what is meant by the 'set' of a saw blade and illustrate your answer. What is the difference in technique between sawing a thin tube and sawing solid bar? (*AEB*)

6. Write an account of the construction and uses of an engineer's try-square. How would you test such a square for accuracy? (*AEB*)

7. For what particular purposes are the following tools used? (*a*) Engineer's square, (*b*) centre square, (*c*) adjustable bevel.
Sketch them. How would you check an engineer's square for accuracy? (*UEI*)

8. (*a*) What is a dot punch, centre punch and pin punch?
(*b*) What metal would you suggest for making these tools and what treatment would you give it?

9. Describe the various types of hammer used in the workshop. Explain how the shaft is fitted to the head. What materials are they made of? (*UEI*)

10. What is (*a*) a bossing mallet, (*b*) a tinman's boxwood mallet, (*c*) a rawhide mallet?

11. Make sketches of (*a*) a parallel jaw engineer's vice, (*b*) a leg vice, (*c*) a machine vice.
Your sketches should show, as far as possible, their construction.

12. What is the purpose of a scraper? Sketch a flat, triangular and half round scraper, describing the uses of each. How would you sharpen and use a flat scraper?

13. One outer face of a 100 x 75 x 75 mm cast iron angle plate is to be hand scraped flat.
(*a*) Sketch a suitable type of scraper. Name the scraper and show clearly the form of the cutting edges.
(*b*) How are these cutting edges prepared and maintained?
(*c*) What method can be used to indicate where metal must be removed by the scraper. (*AEB*)

14. (*a*) Sketch the underside of a surface plate and state the reason for its particular construction.
(*b*) Sketch a scribing block and a vee block. Show how they may be used to find the centre of a round bar of steel of 40 mm dia. (*AEB*)

15. Sketch and describe a surface gauge or scribing block explaining clearly some of its uses. (*UEI*)

16. What are the main uses of a surface plate? Describe one and discuss the precautions necessary in its use. (*UEI*)

17. (*a*) Describe, with sketches, how the scriber is locked to the spindle of a surface gauge.
(*b*) What is a marking out table?

18. Sketch a vee block and describe two of its uses. (*UEI*)

19. Sketch an angle plate and describe two of its uses. (*UEI*)

20. List the precautions you would take when threading a blind hole in mild steel.

21. Write notes on the following: (*a*) tapping size, (*b*) clearance size, (*c*) pitch, (*d*) lead.

22. You have broken a 6 mm tap in a blind hole. Give possible reasons for its breakage and suggest methods of removing it. (*UEI*)

23. Sketch two types of adjustable die holder, showing clearly the method of adjustment. (*UEI*)

24. Stamped upon a die is "M 14 x 2". What does this mean? Why is each size of die usually accompanied by three taps? (*UEI*)

25. Sketch and describe a set of taps and a tap wrench. What precautions are necessary when tapping a blind hole?

26. Discuss the following failures, give likely causes and any obvious remedies: (*a*) a stripped thread, (*b*) a tap broken in the work, (*c*) a drill broken in the work, (*d*) the point of a scriber blunting off quickly. (*AEB*)

27. Draw an enlarged section of the following: (*a*) a tap, (*b*) a reamer, (*c*) a twist drill.

28. Give details of three different types of spanner. If you wished to make a 6 mm open ended spanner what width would you make the slot?
What metal would you use and what treatment would you give it?

29. What is (*a*) a die nut, (*b*) a castle nut, (*c*) a lock nut?

30. What is the purpose of a hand reamer? Explain in detail how it should be used and the precautions you would take. (*UEI*)

31. Sketch one type of lever bench shears showing clearly the action of the levers. (*UEI*)

32. Sketch and describe four different kinds of metalwork chisels, explaining the purpose of each. What metal is used in their manufacture and what treatment is the metal given?

33. Write notes on files giving details of shape, size, gradings, etc. Of what materials are the file, the handle and ferrule made?

34. Sketch six different kinds of tinmans' stakes and explain the purpose of each.

35. The following tools are used in sheet metalwork. Make a sketch of them, to include approximate dimensions, and explain their uses.
(*a*) bick iron, (*b*) creasing iron, (*c*) planishing hammer. (*UEI*)

36. Sketch a hatchet and straight soldering iron. What are the "bits" made of and why? Give one example where a hatchet iron would be an advantage. (*UEI*)

37. (*a*) Make sketches, in good proportion, of four types of rivet used in metalwork. Indicate the nominal length of the rivet in each case. Give an example of the use of each type of rivet.
(*b*) Describe, with the aid of sketches, the process of hand riveting for one of these types of rivet. Name the tools used.
(*c*) Name three materials used in rivet making. What properties are essential in the materials used? (*AEB*)

38. Sketch any form of hand vice with which you are acquainted. Give the details of its construction and name metals of which the different parts are made. (*UL*)

39. Describe, stage by stage, how to make a soldering iron. Give reasons for choosing the metals you would use. Illustrate your answer. (*UL*)

40. Sketch, approximately full size, a centre square. Describe, stage by stage, with sketches where necessary, the procedure to be followed in making the centre square. (*UL*)

41. Draw, approx. full size, a full set of 12 mm taps, naming each tap. Use a practical example to explain why three taps are necessary for each size of thread. (*UC*)

42. Discuss the use of hacksaw blades in relation to the metal to be sawn.

Explain the terms "kerf" and "set" in relation to hacksawing. How is the set produced on (*a*) coarse tooth blades and (*b*) fine tooth blades? (*SUJB*)

43. Make a drawing to show full details of an ISO metric thread.

Explain the difference between pitch and lead.

44. Compare and contrast the following:

(*a*) Surface plate and levelling plate.

(*b*) Smith's drift and drill drift.

(*c*) Pin punch and centre punch. (*SUJB*)

45. Show how two of the following tools or pieces of equipment are constructed:

(*a*) Toolmakers' clamp.

(*b*) A jig to bend numbers of light section bars or rods to the same pattern.

(*c*) A cutter to make up to 50 mm diameter holes in sheet metal.

(*d*) The nozzle of a brazing hearth blow pipe using gas and air. (*OCSEB*)

46. State the purpose, and make clear sketches, of three of the following tools: (*a*) tinman's snips, (*b*) piercing saw, (*c*) folding bars, (*d*) half moon stake. (*OLE*)

47. What information is required when ordering hacksaw blades? Why is there a variety of blades available for general use? What do you take as a general guide in selecting a blade for a particular job? State three precautions to be observed if good service is to be obtained from a hacksaw blade. (*OLE*)

48. Make carefully drawn sketches and describe the uses of any three of the following: (*a*) a pair of inside callipers, (*b*) a raising hammer, (*c*) a creasing iron, (*d*) a drawplate. (*WJEC*)

49. (*a*) Make sectional profile sketches of any three of the following screw threads, indicating, in each case, the angle and a suitable use to which the threads are put:

(*i*) ISO metric,

(*ii*) Acme,

(*iii*) Buttress,

(*iv*) Square.

(*b*) Explain how you would drill and tap a 6 mm thread into a piece of 12 mm thick mild steel plate. (*WJEC*)

50. Describe, naming the equipment used, three different methods of marking off the centre at each end of a 75 mm dia. bar about 250 mm long. (*WJEC*)

51. (*a*) Make a sketch of a simple adjustable spanner.

(*b*) Insert four important dimensions.

(*c*) Tabulate a list of the material required to make this spanner. (*SCE*)

52. When would you use a "tap wrench"? (*CSE*)

53. Make a simple freehand sketch of a "set screw" and a "grub screw". (*CSE*)

54. Name two small hand tools used for holding metal while work (*e.g.*, filing or drilling) is being done upon it. (*CSE*)

55. What do you understand by the following:

(*a*) B.D.M.S., (*b*) I S O, (*c*) N.T.S.? (*CSE*)

56. Explain with the aid of sketches how you would use a surface gauge, or scribing block to mark off the position of a hole which has to be drilled central and true across the diameter of a 25 mm diameter bar of mild steel. (*CSE*)

57. Why are vice clamps used? Give an example of when you would use them. (*CSE*)

58. Mention two types of bench vice usually found in a school workshop. List some of their differences. (*CSE*)

59. What is the purpose of the ball pane of an engineer's hammer? (*CSE*)

60. Name four essentials which must be stated when ordering rivets. (*CSE*)

61. What is meant by the term "safe edge" of a file? What use is made of this; give one example? (*CSE*)

62. A planishing hammer usually has one flat and one slightly convex face. Why is this? (*CSE*)

63. Make sketches and explain how you would set to size and use: (*a*) a pair of outside callipers, (*b*) a pair of inside callipers, (*c*) a pair of odd leg callipers. (*CSE*)

64. Make sketches of: (*a*) an open ended spanner, (*b*) one type of adjustable spanner. Your drawings should show clearly how the adjustment for size is made. (*CSE*)

65. Give the full names for the following abbreviations and an example of each to show its use: W.I., H.S.S., C.S., B.D.M.S. (*CSE*)

66. Name six tools you have used when "marking out". (*CSE*)

Measurement and Inspection

1. Explain the construction and use of a micrometer and give any precautions necessary to ensure an accurate reading. Sketch the micrometer readings for (*a*) 5.13 mm and (*b*) 5.31 mm. (*AEB*)

2. Describe four methods of finding the centre of the end of a round rod. (*UEI*)

3. Describe how a metric micrometer works. Sketch part of one showing a reading of 10.33 mm.

4. Explain the principle of the metric vernier. Draw part of one showing a reading of 8.21 mm.

5. Why are limit gauges used? Sketch two types of limit gauges and state suitable metals from which they could be made. (*AEB*)

6. Sketch, describe and give the uses of six different kinds of gauges.

7. Sketch and describe the following: (a) buttress thread, (b) plug tap, (c) plug and ring gauge, (d) double-ended limit plug gauge, (e) flat scraper, (f) dial indicator.
(AEB)

8. What is meant by a vernier scale? Sketch a vernier calliper reading to 0.02 mm and show on your sketch the vernier set to a reading of 6.34 mm.
(AEB)

9. (a) State the principle upon which the micrometer is based. Sketch a type of internal micrometer.

(b) Explain how you would drill a number of blind holes of equal depth.
(AEB)

10. What is the purpose of a height gauge? Sketch one. What provision is made to allow the gauge to be adjusted or set to fine limits?

11. Make twice full size a drawing of a vernier calliper measuring a cylindrical rod 26.12 mm diameter to show clearly that you know how to read the instrument.
(UL)

12. Sketch and describe three different tools that are used to measure internal diameters. State which you consider to be the most accurate and give your reasons.
(WJEC)

13. (a) Make a sketch in good proportion of a 0-25 mm micrometer and name all the principle parts.

(b) It is required to measure a bar 21 mm in diameter using a 0-1 inch micrometer. What should be the reading if 25.4 mm equals one inch?

(c) What is the use of the ratchet?

(d) Why is it considered bad practice to lock a micrometer spindle and then use the instrument as a gap gauge?
(WJEC)

14. A batch of pins has been turned to 20 mm $\pm$ 0.04 mm.

(a) Make a neat sketch, in good proportion, of a suitable limit gauge for checking the pins and insert the important dimensions.

(b) Make a sketch showing the mean dimension as a reading on a 0-25 mm micrometer.

(c) What feature of the pins, apart from the length, cannot be checked by either the limit gauge or the micrometer?
(WJEC)

15. If you were making the stock of a try square from 20 mm x 9 mm bright drawn mild steel, how would you check the two opposite faces for flatness and parallelism?
(CSE)

Processes

1. Describe, in detail, how you would harden and temper a cold chisel, giving your reasons for the various processes you describe.
(AEB)

2. A friend brings you a small cold chisel. He complains that it is easily blunted. Give possible reasons and explain in detail how you would correct the fault.
(UEI)

3. A rod of cast steel (about 12 mm dia. and 200 mm long) is found after hardening to be bent. Describe your method of softening, straightening and rehardening the rod to avoid this trouble.
(UEI)

4. Explain the instruction "temper to a dark straw". What is the function of the colour? Would it be possible to temper without it?
(UEI)

5. Distinguish between the following: (a) hardening and casehardening, (b) soft soldering and hard soldering, (c) annealing and normalizing, (d) silver soldering and brazing.

6. Write notes on (a) casehardening, (b) normalizing, (c) annealing tool steel, aluminium, brass and copper.

7. Explain tempering. How does the tempering process vary for each of the tools named and why? Scriber, cold chisel, screwdriver and spring.
(AEB)

8. Describe the blacksmith's method of producing a hole through a piece of metal by punching. Sketch the punch.
(UEI)

9. Sketch a blacksmith's hardie and flatter and explain their uses.
(UEI)

10. Use simple sketches to show how an eye may be forged on the end of a piece of 6 mm dia. mild steel rod. What length of metal is needed for a 25 mm inside diameter eye?
(UEI)

11. With the aid of sketches (where possible) describe five of the following: (a) drawing down, (b) upsetting, (c) blacksmith's weld, (d) fullering, (e) swaging, (f) tinning, (g) sweating, (h) shrinking.
(AEB)

12. Explain and show the steps in the construction of the following: (a) a safe edge, (b) a lap seam, (c) a wired edge.

13. Describe in detail your method of joining two pieces of tinplate by means of (a) a grooved seam, (b) a lapped and soldered joint.
(UEI)

14. Soft soldering flux is obtainable in the form of a liquid or a paste. What are the important differences between them? Give examples of their different uses.
(UEI)

15. What is the composition of soft solder? Explain the purpose of a soldering iron and a flux. What is sweating?
(UEI)

16. What are the measures necessary to ensure a successful soft soldered joint? What is the purpose of a flux? List some fluxes and the metals for which they are suitable.

17. How would you (a) "tin a bit"; (b) remedy a "burnt iron". What causes a burnt iron? (c) sweat a joint; (d) clean work after soldering?

18. Make a sectional sketch through two strips of copper 25 mm wide and 6 mm thick which have been sweated together. Show on the section what has made the solder unite with the copper. Label the parts.
(UEI)

19. Metals may be joined by hard soldering and soft soldering. Describe each process and say under what circumstances each would be used. Why are fluxes used? Name four of them and state the metals for which each is suitable.
(AEB)

20. Sketch and give the uses of as many rivets as you can. What metals are they made of? Describe your method of fixing a snap head rivet. Explain the faults possible in riveting and precautions necessary to avoid them.
(AEB)

21. How would you prepare and braze two pieces of mild steel to form a "T"?

22. What is a centre punch and what are the reasons for centre punching? How would you centre punch correctly?

23. Sketch and describe a flat chisel. Write notes, with sketches, on the ways in which a flat chisel may be used.

24. Draw about a 50 mm length of the cutting ends of chisels which can be used to:

(*a*) cut a piece of 75 x 25 x 3 mm M.S. along its length,

(*b*) rough out the corners of a square hole which is already drilled,

(*c*) pull back a centre which has wandered when starting drilling. (*UEI*)

25. The following terms apply to threads. What do they mean? (*a*) pitch, (*b*) lead, (*c*) nominal diameter, (*d*) core diameter.

Why is a tapping drill not the same as the core diameter for any particular thread?

26. Describe how you would thread an 8 mm rod of M.S. with a 50 mm long metric thread, emphasizing the precautions you would observe. What difference would there be if the rod were brass? Why is it usual to use the tap before the die?

27. A blind hole 20 mm deep in a mild steel block has to be tapped M 6 x 1 mm. How would you proceed to do it? What precautions are necessary?

28. Explain carefully how you would make a rectangular slot 40 x 6 mm in a piece of steel 3 mm thick. (*UEI*)

29. Describe with sketches the marking out, cutting and filing to shape of a 25 mm square hole in a piece of mild steel 50 x 50 x 6 mm. (*UEI*)

30. Describe how you would accurately mark out, set up and drill an 18 mm hole in a block of M.S. 100 x 50 x 12 mm.

31. How would you accurately mark out, set up and drill a 12 mm hole diametrically through a 50 mm diameter bar of M.S.?

32. (*a*) Describe, with the aid of sketches, a method of marking off the centre lines of holes on the vertical face of a casting by means of a scribing block and surface plate.

(*b*) A gunmetal casting (with rough surfaces) in the shape of a 50 mm square prism 75 mm long is to be finished flat at one square end. Describe how this operation would be performed using hand tools only. (*AEB*)

33. Explain, with sketches, how you would make a slot hole, with radiused ends, 25 x 6 mm through the centre of a mild steel bar 150 mm long and 30 mm diameter. (*AEB*)

34. Set out in tabulated form, and using sketches, the stages involved in making a small ashtray in copper.

35. (*a*) Why is annealing necessary when copper and gilding metal is being shaped?

(*b*) What are the uses of a pickle bath? What chemicals does it contain?

(*c*) Why is it usual to planish articles made of copper?

(*d*) Why is flux necessary in silver soldering? How is excess flux removed? (*UEI*)

36. When some metals are hammered they become hard and brittle. Explain how you would overcome this difficulty when working in aluminium, brass and carbon steel. Examples of work in these metals must be given. What name is given to this operation? (*UEI*)

37. Explain the differences between the processes of hollowing and raising. Give an example of one piece of work that would be formed by hollowing and one that would be formed by raising.

38. In note form, with sketches, describe how you would cast an aluminium disc 75 mm diameter by 25 mm thick.

39. For what purpose are cores used when casting? Describe, with sketches, how a core is made and used.

40. A casting is imperfect because of sand inclusions and blowholes. Discuss the possible causes.

41. Explain what is meant by each of the following terms as applied to the production of castings: (*a*) pouring gate and feeding gate, (*b*) runner, (*c*) core print. Why is it sometimes necessary to use split patterns? (*AEB*)

42. What are the main properties and uses of cast iron? State the precautions that should be taken: (*a*) when designing, and (*b*) when manufacturing, a casting to prevent possible failure in use. (*AEB*)

43. Explain clearly what is meant by three of the following as used in foundry work: (*a*) cope and drag, (*b*) runner, riser and vent, (*c*) solid and split patterns, (*d*) cores and core prints. Use sketches to clarify your answers. (*AEB*)

44. Explain any four of the following terms used in metal workshop practice: between centres, chucking piece, drawing down, sweating, alignment, planishing. Use sketches where necessary. (*UL*)

45. A hexagonal hole with sides 25 mm long has to be cut in a piece of 5 mm thick mild steel, 100 mm square. Describe clearly how you would set out the hexagon and how you would cut the hole. (*UL*)

46. In what kind of work would each of the following processes be employed: tempering, riveting, case-hardening, knurling, boring, moulding, annealing? Describe briefly two of the processes. (*UL*)

47. Assuming that you have to make a cast iron rectangular base for a scribing block by hand methods:

(*a*) Sketch and describe the methods you would use to obtain a flat surface to the base. A filed finish is not acceptable.

(*b*) Make clear sketches of the special tools you would use. (*UC*)

48. Sketch and describe two methods of making a 12 mm square hole through a mild steel bar of section 30 x 8 mm. One of the methods you describe must be a forging method. (*UC*)

49. (*a*) Describe, with sketches, the stages in tapping a blind hole.

(*b*) What is meant by (*i*) tapping size, (*ii*) clearance size, (*iii*) nominal size? (*UC*)

50. Explain, in detail, naming any other tools or equipment you would need, how you would use a surface gauge (scribing block) for the following purposes:

(*a*) "centring" a piece of round rod in preparation for turning between centres,

(*b*) "setting out" a 25 mm square hole to be cut through a 75 mm square plate, with its edges parallel to the sides of the plate. (*UL*)

51. Show by simple, but reasonably accurate, sketches, the forms to which you would grind (*a*) a flat cold chisel, (*b*) a centre punch, (*c*) a scriber point, (*d*) a screwdriver. How would you avoid 'drawing the temper' of these tools using a dry emery wheel? (*UC*)

52. The following three forms of rivet are commonly used: snap head, countersunk head and flat head. Describe, with the aid of sketches, the correct method of closing each type of rivet and give an example of one use of each. (*UC*)

53. What do you understand by case-hardening? Describe with sketches how the process of case-hardening may be carried out in the school workshop and give two examples where it is used. (*UL*)

54. Describe three of the following processes used for finished metalwork, giving one example of the use of each: (*a*) armour bright, (*b*) anodizing, (*c*) scraper finish, (*d*) colouring of copper, (*e*) galvanizing, (*f*) blue finish on steel. (*UC*)

55. Metals and alloys become work—or age—hardened. Name and describe suitable treatment to render each of the following workable again: copper, zinc, duralumin, brass. (*UC*)

56. (*a*) Show, with the aid of a sketch, a typical small two-part moulding box (or snap flask) used for simple casting and name the parts.

(*b*) Make a sectional sketch of the moulding box with a simple pattern in position. Explain why an upper and a lower portion is necessary. (*UC*)

57. (*a*) Compare the processes of annealing mild steel, copper and aluminium with a gas blow torch.

(*b*) Use a practical example to explain why oil is sometimes used instead of water when quenching tool steel during the hardening process.

(*c*) Explain the term 'work hardened' and give two practical examples which illustrate the usefulness of retaining metal in its work-hardened state. (*UC*)

58. In the process of hardening and tempering cast steel articles, explain how to produce (*a*) a uniform temper throughout and (*b*) a temper at one end only. Describe how to harden and temper a screwdriver with one heating and how to harden and temper a dowel plate. (*SUJB*)

59. Differentiate between soft-soldering and hard-soldering. What are the important factors ensuring a sound joint in each case? (*OCSEB*)

60. Describe in detail three of the following processes: (*a*) annealing, (*b*) knurling, (*c*) upsetting or jumping up, (*d*) reaming. (*OCSEB*)

61. Sketch a simple screwdriver which could be made in your school workshop and describe carefully how you would make it. Which parts need hardening and tempering? Explain exactly how you would do this. (*OLE*)

62. Explain each of the following processes or operations and state for what purpose each is used: (*a*) tinning, (*b*) planishing, (*c*) countersinking, (*d*) blueing. (*OLE*)

63. (*a*) Name three advantages of aluminium over the other non-ferrous metals used in the workshop.

(*b*) Two pieces of aluminium are to be jointed. How would you make this joint?

(*c*) Describe the procedure in annealing aluminium (*SCE*)

64. Make labelled sketches to explain what is meant in tinplate work, by: (*a*) a safe edge or beaded edge (*b*) a wired edge. (*CSE*)

65. Name one permanent joint and one temporary joint used in metalworking. (*CSE*)

66. What material would you: (*a*) case harden, (*b*) harden and temper? (*CSE*)

67. Which tool or appliance would you use to provide the heat when you were: (*a*) silver soldering a joint in 0.9 mm copper, (*b*) soft soldering a joint in tinplate? (*CSE*)

68. Four identical copper washers are required in the science laboratory. Explain how you would make them from 1.5 mm copper sheet. The internal diameter is to be 25 mm and the external diameter 50 mm. (*CSE*)

69. Explain briefly the following forging terms: (*a*) drawing down, (*b*) upsetting or jumping up. (*CSE*)

70. Name the tools used to cut a thread in a drilled hole. Name them in the order in which they would be used if the hole was a "blind" one. (*CSE*)

71. You are required to make from 0.9 mm copper sheet a small bowl, 50 mm high and 125 mm in diameter. Explain in detail all the steps you would take to complete this. Tabulate your answer and illustrate with sketches. (*CSE*)

72. Two pieces of metal have to be joined together by means of rivets. Explain how you would do this:

(*a*) to produce a flush finish, (*b*) so that the rivet heads protrude above the metal. Sketch any special tool that you would use to close the rivets. (*CSE*)

73. Explain in detail how you would cut, by hand methods, a 10 mm thread on the end of a bar of mild steel. Make a sketch of the tool you would use to make the thread. (*CSE*)

74. Make a list of the points you would consider when designing a small shovel for general household use. Sketch a suitable one. (*CSE*)

75. Design a pulley extractor which will remove pulleys of diameter 75 to 150 mm from shafting. You are to make use of the fact that the shaft ends are usually centre drilled. (*CSE*)

76. What is meant by annealing? How would you anneal aluminium? (*CSE*)

77. Explain the need for "draft" on patterns used in casting. (*CSE*)

Machine tools

Coolants

1. Name two metals that require a lubricant when being drilled and one metal that can be drilled dry. Suggest a suitable lubricant in each case and explain its purpose. What might happen if the metals were drilled dry? (*UEI*)

2. (*a*) Some metals need a lubricant or coolant for machining, others do not. Explain this with reference to particular metals.

(*b*) Why is it necessary for a power drill to have a range of speeds? (*AEB*)

3. Distinguish clearly between the action of a coolant and a lubricant. Give workshop examples of the functions being carried out separately and being carried out together. On what principle does a lubricant operate? (*SUJB*)

1. Explain the terms "rake" and "clearance" when applied to turning tools. Sketch a tool suitable for turning mild steel bar and give approximate values of the various angles that should be ground on it.   (*AEB*)

2. Sketch a side cutting tool, showing clearly the rake and clearance angles. How do these angles become altered when the tool is not set at centre height?

3. Sketch a parting tool, knife tool and round nose tool. Indicate the different rake and clearance angles necessary for cutting mild steel, brass and aluminium.
(*AEB*)

4. Sketch and describe the following lathe tools and state the purpose for which each is used. What metals would be suitable for them?
    (*a*) boring tool, (*b*) parting tool, (*c*) knife tool, (*d*) lathe steady.   (*AEB*)

5. (*a*) Show on diagrams the rake and clearance angles necessary on a lathe tool.
    (*b*) With the help of diagrams describe two methods of taper turning.   (*AEB*)

6. What is meant by the terms "rake" and "clearance" as applied to cutting edges?
    (*a*) Show, with the aid of sketches, how and why these angles vary for three of the following materials: brass, cast iron, tool steel, mild steel, aluminium.
    (*b*) How does an error in setting a lathe tool to centre height affect these angles?   (*AEB*)

7. (*a*) How would you ensure that a lathe tool is set to the correct height?
    (*b*) What provision is sometimes made to allow large pieces of work to be turned on a lathe?

8. Sketch and describe the construction of a three-jaw concentric chuck. If the three-jaws are taken out, how would you replace them correctly? What provision is made to allow large stock to be gripped?

9. Explain what a four-jaw chuck is and how it works. Describe a turning operation using a four-jaw chuck.

10. What is the purpose of a faceplate? Sketch and describe a set-up needing the use of a faceplate.

11. Describe four methods of estimating the necessary tailstock set-over when taper turning on centres.

12. Explain how a screwcutting tool has to be ground and set up for screwcutting in the lathe. Describe how you would use a thread dial indicator.

13. A lathe has a leadscrew of 3 mm pitch. Calculate the gear trains necessary for cutting threads of the following pitch: 1.5, 2, 2.5, 3, 3.5 4. Gears run from 20 to 120 in steps of 5 plus one wheel of 63 teeth.

14. A lathe has a leadscrew of 3.5 mm pitch. Calculate the gear trains necessary for cutting threads of the following pitch: 1, 2, 3, 4, 5. Gears run from 20 to 120 in steps of 5 plus one wheel of 63 teeth.

15. Sketch and describe a fixed and travelling steady. What are their purposes?   (*AEB*)

16. Write notes on the following: (*a*) gap bed, (*b*) dead and live centres, (*c*) running centre and half centre, (*d*) tumbler gears, (*e*) apron, (*f*) saddle.

17. Distinguish between the following: (*a*) feed shaft and lead screw, (*b*) thread dial indicator and dial indicator, (*c*) screwpitch gauge and screwcutting gauge, (*d*) driving plate and faceplate.

18. Describe three different types of lathe toolholder that you are familiar with. What are the merits of each type?   (*AEB*)

19. Explain the use of the following parts of the lathe: (*a*) headstock, (*b*) compound slide, (*c*) back gear, (*d*) tailstock. Sketch a side view of the tailstock.   (*AEB*)

20. For what kind of work and turning operations are the following used? (*a*) face plate, (*b*) three-jaw chuck, (*c*) driving plate, (*d*) four-jaw chuck. Describe, with a sketch, a turning operation using either a faceplate or a driving plate.   (*AEB*)

21. (*a*) Describe the method of adjusting the cutting tool of a lathe to the correct height.
    (*b*) Describe, with the aid of sketches, how adjustments can be made to take up slackness on the sliding surfaces of a lathe.   (*AEB*)

22. A lathe having a lead screw of 2.5 mm pitch is to be used to cut external threads of 1.25 and 2.0 mm pitch.
    (*a*) Use sketches to show clearly the shape of the cutting tool that should be ground on an H.S.S. tool bit for use on the lathe.
    (*b*) How would you ensure that the cutting tool picks up the thread groove accurately for each successive depth of cut in each case?
    (*c*) What is an external hand chaser? How is it used?   (*AEB*)

23. Make an outline sketch of a lathe set-up for turning a job between centres. Name the parts.
    (*a*) Explain the important points concerning the live and dead centres.
    (*b*) How should the set-up be corrected if it were found to be turning 0.1 mm out of parallel?
    (*c*) Name two methods of turning tapers on work being turned between centres.   (*AEB*)

24. What is meant by the terms "cutting speed" and "feed rate" as applied to lathes and drilling machines? Why is it necessary to have a range of spindle speeds on these machines?
    (*a*) Sketch one method of providing such a range of speeds on a drilling machine.
    (*b*) Calculate a suitable number of revolutions per minute for turning a 30 mm bar of M.S. at 25 m per min.
(*AEB*)

25. (*a*) What are the essential points to be observed when setting a lathe tool to ensure correct thread form when cutting a Vee thread?
    (*b*) Sketch the end view of the drive from the mandrel to the lead screw of the lathe, indicating the wheels required to cut a thread of 2 mm with a lead screw of 4 mm pitch. Gears from 20 to 120 teeth by steps of 5 teeth are available.   (*AEB*)

26. (*a*) Describe three methods of finding the centre of the end of a cylindrical bar.
    (*b*) How would you prepare the bar for mounting on centres?   (*AEB*)

27. A piece of M.S. rod 200 mm long and 25 mm diameter has already been fitted between centres on a lathe.
    (*a*) Describe with sketches the tool you would use for parallel turning and show how you would set it in the tool-post.

(b)   How would you check for parallelism after the first complete cut?

(c)   If you find the rod not parallel, what is the likely cause and how would you remedy this fault?   (*AEB*)

28.   Describe, with the aid of sketches, how you would turn on a lathe (a) a short or quick taper, (b) a long or gradual taper.

29.   Describe, with the aid of sketches, the setting up and turning on a lathe of:

(a)   a job requiring the use of a four-jaw chuck;

(b)   a job requiring the use of a faceplate.   (*AEB*)

30.   (a)   Make sketches to show clearly the sectional details of the bed of a precision centre lathe.   State the purpose and importance of each of the slide surfaces. From what material would such a lathe bed be normally made?

(b)   Show, with the aid of sketches, one method of adjusting for wear on a machine slide.   Name all the parts of the slide.   (*AEB*)

31.   (a)   Explain what is meant by straight knurling and diamond knurling.   Make sketches to show the details of the tools used in each case.

(b)   Name the materials from which each part of one of the tools is made and indicate the heat treated condition desirable.   Give reasons.

(c)   How is the knurling tool set in the lathe?
(*AEB*)

32.   Sketch, approximately full size, a lathe carrier. Describe the purpose for which it is used and show by a sketch its position when in use on the lathe.   (*UL*)

33.   Explain, with sketches, the meaning of the terms "rake" and "clearance" as applied to turning tools.

Approximately full size, draw a plan and an elevation viewed from the tailstock of a roughing tool in position on the lathe for turning a 30 mm diameter mild steel bar.   (*UL*)

34.   A 155 mm length of 25 mm dia. mild steel, with sawn ends, is to have a finished length of 150 mm with a 9 mm hole drilled 25 mm deep in one end.   Describe, with sketches, the stages to be followed in doing the work using a lathe.   (*UL*)

35.   Show by means of sketches and brief descriptions how:

(a)   the tailstock is held to the bed of a lathe,

(b)   the centre is held in the spindle of the tailstock,

(c)   the spindle is moved in the tailstock, as when bringing the centre up to the work,

(d)   the spindle is locked in position in the tailstock.
(*UL*)

36.   When is it advisable to use a mandrel for turning a workpiece?   Describe one and show how the work would be mounted on it.   (*UL*)

37.   (a)   Use two orthographic views in each case to illustrate three methods of mounting work in a centre lathe.

(b)   Justify each of the methods of mounting used in (a).   (*UC*)

38.   Describe briefly, with sketches where helpful, the meaning of five of the following lathework terms: centre, cross slide, tolerance, radiusing, surfacing, rake, parting, feed.   (*SUJB*)

39.   (a)   Describe any differences you have noted in the operation of turning on the lathe: (i) brass, (ii) cast iron, (iii) mild steel.

(b)   How are diameters measured on turned work?

(c)   List some of the principal safety precautions to be observed when using the lathe.   (*OCSEB*)

40.   (a)   Name three materials used for the cutting edges of lathe tools and state with reasons which of them you consider to be the most satisfactory for use in the school workshop.

(b)   Describe the provisions made for adjusting the lathe tool to correct height in the following: (i) a single pillar type tool post, (ii) a fourway tool post, (iii) a lathe tool holder.   Illustrate your answer.   (*WJEC*)

41.   Describe, with the aid of sketches, two methods of machining tapers using a centre lathe.   State the advantages and disadvantages of each method described.
(*WJEC*)

42.   (a)   Sketch, freehand, three views in orthographic projection showing the side rake and the side clearance angle of a knife tool suitable for cutting mild steel. Indicate each angle.

(b)   Why is it important that the point of a lathe tool should be set at the centre height of the machine?

(c)   On an instruction sheet issued to a machinist the following statement appeared: 'The cutting speed to be 24 m/min.'   Explain what this means with reference to plain turning.   (*WJEC*)

43.   (a)   Make neat sketches showing the plan view of three different lathe tools.   Name each one and describe the principal use to which one of the tools is put.

(b)   If a lathe tool is mounted in a lathe with its point above centre, what is the effect on (i) the effective clearance angle, (ii) the effective rake angle?

(c)   List three safety precautions to be taken when using a pedestal off-hand grinding machine for regrinding a lathe tool.   (*WJEC*)

44.   Explain four of the following terms: Tailstock, compound slide, tool post, headstock, tumbler gears, chuck, combination drill, knurling tool.   (*SCE*)

45.   A piece of 25 mm diameter bright mild steel bar is supplied already faced to 150 mm in length.

(a)   How would you prepare the bar to be turned between centres?

(b)   Make a simple sketch of the bar in position between centres and indicate clearly the name of each lathe component and accessory between the headstock and tailstock and above the bed.   Exclude the toolpost and cutting tool.   (*SCE*)

46.   (a)   Sketch a lathe tailstock and name the parts.

(b)   Indicate how the tailstock may be fixed to the bed of the lathe.   (*SCE*)

47.   Draw the outline of a lathe and name four main parts.   (*CSE*)

48.   Explain in a few words and a sketch what is meant by the term "knurling".   (*CSE*)

49.   Explain the use of a "combination" or "slocombe" centre drill.   (*CSE*)

50.   Describe in detail how you would use a lathe to drill a 6 mm hole down the axis of a 25 mm diameter bar of mild steel 50 mm long.   (*CSE*)

51. Explain how you would prepare a 150 mm length of 20 mm diameter mild steel for turning between centres in a lathe. Make a "front elevation" free-hand sketch of the piece of metal set up in the lathe. (*CSE*)

52. Which chuck would you put on the mandrel of a lathe, to hold: (*a*) hexagonal bar, (*b*) square bar? (*CSE*)

Power Drill

1. Sketch and describe in detail a taper shank twist drill. What conditions must be observed to ensure that a drill will cut with the maximum accuracy and efficiency? (*AEB*)

2. Describe the chief methods of holding and securing work to the drilling machine table and give any precautions necessary for safety. (*AEB*)

3. Give an explanation of the following: (*a*) a carbon steel drill, (*b*) an H.S. drill, (*c*) a pilot drill, (*d*) a countersink drill. (*UEI*)

4. What is a straight fluted drill? Sketch one. When would you use such a drill?

5. Describe, with a sketch, how to extract a drill with a taper drift.

6. Describe, with sketches, how the feed mechanism of a sensitive drill works.

7. What is a flat drill? Sketch two different types, explaining the advantage of one over the other. Why is a flat drill relatively inefficient?

8. Sketch the following and give details of their uses: (*a*) combination drill, (*b*) countersink, (*c*) counterbore.

9. What is a reamer and how does it differ from a straight fluted drill? How would you use a reamer?

10. What is the clearance angle on a twist drill? What is the difference between a straight shank and a morse taper drill and what are their individual merits? (*AEB*)

11. Sketch a twist drill showing clearly the cutting and clearance angles. If a drill cuts badly or not at all, what, in your opinion, may be wrong?

12. (*a*) Make sketches of a flat drill. Show the cutting angles. State for what purposes this drill would be used.

   (*b*) Describe with the aid of sketches the procedure to be followed in drilling a 6 mm hole diametrically through a bar 30 mm diameter and 200 mm long. (*AEB*)

13. A 12 mm diameter reamed hole is to be made in a steel block. State the operations required to produce the hole after it has been marked out. Give reasons for each of the operations and details of the equipment required. Explain why it is probable that a more accurate result would be obtained if taper shank drills were used. (*AEB*)

14. Make a longitudinal sectional elevation through the chuck of a hand drill. What faults in the chuck would cause a drill to wobble?

15. Sketch and describe the following:
   (*a*) Fixing a cylindrical bar on the drilling machine when drilling a hole in the circular surface.
   (*b*) The use of a depth gauge micrometer.
   (*c*) The method of drilling a hole in a surface inclined to the vertical line of the drill. (*UEI*)

16. The centres of a number of 12 mm diameter holes have been set out on a sheet of brass 1.2 mm thick, measuring 150 x 50 mm.
   (*a*) Describe, in detail, the operations which would be necessary to drill these holes using a power drilling machine.
   (*b*) What precautions would you take before, during and after drilling? (*AEB*)

17. (*a*) Describe in detail the operations necessary to produce a hand reamed hole 12 mm diameter through a piece of bright mild steel 20 mm thick. Give reasons for each stage of the work.
   (*b*) Sketch the reamer used. Include a sectional sketch to show clearly the form of the cutting edges. Name all parts.
   (*c*) From what material would such a reamer be made? In what heat-treated condition would you expect the reamer to be? (*AEB*)

18. Why is it good practice to drill a small pilot hole first when a large diameter hole has to be drilled? What causes a drill to make an oversize hole?

19. When sharpening a drill, what essential points must be observed? Make sketches to show correct and incorrect angles at the point. What is meant by peripheral speed in drilling? How and why does it vary? (*AEB*)

20. What advantages are claimed for the twist drill over the flat drill? Make an annotated diagram of the cutting end of a twist drill. (*UL*)

21. The revolutions per minute for a small drill are greater than for a large drill when cutting the same material. Account for this. What is meant by peripheral speed? Relate this to r.p.m. What are the probable causes of a drill cutting (*a*) off-centre, (*b*) oversize? What precautions would you take when drilling thin metal? (*OLE*)

22. Explain, with the aid of suitable sketches, the reasons that cause a twist drill to cut an oversize hole. Make an enlarged sketch of the end of a twist drill to indicate clearly three of the following features: (*a*) web, (*b*) land, (*c*) body clearance, (*d*) cutting edge. (*WJEC*)

23. What is meant by "chain drilling"? (*CSE*)

24. What is meant by: (*a*) a clearance hole, (*b*) a tapping hole? (*CSE*)

25. Explain in detail how you would use a power drill to make a 12 mm diameter hole through B.D.M.S. 30 x 30 x 16 mm. (*CSE*)

Bench or Pedestal Grinder

1. Show clearly how a grinding wheel should be fitted to a spindle. What precautions are necessary in its use? (*AEB*)

2. Write notes on grinding wheels giving details of material used, bond, grade, etc. How would you dress a wheel and why? (*AEB*)

Safety Measures

1. Write a short account of the safety measures necessary when working on (*a*) a lathe, (*b*) a grinding wheel. (*AEB*)

2. What safety precautions would you take before, during and after drilling on a power drill?

3. Indicate two safety measures to be observed in each of the following:
    (a) using a drilling machine,
    (b) grinding a lathe tool,
    (c) hammering heated metal on the anvil,
    (d) turning metal on the lathe.   (SCE)

Miscellaneous Questions

1. Give the meaning and explanation of the following: (a) pitch, (b) screw pitch gauges, (c) silver steel, (d) folding bars.   (UEI)

2. Explain the term "clearance" in connection with cutting tools. By sketching the relevant portions only show where it can be found on (a) a twist drill, (b) a crosscut chisel.   (UEI)

3. Explain what is meant by: (a) annealing steel, (b) work hardened copper, (c) cherry red heat, (d) countersinking.   (UEI)

4. What is meant by each of the following: (a) draw filing, (b) pinning, (c) second cut?   (UEI)

5. Explain the following: (a) point hardening, (b) fettling, (c) limit gauge, (d) alignment, (e) plug gauge, (f) woodruff key, (g) pickling, (h) pinning.

6. Write notes on: (a) limits, (b) limit gauges, (c) tolerances, (d) parallel strips, (e) hermaphrodite (or Jenny) callipers, (f) spot facing.

7. Write notes on: (a) spot facing, (b) the use of a die nut, (c) the set of a blade, (d) morse tapers.

8. What is (a) a jig, (b) a template, (c) a development?

9. (a) Explain, with diagrams, how a forge works.
    (b) How would you maintain the fire in good condition?

10. For what purposes are the following used: (a) hot and cold setts, (b) swages, (c) fullers, (d) flatters?

11. Explain the difference between four of the following pairs: (a) normalizing and annealing, (b) hardening and tempering, (c) hard soldering and soft soldering, (d) crucible steel and mild steel, (e) duralumin and aluminium.   (AEB)

12. (a) In what circumstances would you use a reamer?
    (b) Why does a twist drill sometimes become "blued" when in use?
    (c) State the coolants (if any) you would use when machining the following: mild steel, brass, bronze, aluminium, cast iron.
    (d) Describe the operations in cutting a 10 mm thread on the end of a rod.   (AEB)

13. Write brief notes on five of the following giving diagrams where appropriate: swaging, fullering, fettling, casehardening, limit gauge, clearance, alignment.   (AEB)

14. How would you hold a piece of threaded rod in a vice without damaging the thread?   (UEI)

15. (a) By means of a drawing of a screw thread, show the following: core diameter, nominal diameter, root, crest and pitch.
    (b) Make drawings to show pitch angles and details of the following threads: ISO metric, Square, Acme and Buttress.

16. Explain, with sketches, how the following are held in position:
    (a) the circular split die in a die stock,
    (b) the centre in the tailstock of a lathe,
    (c) the blade in a hacksaw.   (UL)

17. Describe, with drawings, the characteristics of five of the following fittings: locknut, self-tapping screw, thumbscrew, copper cotter pin, spring washer, Phillips type screw, hexagon head machine screw, raised cheese-head screw.   (SUJB)

18. Make sketches and describe the use of five of the following: socket grub screw, coach bolt, carriage bolt, 20 mm half round steel, raised head screw, socket key, morse sleeve drift, screw gauge.   (SUJB)

19. Explain briefly five of the following terms: blowhole, cope, hand reamer, tap, coolant, screw-cutting gauge, flux, swage, parting tool.   (SCE)

BRITISH STANDARD WHITWORTH SCREWTHREADS (B.S.W.)

Outside Dia. (in.)	Core Dia. (in.)	Threads per Inch	Tapping Size Drill	Clearing Size Drill
$\frac{1}{16}$	0.0412	60	No. 56	No. 52
$\frac{3}{32}$	0.0671	48	No. 50	No. 41
$\frac{1}{8}$	0.0930	40	No. 40	No. 30
$\frac{5}{32}$	0.1162	32	No. 31	4 mm
$\frac{3}{16}$	0.1342	24	$\frac{9}{64}$ in.	No. 12
$\frac{7}{32}$	0.1654	24	No. 18	No. 2
$\frac{1}{4}$	0.1860	20	11	6 mm
$\frac{5}{16}$	0.2414	18	Letter D	Letter O
$\frac{3}{8}$	0.2950	16	Letter N	Letter W
$\frac{7}{16}$	0.3461	14	Letter S	$11\frac{1}{2}$ mm
$\frac{1}{2}$	0.3933	12	Letter X	$\frac{33}{64}$ in.
$\frac{5}{8}$	0.5086	11	$\frac{33}{64}$ in.	$\frac{41}{64}$ in.
$\frac{3}{4}$	0.6220	10	$\frac{5}{8}$ in.	$\frac{49}{64}$ in.
$\frac{7}{8}$	0.7328	9	$\frac{47}{64}$ in.	$\frac{57}{64}$ in.
1	0.8400	8	$\frac{27}{32}$ in.	$1\frac{1}{64}$ in.

BRITISH STANDARD FINE SCREWTHREADS (B.S.F.)

Outside Dia. (in.)	Core Dia. (in.)	Threads per Inch	Tapping Size Drill	Clearing Size Drill
$\frac{7}{32}$	0.1731	28	No. 16m	No. 2m
$\frac{1}{4}$	0.2007	26	No. 4m	Letter F
$\frac{9}{32}$	0.2320	26	Letter B	Letter L
$\frac{5}{16}$	0.2543	22	$\frac{17}{64}$ in.	Letter O
$\frac{3}{8}$	0.3110	20	$\frac{21}{64}$ in.	Letter W
$\frac{7}{16}$	0.3664	18	$\frac{3}{8}$ in.	11.3 mm
$\frac{1}{2}$	0.4200	16	$\frac{7}{16}$ in.	13.0 mm
$\frac{9}{16}$	0.4825	16	$\frac{1}{2}$ in.	$\frac{37}{64}$ in.
$\frac{5}{8}$	0.5335	14	$\frac{35}{64}$ in.	$\frac{41}{64}$ in.
$\frac{11}{16}$	0.5960	14	$\frac{39}{64}$ in.	$\frac{45}{64}$ in.
$\frac{3}{4}$	0.6433	12	$\frac{41}{64}$ in.	$\frac{49}{64}$ in.
$\frac{13}{16}$	0.7058	12	$\frac{23}{32}$ in.	$\frac{53}{64}$ in.
$\frac{7}{8}$	0.7586	11	$\frac{49}{62}$ in.	$\frac{57}{64}$ in.
1	0.8719	10	$\frac{57}{64}$ in.	$1\frac{1}{64}$ in.

BRITISH ASSOCIATION STANDARD THREADS (B.A.)

No.	Outside Dia. (in.)	Core Dia. (in.)	Threads per Inch	Tapping Size Drill	Clearing Size Drill
0	0.2360	0.1887	25.4	No. 12	Letter B
1	0.2090	0.1665	28.2	No. 19	No. 3
2	0.1850	0.1467	31.4	No. 26	$\frac{3}{16}$ in.
3	0.1610	0.1266	34.8	No. 30	No. 19
4	0.1420	0.1108	38.5	No. 34	No. 27
5	0.1260	0.0981	43.0	$2\frac{1}{2}$ mm	No. 30
6	0.1100	0.0849	47.9	No. 44	No. 34
7	0.0980	0.0753	52.9	No. 48	No. 39
8	0.0870	0.0657	59.1	No. 51	No. 43
9	0.0750	0.0565	65.1	$1\frac{1}{2}$ mm	No. 48
10	0.067	0.0504	72.6	No. 55	No. 50

UNIFIED AND AMERICAN THREADS— COARSE (U.N.C. AND N.C.)

Nominal Size	Threads per Inch	Core Dia.	Tap Drill Size
$\frac{1}{4}$	20	0.1959	$\frac{13}{64}$
$\frac{5}{16}$	18	0.2524	G
$\frac{3}{8}$	16	0.3073	8.0 mm
$\frac{7}{16}$	14	0.3602	U
$\frac{1}{2}$	13	0.4167	10.75 mm
$\frac{9}{16}$	12	0.4723	$\frac{31}{64}$
$\frac{5}{8}$	11	0.5266	13.75 mm
$\frac{3}{4}$	10	0.6417	$\frac{21}{32}$
$\frac{7}{8}$	9	0.7547	19.5 mm
1	8	0.8647	$\frac{7}{8}$

UNIFIED AND AMERICAN THREADS— FINE (U.N.F. AND N.F.)

Nominal Size	Threads per Inch	Core Dia.	Tap Drill Size
$\frac{1}{4}$	28	0.2113	5.5 mm
$\frac{5}{16}$	24	0.2674	7.0 mm
$\frac{3}{8}$	24	0.3299	8.5 mm
$\frac{7}{16}$	20	0.3834	$\frac{25}{64}$
$\frac{1}{2}$	20	0.4459	$\frac{29}{64}$
$\frac{9}{16}$	18	0.5024	13.0 mm
$\frac{5}{8}$	18	0.5649	14.5 mm
$\frac{3}{4}$	16	0.6823	17.5 mm
$\frac{7}{8}$	14	0.7977	20.5 mm
1	12	0.9098	$\frac{29}{64}$

IMPERIAL STANDARD WIRE GAUGE

No.	Dia. (in.)	No.	Dia. (in.)	No.	Dia. (in.)
7/0	0.500	13	0.092	32	0.0108
6/0	0.464	14	0.080	33	0.0100
5/0	0.432	15	0.072	34	0.0092
4/0	0.400	16	0.064	35	0.0084
3/0	0.372	17	0.056	36	0.0076
2/0	0.348	18	0.048	37	0.0068
1/0	0.324	19	0.040	38	0.0060
1	0.300	20	0.036	39	0.0052
2	0.276	21	0.032	40	0.0048
3	0.252	22	0.028	41	0.0044
4	0.232	23	0.024	42	0.0040
5	0.212	24	0.022	43	0.0036
6	0.192	25	0.020	44	0.0032
7	0.176	26	0.018	45	0.0028
8	0.160	27	0.0164	46	0.0024
9	0.144	28	0.0148	47	0.0020
10	0.128	29	0.0136	48	0.0016
11	0.116	30	0.0124	49	0.0012
12	0.104	31	0.0116	50	0.0010

CUTTING SOLUTIONS FOR VARIOUS MATERIALS

Material	Turning, Drilling, Reaming, Milling	Tapping and Screwing
Steel	Soluble oil	Soluble oil
Cast Iron	Dry	Dry
Brass Bronze	Dry Soluble oil Mineral/lard oil	Dry Soluble oil
Aluminium	Dry Kerosene Soluble oil	Dry Kerosene Soluble oil
Copper	Mineral/lard oil	Mineral/lard oil

APPROXIMATE R.P.M. FOR H.S. DRILLS

Drill Size	Mild Steel	Brass	Aluminium
3 mm	3000	5000	6000
5 mm	2000	3500	4500
6 mm	1600	2500	3500
8 mm	1300	2000	3000
9 mm	1000	1800	2500
10 mm	900	1600	2000
12 mm	700	1300	1500

DRILL SIZES AND DECIMAL EQUIVALENTS

Frac.	Drill No. or Letter	inches	Frac.	Drill No. or Letter	inches	Frac.	Drill No. or Letter	inches	Frac.	Drill No. or Letter	inches
	80	0.0135		50	0.0700		22	0.1570	17/64		0.2656
	79	0.0145		49	0.0730		21	0.1590		H	0.2660
1/64		0.0156		48	0.0760		20	0.1610		I	0.2720
	78	0.0160	5/64		0.0781		19	0.1660		J	0.2770
	77	0.0180		47	0.0785		18	0.1695		K	0.2810
	76	0.0200		46	0.0810	11/64		0.1719	9/32		0.2812
	75	0.0210		45	0.0820		17	0.1730		L	0.2900
	74	0.0225		44	0.0860		16	0.1770		M	0.2950
	73	0.0240		43	0.0890		15	0.1800	19/64		0.2969
	72	0.0250		42	0.0935		14	0.1820		N	0.3020
	71	0.0260	3/32		0.0937		13	0.1850	5/16		0.3125
	70	0.0280		41	0.0960	3/16		0.1875		O	0.3160
	69	0.0292		40	0.0980		12	0.1890		P	0.3230
	68	0.0310		39	0.0995		11	0.1910	21/64		0.3281
1/32		0.0312		38	0.1015		10	0.1935		Q	0.3320
	67	0.0320		37	0.1040		9	0.1960		R	0.3390
	66	0.0330		36	0.1065		8	0.1990	11/32		0.3437
	65	0.0350	7/64		0.1094		7	0.2010		S	0.3480
	64	0.0360		35	0.1100	13/64		0.2031		T	0.3580
	63	0.0370		34	0.1110		6	0.2040	23/64		0.3594
	62	0.0380		33	0.1130		5	0.2055		U	0.3680
	61	0.0390		32	0.1160		4	0.2090	3/8		0.3750
	60	0.0400		31	0.1200		3	0.2130		V	0.3770
	59	0.0410	1/8		0.1250	7/32		0.2187		W	0.3860
	58	0.0420		30	0.1285		2	0.2210	25/64		0.3906
	57	0.0430		29	0.1360		1	0.2280		X	0.3970
	56	0.0465		28	0.1405		A	0.2340		Y	0.4040
3/64		0.0469	9/64		0.1406	15/64		0.2344	13/32		0.4062
	55	0.0520		27	0.1440		B	0.2380		Z	0.4130
	54	0.0550		26	0.1470		C	0.2420	27/64		0.4219
	53	0.0595		25	0.1495		D	0.2460	7/16		0.4375
1/16		0.0625		24	0.1520	1/4	E	0.2500	29/64		0.4531
	52	0.0635		23	0.1540		F	0.2570	15/32		0.4687
	51	0.0670	5/32		0.1562		G	0.2610	31/64		0.4844
									1/2		0.5000

CONVERSION TABLE—APPROXIMATE R.P.M. FOR VARIOUS DIAMETERS OF WORK, CUTTER, DRILL, ETC.

Dia. mm	Cutting speed in metres per minute												
	10	15	20	25	30	35	40	45	50	60	80	100	120
	Revolutions per minute												
1	3200	4800	6400	8000	9600								
2	1600	2400	3200	4000	4800	5600	6400	7200	8000	9600			
3	1070	1600	2130	2670	3200	3720	4240	4750	5300	6360	8470		
4	800	1200	1600	2000	2400	2800	3200	3600	4000	4800	6400	8000	9600
6	530	800	1060	1320	1590	1850	2120	2480	2650	3180	4240	5300	6350
8	400	600	800	1000	1200	1400	1600	1800	2000	2400	3200	4000	4800
10	320	480	640	790	960	1110	1270	1430	1590	1910	2540	3180	3820
12	270	400	530	670	800	930	1070	1200	1330	1600	2130	2670	3200
14	230	340	450	570	680	800	910	1020	1140	1360	1820	2270	2730
16	200	300	400	500	600	700	800	900	1000	1200	1600	2000	2400
18	175	265	350	440	530	620	710	800	880	1060	1420	1770	2120
20	160	240	320	400	480	560	640	720	800	950	1270	1590	1910
25	125	190	255	320	380	450	510	570	660	760	1020	1250	1520
30	106	160	210	270	320	370	420	480	530	640	850	1060	1270
40	79	120	160	200	240	280	320	360	400	480	640	800	960
50	64	95	125	160	190	225	255	290	320	380	510	630	760
75	42	64	85	110	125	150	170	190	210	255	340	420	510
100	32	48	64	80	96	110	130	145	160	190	255	320	380
200	16	24	32	40	48	56	64	72	80	96	125	160	190

The information given in this table is based on a chart first issued by the Schools Council from page 35 of the Council's *Measure for Measure: A Guide to Metrication for Workshop Crafts and Technical Studies* (Evans/Methuen Educational, 1970).

A SET OF METRIC DRILLS

To date, the metric sets of drills are available only in steps of 0.5 mm or 0.1 mm. The first produces a set that is not complete enough and the second a set which consists of too many drills.

For general use in schools and colleges a set of drills should be capable of providing sizes equivalent to:

1 the ISO metric thread diameters
2 the normal diameters of the preferred sizes of rod
3 the tapping sizes and clearance sizes for the ISO threads
4 the reaming sizes for either imperial reamers (until they go out of use) and/or metric reamers.

Although in no logical progression, the drill sizes that satisfy these requirements are given in the following table:

1.0	2.5	4.6	8.2	11.2	16.2
1.1	2.6	5.0	8.5	12.0	17.0
1.2	3.0	5.2	9.0	12.2	17.5
1.4	3.2	6.0	9.3	12.5	18.0
1.6	3.3	6.2	9.5	14.0	18.2
1.8	3.5	6.8	10.0	14.2	18.8
2.0	4.0	7.0	10.2	15.0	20.0
2.1	4.2	7.8	10.3	15.5	20.2
2.2	4.5	8.0	11.0	16.0	

A convenient set of drills from this range would be from 2.0 mm to 12.0 mm or 2.0 mm to 20.0 mm.

249

Nom. Dia.	Pitch	Basic Major Diameter	Basic Effective Diameter	Basic Minor Diameter of External Threads	Basic Minor Diameter of Internal Threads	Recommended Tapping Drill Size	Clearance Drill Size
mm	mm	mm	mm	mm	mm	mm	mm
1.6	0.35	1.600	1.373	1.171	1.221	1.25	1.65
1.8	0.35	1.800	1.573	1.371	1.421	1.45	1.85
2	0.4	2.000	1.740	1.509	1.567	1.6	2.05
2.2	0.45	2.200	1.908	1.648	1.713	1.75	2.25
2.5	0.45	2.500	2.208	1.948	2.013	2.05	2.6
3	0.5	3.000	2.675	2.387	2.459	2.5	3.1
3.5	0.6	3.500	3.110	2.764	2.850	2.9	3.6
4	0.7	4.000	3.545	3.141	3.242	3.3	4.1
4.5	0.75	4.500	4.013	3.580	3.688	3.8	4.6
5	0.8	5.000	4.480	4.019	4.134	4.2	5.1
6	1.0	6.000	5.350	4.773	4.917	5.0	6.1
7	1.0	7.000	6.350	5.773	5.917	6.0	7.2
8	1.25	8.000	7.188	6.466	6.647	6.8	8.2
10	1.5	10.000	9.026	8.160	8.376	8.5	10.2
12	1.75	12.000	10.863	9.853	10.106	10.2	12.2
14	2.0	14.000	12.701	11.546	11.835	12.0	14.25
16	2.0	16.000	14.701	13.546	13.835	14.0	16.25
18	2.5	18.000	16.376	14.933	15.294	15.5	18.25
20	2.5	20.000	18.376	16.933	17.294	17.5	20.25
22	2.5	22.000	20.376	18.933	19.294	19.5	22.25
24	3.0	24.000	22.051	20.319	20.752	21.0	24.25
27	3.0	27.000	25.051	23.319	23.752	24.0	27.25
30	3.5	30.000	27.727	25.706	26.211	26.5	30.5
33	3.5	33.000	30.727	28.706	29.211	29.5	33.5
36	4.0	36.000	33.402	31.093	31.670	32.0	36.5
39	4.0	39.000	36.402	34.093	34.670	35.0	39.5

The information given in this table is based on a chart first issued by the Sheffield Twist Drill and Steel Co. Ltd.

METRIC CONVERSION CHART—MM TO INCHES, FRACTIONS AND B.A. SIZES

mm	in.	mm	in.	mm	in.	mm	in.	mm	in.	Fractions	mm	in.	B.A. Equiv.	Fractions	mm	in.	Fractions
.01	.00039	.26	.01024	.51	.02008	.76	.02992	1.59	0.062	$\frac{1}{16}$	6.35	0.250	—	$\frac{1}{4}$	17.00	0.670	—
.02	.00079	.27	.01063	.52	.02047	.77	.03032	2.00	0.079	—	7.00	0.276	—	—	17.46	0.688	$\frac{11}{16}$
.03	.00118	.28	.01102	.53	.02087	.78	.03071	2.20	0.087	—	7.14	0.281	8	$\frac{9}{32}$	18.00	0.709	—
.04	.00157	.29	.01142	.54	.02126	.79	.03110	2.38	0.094	$\frac{3}{32}$	7.94	0.312	—	$\frac{5}{16}$	19.00	0.748	—
.05	.00197	.30	.01181	.55	.02165	.80	.03150	2.50	0.098	—	8.00	0.315	7	—	19.05	0.750	$\frac{3}{4}$
.06	.00236	.31	.01220	.56	.02205	.81	.03189	2.80	0.110	—	8.73	0.344	—	$\frac{11}{32}$	20.00	0.787	—
.07	.00276	.32	.01260	.57	.02244	.82	.03228	3.00	0.118	—	9.00	0.354	6	—	20.64	0.813	$\frac{13}{16}$
.08	.00315	.33	.01299	.58	.02283	.83	.03268	3.17	0.125	$\frac{1}{8}$	9.52	0.375	—	$\frac{3}{8}$	22.22	0.875	$\frac{7}{8}$
.09	.00354	.34	.01339	.59	.02323	.84	.03307	3.20	0.126	—	10.00	0.394	5	—	23.81	0.938	$\frac{15}{16}$
.10	.00394	.35	.01378	.60	.02362	.85	.03346	3.50	0.138	—	10.32	0.406	—	$\frac{13}{32}$	25.00	0.984	—
.11	.00433	.36	.10417	.61	.02402	.86	.03386	3.60	0.142	—	11.00	0.433	4	—	25.40	1.000	—
.12	.00472	.37	.01457	.62	.02441	.87	.03425	3.97	0.156	$\frac{5}{32}$	11.11	0.438	—	$\frac{7}{16}$	30	1.181	—
.13	.00512	.38	.01496	.63	.02480	.88	.03465	4.00	0.158	—	11.91	0.468	—	$\frac{15}{32}$	35	1.378	—
.14	.00551	.39	.01535	.64	.02520	.89	.03504	4.10	0.161	—	12.00	0.472	3	—	40	1.575	—
.15	.00591	.40	.01575	.65	.02559	.90	.03543	4.50	0.177	—	12.70	0.500	—	$\frac{1}{2}$	45	1.772	—
.16	.00630	.41	.01614	.66	.02598	.91	.03583	4.70	0.185	—	13.00	0.512	2	—	50	1.969	—
.17	.00669	.42	.01654	.67	.02638	.92	.03622	4.76	0.187	$\frac{3}{16}$	14.00	0.551	—	—	100	3.937	—
.18	.00709	.43	.01693	.68	.02677	.93	.03661	5.00	0.197	—	14.29	0.563	1	$\frac{9}{16}$	200	7.874	—
.19	.00748	.44	.01732	.69	.02717	.94	.03701	5.30	0.209	—	14.00	0.591	—	—			
.20	.00787	.45	.01772	.70	.02756	.95	.03740	5.56	0.219	$\frac{7}{32}$	15.87	0.625	—	$\frac{5}{8}$			
.21	.00827	.46	.01811	.71	.02795	.96	.03780	6.00	0.236	—	16.00	0.630	0	—			
.22	.00866	.47	.01850	.72	.02835	.97	.03819										
.23	.00906	.48	.01890	.73	.02874	.98	.03858										
.24	.00945	.49	.01929	.74	.02913	.99	.03898										
.25	.00984	.50	.01969	.75	.02953	1	.0394										

Abbreviations

S I abbreviations: no stops are used and there are no plural forms.

Abbreviations for engineering drawing: abbreviations are the same in the plural; capital or lower case letters may be used; full stops are not used except where the abbreviation makes a word, e.g. fig. for figure (B.S. 308).

Other abbreviations: the Oxford dictionary suggests (1) using a stop when the abbreviation curtails the word, e.g. temp. for temperature, (2) omitting the full stop when the first and last letters of the word are retained, e.g. std for standard.

A/F	Across the Flats	I S O	International Standards Organization
A.N.C.	American National Coarse		
A.N.F.	American National Fine	L.H.	Left Hand
Assy	Assembly	Lg	Long
B.A.	British Association	Matl	Material
B.D.M.S.	Bright Drawn Mild Steel	Max.	Maximum
B.G.	Birmingham Gauge	m	Metre
B.M.S.	Bright Mild Steel	Min.	Minimum
B.S.B.	British Standard Brass	mm	Millimetre
B.S.F.	British Standard Fine	M.P.	Melting Point
B.S.I.	British Standards Institute	M.S.	Mild Steel
B.S.P.	British Standard Pipe		
B.S.W.	British Standard Whitworth	N.P.	Nickel Plated
		No.	Number
C.I.	Cast Iron		
C.S.	Cast Steel	P.C.D.	Pitch Circle Diameter
Crs	Centres		
C.L. or ₵	Centreline	R	Radius
Cham.	Chamfered	R.P.M.	Revolutions per Minute
Ch. Hd	Cheese Head	Rev/Min	Revolutions per Minute
C.R.C.A.	Cold Rolled Close Annealed	R.H.	Right Hand
C'bore	Counterbore	Rd Hd	Round Head
Csk	Countersink		
Csk Hd	Countersunk Head	S'face	Spotface
Cyl.	Cylinder	Sq.	Square—in a note, B.S. 308
		□	Square—preceding a dimension, B.S. 308
d	Diameter—S I System	Std	Standard
dia.	Diameter—in a note, B.S. 308	S.W.G.	Standard Wire Gauge
∅	Diameter—preceding a dimension, B.S. 308	S I	Système International
Fig.	Figure	Temp.	Temperature
		T.P.I.	Teeth per Inch
g	Gramme		
		U.N.C.	Unified National Coarse
Hex.	Hexagon	U.N.F.	Unified National Fine
Hex. Hd	Hexagonal Head		
H.C.S.	High Carbon Steel	Vol.	Volume
H.S.S.	High Speed Steel		
H.T.	High Tensile Steel	Wt	Weight
		W.G.	Wire Gauge
I.S.W.G.	Imperial Standard Wire Gauge	W.I.	Wrought Iron
in.	Inch		